PLANE TRIGONOMETRY

Part 1

SL LONEY

Sydney Luxton Loney

arihant

ARIHANT PRAKASHAN (Series), MEERUT

ARIHANT PRAKASHAN (Series), MEERUT

卐 ADMINISTRATIVE & PRODUCTION OFFICES

Regd. Office
'Ramchhaya' 4577/15, Agarwal Road, Darya Ganj, New Delhi - 110002
Tele: 011- 47630600, 43518550; Fax: 011- 23280316

Head Office
Kalindi, TP Nagar, Meerut (UP) - 250002
Tel: 0121-2401479, 2512970, 4004199; Fax: 0121-2401648

卐 SALES & SUPPORT OFFICES

Agra, Ahmedabad, Bengaluru, Bhubaneswar, Bareilly, Chennai, Delhi, Guwahati, Hyderabad, Jaipur, Jhansi, Kolkata, Lucknow, Meerut, Nagpur & Pune.

卐 ISBN 978-93-5176-175-4

卐 PRICE ₹ 95.00

Printed & Bound By
Arihant Publications (I) Ltd. (Press Unit)

For further information about the books published by Arihant, log on to **www.arihantbooks.com** or e-mail at **info@arihantbooks.com**

PREFACE

The following work will, I hope to be a fairly complete elementary text - book on Plane Trigonometry, suitable for Schools and the Pass and Junior Honour classes of Universities. In the higher portion of the book I have endeavoured to present to the student, as a simply as possible, the modern treatment of complex quantities, and I hope it will be gound that he will have little to unlearn when he commences to read treatises of more difficult character.

As Trigonomery consists largely of formulae and applications thereof, I have prefixed a list of the principle formulae which the student should commit to memory. These more important formulae are distinguished in the text by the use of thick type. Other formulae are subsidiary and of less importance.

The number of examples is very large. A selection only should be solved by the student on a first reading.

On a first reading also the articles marked with an asterisk should be omitted.

Considerable attention has been paid to the printing of books and I am under great obligation to the Syndics of the Press for their liberality in this matter, and to the officers and workmen of the press for the trouble they have taken.

I am indebted to Mr WJ Dobbs, BA late Scholar of St. John's College for his kindness in reading and correcting the poor-sheets and for many valuable suggestions.

For any corrections and suggestions for improvement I shall be thankful.

SL Loney

Royal Holloway College
Egham, Surrey
September 12, 1893

Preface to the Second Edition

The Second Edition has been carefully revised, and it is hoped that few serious mistakes remain either in the text or the answers.

Some changes have been made in the chapter on logarithms and logarithmic tables, and an additional chapter has been added to Projections.

April 25, 1895

Preface to the Fifth Edition

This Edition (the Seventeenth Impression) has been reset; some additions have been made to the text, and Table of the Radian Measured of angles have been added.

July 7, 1925

Preface to the Sixth Edition

Worked examples and exercises and have revised to conform to the Metric System and with the answers is a note on their acceptable accuracy.

CONTENTS

1

MEASUREMENT OF ANGLES; SEXAGESIMAL, CENTESIMAL, AND CIRCULAR MEASURE

➤ **1.** In Geometry angles are measured in terms of a right angle. This, however, is an inconvenient unit of measurement on account of its size.

➤ **2.** In the **Sexagesimal** system of measurement a right angle is divided into 90 equal parts called **Degrees**. Each degree is divided into 60 equal parts called **Minutes**, and each minute into 60 equal parts called **Seconds**.

The symbols $1°$, $1'$, and $1''$ are used to denote a Degree, a Minute, and a Second respectively.

Thus, 60 Seconds ($60''$) make One Minute ($1'$),

60 Minutes ($60'$) make One Degree ($1°$),

and 90 Degrees ($90°$) make One Right Angle.

This system is well established and is always used in the practical applications of Trigonometry. It is not however very convenient on account of the multipliers 60 and 90.

➤ **3.** On this account another system of measurement called the **Centesimal,** or French, system has been proposed. In this system the right angle is divided into 100 equal parts, called **Grades;** each grade is subdivided into 100 **Minutes,** and each minute into 100 **Seconds.**

The symbols is 1^g, $1'$ and $1''$ are used to denote a Grade, a Minute and a Second respectively.

Thus, 100 Seconds($100''$) make One Minute ($1'$),

100 Minutes($100'$) make One Grade (1^g),

100 Grades (100^g) make One Right Angle.

➤ **4.** This system would be much more convenient to use than the ordinary Sexagesimal system.

As a preliminary, however, to its practical adoption, a large number of tables would have to be recalculated. For this reason the system has in practice never been used.

➤ **5.** *To convert Sexagesimal into Centesimal Measure, and vice- versa.* Since, a right angle is equal to 90° and also to 100^g, we have

$$90° = 100^g$$

$$\therefore \qquad 1° = \frac{10^g}{9}, \text{ and } 1^g = \frac{9°}{10}.$$

Hence, to change degrees into grades, add on one-ninth; to change grades into degrees, subtract one-tenth.

<u>**EXAMPLE**</u> $36° = \left(36 + \frac{1}{9} \times 36\right)^g = 40^g$

and $64^g = \left(64 - \frac{1}{10} \times 64\right)^\circ = (64 - 6.4)° = 57.6°$

If the angle does not contain in integral number of degrees, we may reduce it to a fraction of a degree and then change to grades.

In practice it is generally found more convenient to reduce any angle to a fraction of a right angle. The method will be seen in the following examples:

<u>**EXAMPLE 1**</u> *Reduce* $63°14'51''$ *to Centesimal measure.*

We have $51'' = \frac{17'}{20} = 0.85'$,

and $14'\,51'' = 14.85' = \frac{14.85°}{60} = 0.2475°$,

$$\therefore \qquad 63°14'51'' = 63.2475° = \frac{63.2475}{90} \text{ rt. angle}$$

$$= 0.70275 \text{ rt. angle}$$

$$= 70.275^g = 70^g 27.5'$$

$$= 70^g\, 27'\, 50''$$

<u>**EXAMPLE 2**</u> *Reduce* $94^g 23' 87''$ *to Sexagesimal measure.*

$$94^g 23' 87'' = 0.942387 \text{ right angle}$$

$$= \frac{90}{84.814834 \text{ degrees}}$$

$$= \frac{60}{48.8898 \text{ minutes}}$$

$$= \frac{60}{53.3880 \text{ seconds}}$$

$$\therefore \quad 94^g 23' 87'' = 84° 48' 53.388''$$

➤ **6. Angles of any size:** Suppose AOA' and BOB' to be two fixed lines meeting at right angles in O, and suppose a revolving line OP (turning about a fixed point at O) to start from OA and revolve in a direction opposite to that of the hands of a watch.

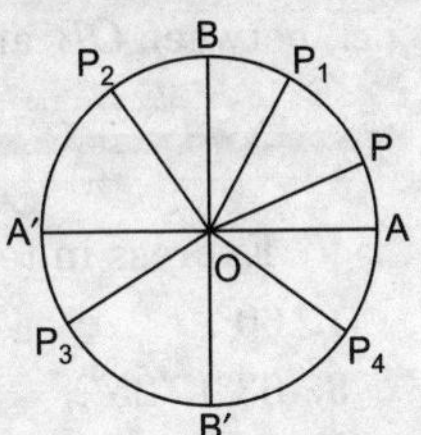

For any position of the revolving line between OA and OB such as OP_1, it will have turned through an angle AOP_1, which is less than a right angle.

For any position between OB and OA', such as OP_2, the angle AOP_2 through which it has turned is greater than a right angle.

For any position OP_3, between OA' and OB' the angle traced out is AOP_3, *i.e.*, $AOB + BOA' + A'OP_3$, *i.e.*, 2 right angles + $A'OP_3$, so that the angle described is greater than two right angles.

For any position OP_4, between OB' and OA, the angle turned through is similarly greater than three right angles.

When the revolving line has made a complete revolution, so that it concides once more with OA, the angle through which it has turned is 4 right angles.

If the line OP still continue to revolve, the angle through which it has turned, when it is for the second time in the position OP_1, is not AOP_1 but 4 right angles + AOP_1.

Similarly, when the revolving line, having made two complete revolutions, is once more in the position OP_2, the angle it has traced out is 8 right angles + AOP_2.

➤ **7.** If the revolving line OP be between OA and OB, it is said to be in the first quadrant; if it be between OB' and OA', it is in the second quadrant; if between OA' and OB', it is in the third quadrant; if it is between OB' and OA' it is in the fourth quadrant.

➤ **8.**

EXAMPLE *What is the position of the revolving line when it has turned through* (1) 225°, (2) 480° and (3) 1050°?

(1) Since 225° = 180° + 45°, the revolving line has turned through 45° more than two right angles, and it is therefore in the third quadrant and halfway between OA' and OB'.

(2) Since $480° = 360° + 120°$, the revolving line has turned through 120° more than one complete revolution, and it is therefore in the second quadrant, *i.e.*, between OB and OA' and makes an angle of 30° with OB.

(3) Since $1050° = 11 \times 90° + 60°$, the revolving line has turned through 60° more than eleven right angles, and is therefore in the fourth quadrant, *i.e.*, between OB' and OA, and makes 60° with OB'.

EXAMPLES I

Express in terms of a right angle the angles

1. 60°. **2.** 75°15′.

3. 63°17′25″. **4.** 130°30′.

5. 210°30′30″. **6.** 370°20′48″.

Express in grades, minutes and seconds the angles

7. 30°. **8.** 81°.

9. 138°30′. **10.** 35°47′15″.

11. 235°12′36″. **12.** 475°13′48″.

Express in terms of right angles, and also in degrees, minutes, and seconds the angles

13. 120^g. **14.** $45^g35'24''$.

15. $39^g45'36''$. **16.** $255^g8'9''$.

17. $759^g0'5''$.

Mark the position of the revolving line when it has traced out the following angles

18. $\frac{4}{3}$ right angle **19.** $3\frac{1}{2}$ right angles

20. $13\frac{1}{3}$ right angles **21.** 120°

22. 315° **23.** 745°

24. 1185° **25.** 150^g

26. 420^g **27.** 875^g

28. How many degrees, minutes, and seconds are respectively passed over in $11\frac{1}{9}$ minutes by the hour and minute hands of a watch?

29. The number of degrees in one acute angle of a right-angled triangle is equal to the number of grades in the other; express both the angles in degrees.

30. Prove that the number of Sexagesimal minutes in any angle is to the number of Centesimal minutes in the same angle as 27: 50.

31. Divide 44°8′ into two parts such that the number of Sexagesimal seconds in one part may be equal to the number of Centesimal seconds in the other part.

CIRCULAR MEASURE

➤ **9.** A third system of measurement of angles has been devised, and it is this system which is used in all the higher branches of Mathematics.

The unit used is obtained thus, Take any circle *APBB′*, whose centre is *O*, and from any point *A* measure off an arc *AP* whose length is equal to the radius of the circle. Join *OA* and *OP*.

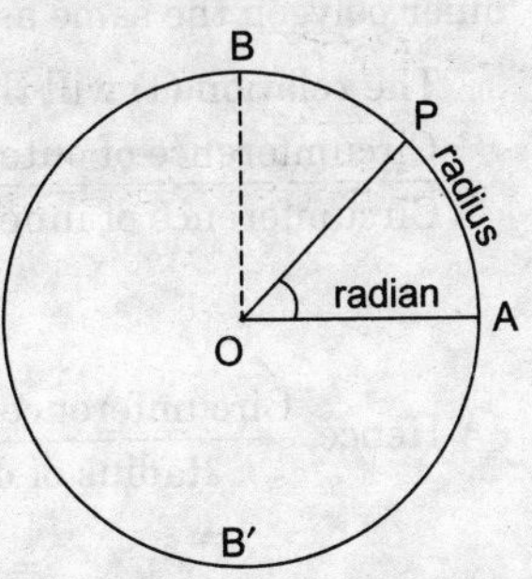

The angle *AOP* is the angle which is taken as the unit of circular measurement, *i.e.*, it is the angle in terms of which in this system we measure all others.

This angle is called A Radian and is often denoted by 1^C.

➤ **10.** It is clearly essential to the proper choice of unit that it should be a *constant* quantity; hence we must show that the radian is a constant angle. This we shall do in the following articles.

➤ **11. Theorem :** *The length of the circumference of a circle always bears a constant ratio to its diameter.*

Take any two circles whose common centre is *O*. In the larger circle inscribe a regular polygon of *n* sides, *ABCD*...

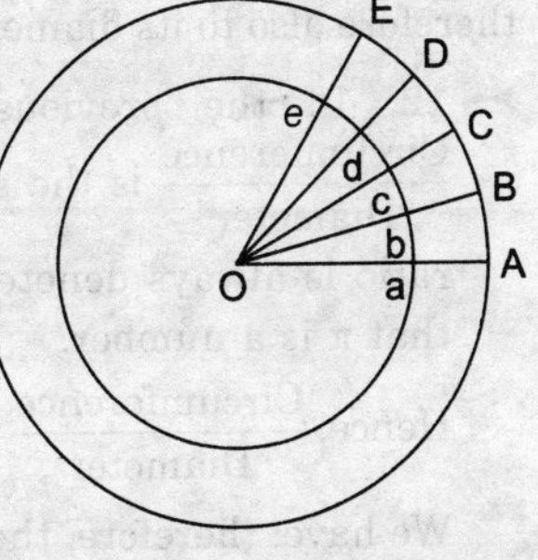

Let *OA*, *OB*, *OC*,... meet the smaller circle in the points *a*, *b*, *c*, *d*,... and join *ab*, *bc*, *cd*,... .

Then, by Geometry, *abcd*... is a regular polygon of *n* sides inscribed in the smaller circle.

Since, $Oa = Ob$, and $OA = OB$, the lines *ab* and *AB* must be parallel, and hence

$$\frac{AB}{ab} = \frac{OA}{Oa}$$

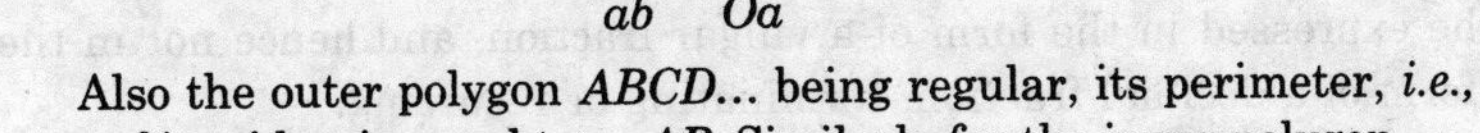

Also the outer polygon *ABCD*... being regular, its perimeter, *i.e.*, the sum of its sides, is equal to $n \cdot AB$. Similarly for the inner polygon

Hence we have

$$\frac{\text{Perimeter of the outer polygon}}{\text{Perimeter of the inner polygon}} = \frac{n \cdot AB}{n \cdot ab} = \frac{AB}{ab} = \frac{OA}{Oa} \qquad ...(1)$$

This relation exists whatever be the number of sides in the polygons.

Let then the number of sides be indefinitely increased (*i.e.*, let n become inconceivably great) so that finally the perimeter of the outer polygon will be the same as the circumference of the outer circle, and the perimeter of the inner polygon the same as the circumference of the inner circle.

The relation (1) will then become

$$\frac{\text{Circumference of outer circle}}{\text{Circumference of inner circle}} = \frac{OA}{Oa}$$

$$= \frac{\text{Radius of outer circle}}{\text{Radius of inner circle}}$$

Hence, $\dfrac{\text{Circumference of outer circle}}{\text{Radius of outer circle}}$

$$= \frac{\text{Circumference of inner circle}}{\text{Radius of inner circle}}.$$

Since, there was no restriction whatever as to the sizes of the two circles, it follows that the quantity

$$= \frac{\text{Circumference of any circle}}{\text{Radius of that circle}}$$

is **the same for all circles**.

Hence, the ratio of the circumference of a circle to its radius, and therefore also to its diameter, is a constant quantity.

➤ **12.** In the previous article we have shown that the ratio $\dfrac{\text{Circumference}}{\text{Diameter}}$ is the same for all circles. The value of this constant ratio is always denoted by the Greek letter π [pronounced "Pi"] so that π is a number.

Hence, $\dfrac{\text{Circumference}}{\text{Diameter}}$ = the constant number π.

We have, therefore, the following theorem; **The circumference of a circle is always equal to π times its diameter or 2π times its radius.**

➤ **13.** Unfortunately the value of π is not a whole number, nor can it be expressed in the form of a vulgar fraction, and hence not in the form of a decimal fraction, terminating or recurring.

The number π is an incommensurable magnitude, i.e., a magnitude whose value cannot be exactly expressed as the ratio of two whole numbers.

Its value, correct to 8 places of decimals, is

3.14159265...

The fraction $\frac{22}{7}$ gives the value of π correctly for the first two decimal places; for $\frac{22}{7} = 3.14285\ldots$.

The fraction $\frac{355}{113}$ is a more accurate value of π , being correct to 6 places of decimals; for $\frac{355}{113} = 3.14159203\ldots$.

[N.B. The fraction $\frac{355}{113}$ may be remembered thus; write down the first three odd numbers repeating each twice, thus 113355; divide the number thus obtained into two parts and let the first part be divided into the second, thus 113)355(.

The quotient is the value of π to 6 places of decimals]

To sum up. **An approximate value of π, correct to 2 places of decimals, is the fraction $\frac{22}{7}$; a more accurate value is 3.14159... .**

By division, we can show that

$$\frac{1}{\pi} = 0.3183098862\ldots$$

➤ **14.**

EXAMPLE 1 *The diameter of a wheel is 28 cm; through what distance does its centre move during one revolution of the wheel along the ground?*

The radius r is here 14 cm

The circumference therefore $= 2 \cdot \pi \cdot 14 = 28\pi$ cm

If we take $\pi = \frac{22}{7}$, the circumference $= 28 \times \frac{22}{7}$ cm = 88 cm. approximately.

If we give π the more accurate value 3.14159265..., the circumference

$$= 28 \times 3.14159265\ldots \text{ cm} = 87.96459 \text{ cm}.$$

EXAMPLE 2 *What must be the radius of a circular running path, round which an athlete must run 5 times in order to describe* 1760 *metres?*

The circumference must be $\frac{1}{5} \times 1760$, *i.e.,* 352 metres.

Hence, if r be the radius of the path in metres, we have $2\pi r = 352$,

i.e., $$r = \frac{176}{\pi} \text{ metres}$$

Taking, $\pi = \frac{22}{7}$, we have $r = \frac{176 \times 7}{22} = 56$ metres

Taking the more accurate value $\frac{1}{\pi} = 0.31831$, we have

$$r = 176 \times 0.31831 = 56.02256 \text{ metres}$$

EXAMPLES II

1. If the radius of the earth be 6400 km, what is the length of its circumference?
2. The wheel of a railway carriage is 90 cm in diameter and makes 3 revolutions in a second; how fast is the train going?
3. A mill sail whose length is 540 cm makes 10 revolutions per minute. What distance does its end travel in an hour?
4. Assuming that, the earth describes in one year a circle, of 149,700,000 km radius, whose centre is the sun, how many miles does the earth travel in a year?
5. The radius of a carriage wheel is 50 cm, and in $\frac{1}{9}$ th of a second it turns through 80° about its centre, which is fixed; how many km does a point on the rim of the wheel travel in one hour?

➤ 15. Theorem: *The radian is a constant angle.*

Take the figure of Art. 9. let the arc *AB* be a quadrant of the circle, *i.e.*, one-quarter of the circumference.

By Art .12, the length of *AB* is therefore $\frac{\pi r}{2}$, where r is the radius of the circle.

By Geometry, we know that angles at the centre of any circle are to one another as the arcs on which they stand.

Hence,
$$\frac{\angle AOP}{\angle AOB} = \frac{\text{arc.}\,AP}{\text{arc.}\,AB} = \frac{r}{\frac{\pi r}{2}} = \frac{2}{\pi}$$

i.e.,
$$\angle AOP = \frac{2}{\pi}\cdot \angle AOB.$$

But we defined the angle *AOP* to be a Radian.

Hence,
$$\text{a Radian} = \frac{2}{\pi}\cdot \angle AOB$$
$$= \frac{2}{\pi} \text{ of a right angle.}$$

Since, a right angle is a constant angle, and since we have shown (Art. 12) that π is a constant quantity, it follows that a Radian is a constant angle, and is therefore the same whatever be the circle from which it is derived.

➤ 16. Magnitude of a Radian:

By the previous article, a Radian $= \frac{2}{\pi} \times$ a right angle $= \frac{180°}{\pi}$

$$= 180° \times 0.3183098862... = 57.2957795°$$

$$= 57°17'44.8'' \text{ nearly}$$

➤ **17.** Since, a Radian $= \frac{2}{\pi}$ of a right angle,

therefore a right angle $= \frac{\pi}{2}$ radians.

so, that $180° = 2$ right angles $= \pi$ radians

and $360° = 4$ right angles $= 2\pi$ radians.

Hence, when the revolving line (Art. 6) has made a complete revolution, it has described an angle equal to 2π radians; when it has made three complete revolutions, it has described an angle of 6π radians; when it has made n revolutions, it has described an angle of $2n\pi$ radians.

➤ **18.** In practice the symbol "c" is generally omitted and instead of "an angle π^c" we find written "an angle π".

The student must notice this point carefully. If the unit, in terms of which the angle is measured, be not mentioned, he must mentally supply the word "radians". Otherwise he will easily fall into the mistake of supposing that π stands for 180°. It is true that π radians (π^c) is the same as 180°, but π itself is a number, and a number only.

➤ **19.** To convert Circular Measure into Sexagesimal Measure or Centesimal Measure and vice versa.

The student should remember the relations

Two right angles $= 180° = 200^g = \pi$ radians.

The conversion is then merely Arithmetic.

EXAMPLE 1 $0.45\pi^c = 0.45 \times 180° = 81° = 90^g$

(2) $3^c = \frac{3}{\pi} \times \pi^c = \frac{3}{\pi} \times 180° = \frac{3}{\pi} \times 200^g.$

(3) $40°15'36'' = 40°15\frac{3'}{5} = 40.26°$

$$= 40.26 \times \frac{\pi^c}{180} = 0.2236\,\pi \text{ radians.}$$

(4) $40^g15'36'' = 40.1536^g = 40.1536 \times \frac{\pi}{200}$ radians

$$= 0.200768\,\pi \text{ radians.}$$

➤ **20.**

EXAMPLE 1 *The angles of a triangle are in A.P. and the number of grades in the least is to the number of radians in the greatest as* $40 : \pi$; *find the angle in degrees.*

Let the angle be $(x - y)°$, $x°$ and $(x + y)°$

Since, the sum of the three angles of a triangle is 180°, we have

$$180 = x - y + x + x + y = 3x$$

so that $$x = 60.$$

The required angles are therefore

$$(60 - y)°, 60°, \text{ and } (60 + y)°$$

Now, $$(60 - y)° = \frac{10}{9} \times (60 - y)^g$$

and $$(60 + y)° = \frac{\pi}{180} \times (60 + y) \text{ radians}$$

Hence, $$\frac{10}{9}(60 - y) : \frac{\pi}{180}(60 + y) :: 40 : \pi$$

$\therefore$ $$\frac{200}{\pi}\frac{60 - y}{60 + y} = \frac{40}{\pi}$$

i.e., $$5(60 - y) = 60 + y$$

i.e., $$y = 40.$$

The angles are therefore 20°, 60° and 100°.

EXAMPLE 2 *Express in the three systems of angular measurement the magnitude of the angle of a regular decagon.*

By Geometry, we know that all the interior angles of any rectilinear figure together with four right angles are equal to twice as many right angles as the figure has sides.

Let the angle of a regular decagon contain x right angles, so that all the angles are together equal to $10x$ right angles.

The corollary therefore states that

$$10x + 4 = 20$$

so that $$x = \frac{8}{5} \text{ right angles.}$$

But one right angle $= 90° = 100^g = \frac{\pi}{2}$ radians

Hence, the required angle $= 144° = 160^g = \frac{4\pi}{5}$ radians

EXAMPLES III

Express in degrees, minutes, and seconds the angles

1. $\frac{\pi^c}{3}$ **2.** $\frac{4\pi^c}{3}$

3. $10\,\pi^c$ **4.** $1°$

5. 8^c

Express in grades, minutes and seconds the angles

6. $\frac{4\pi^c}{5}$ **7.** $\frac{7\pi^c}{6}$

8. $10\,\pi^c$

Express in radians the following angles:

9. $60°$ **10.** $110°30'$

11. $175°45'$ **12.** $47°25'36''$

13. $395°$ **14.** 60^g

15. $110^g30'$ **16.** $345^g25'36''$

17. The difference between the two acute angles of a right-angled triangle is $\frac{2}{5}\pi$ radians; express the angles in degrees.

18. One angle of a triangle is $\frac{2}{3}x$ grades and another is $\frac{3}{2}x$ degrees, while the third is $\frac{\pi x}{75}$ radians; express them all in degrees.

19. The circular measure of two angles of a triangle are respectively $\frac{1}{2}$ and $\frac{1}{3}$; what is the number of degrees in the third angle?

20. The angles of a triangle are in A.P. and the number of degrees in the least is to be number of radians in the greatest as 60 to π; find the angles in degrees.

21. The angles of a triangle are in A.P. and the number of radians in the least angle is to the number of degrees in the mean angle as $1:120$. Find the angles in radians.

22. Find the magnitude, in radians and degrees, of the interior angle of (1) a regular pentagon, (2) a regular heptagon, (3) a regular octagon, (4) a regular duodecagon, and (5) a regular polygon of 17 sides.

23. The angle in one regular polygon is to that in another as $3:2$; also the number of sides in the first is twice that in the second; how many sides have the polygons?

24. The number of sides in two regular polygons are as $5:4$; and the difference between their angles is $9°$; find the number of sides in the polygons.

25. Find the two regular polygons such that the number of their sides may be as 3 to 4 and the number of degrees in an angle of the first to the number of grades in angle of the second as 4 to 5.

26. The angles of a quadrilateral are in A.P. and the greatest is double the least; express the least angle in radians.

27. Find the radians, degrees and grades the angle between the hour hand and the minute-hand of a clock at (1) half-past three, (2) twenty minutes to six, (3) a quarter past eleven.

28. Find the times (1) between four and five o'clock when the angle between the minute-hand and the hour-hand is 78°, (2) between seven and eight o'clock when this angle is 54°.

➤ **21. Theorem** : *The number of radians in any angle whatever is equal to a fraction, whose numerator is the arc which the angle subtends at the centre of any circle, and whose denominator is the radius of that circle.*

Let AOP be the angle which has been described by a line starting from OA and revolving into the positions OP.

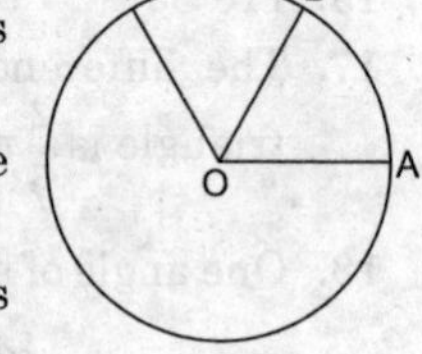

With centre O and any radius, describe a circle cutting OA and OP in the points A and P.

Let the angle AOB be a radian, so that the arc AB is equal to the radius OA.

By Geometry, we have

$$\frac{\angle AOP}{\text{A Radian}} = \frac{\angle AOP}{\angle AOB} = \frac{\text{arc } AP}{\text{arc } AB} = \frac{\text{arc } AP}{\text{Radius}}$$

so that $$\angle AOP = \frac{\text{arc } AP}{\text{Radius}} \text{ of a Radian}$$

Hence the theorem is proved.

➤ **22.**

EXAMPLE 1 *Find the angle subtended at the centre of a circle of radius 3 cm by an arc of length 1 cm.*

The number of radians in the angle $= \dfrac{\text{arc}}{\text{radius}} = \dfrac{1}{3}$

Hence the angle $= \dfrac{1}{3}$ radian $= \dfrac{1}{3} \times \dfrac{2}{\pi}$ right angle $= \dfrac{2}{3\pi} \times 90° = \dfrac{60°}{\pi} = 19\dfrac{1}{11}°$

on taking π equal to $\dfrac{22}{7}$.

EXAMPLE 2 *In a circle of 5 cm radius, what is the length of the arc which subtends an angle of 33°15′ at the centre?*

If x cm be the required length, we have

$$\frac{x}{5} = \text{number of radians in } 33°15'$$

$$= \frac{33\frac{1}{4}}{180}\pi \qquad \text{(Art. 19)}$$

$$= \frac{133}{720}\pi$$

$\therefore$
$$x = \frac{133}{144}\pi \text{ cm} = \frac{133}{144} \times \frac{22}{7} \text{ cm nearly}$$

$$= 2\frac{65}{72} \text{ cm nearly.}$$

EXAMPLE 3 *Assuming the average distance of the earth from the sun to be* 149,700,000 *km., and the angle subtended by the sun at the eye of a person on the earth to be* 32′, *find the sun's diameter.*

Let D be the diameter of the sun in km.

The angle subtended by the sun being very small, its diameter is very approximately equal to a small arc of a circle whose centre is the eye of the observer. Also the sun subtends an angle of 32′ at the centre of this circle.

Hence, by Art. 21, we have

$$\frac{D}{149{,}700{,}000} = \text{the number of radians in } 32'$$

$$= \text{the number of radians in } \frac{8°}{15}$$

$$= \frac{8}{15} \times \frac{\pi}{180} = \frac{2\pi}{675}$$

$\therefore$
$$D = \frac{299{,}400{,}000}{675}\pi \text{ km}$$

$$= \frac{299{,}400{,}000}{675} \times \frac{22}{7} \text{ km approximately}$$

$$= 1{,}390{,}000 \text{ km nearly.}$$

EXAMPLE 4 *Assuming that a person of normal sight can read print at such a distance that the letters subtend an angle of* 5′ *at his eye, find what is the height of the letters that he can read at a distance* (1) *of* 12 *metres, and* (2) 1320 *metres.*

Let x be the required height in metres.

In the first case, x is very nearly equal to the arc of a circle, of radius 12 m, which subtends an angle of 5′ at its centre.

Hence,
$$\frac{x}{12} = \text{number of radians in } 5'$$

$$= \frac{1}{12} \times \frac{\pi}{180}$$

$$\therefore \qquad x = \frac{\pi}{180} \text{ m} = \frac{1}{180} \times \frac{22}{7} \text{ metres nearly}$$

$$= \text{about } 1.7 \text{ cm}$$

In the second case, the height y is given by

$$\frac{y}{1320} = \text{number of radians in } 5'$$

$$= \frac{1}{12} \times \frac{\pi}{180}$$

so that
$$y = \frac{11}{18}\pi = \frac{11}{18} \times \frac{22}{7} \text{ metres}$$

$$= \text{about } 1.9 \text{ metres.}$$

EXAMPLES IV

[Assume $\pi = 3.14159\ldots$ and $\frac{1}{\pi} = 0.31831$]

1. Find the number of degrees subtended at the centre of a circle by an arc whose length is 0.357 times the radius.
2. Express in radians and degrees the angle subtended at the centre of a circle by an arc whose length is 15 cm, the radius of the circle being 25 cm.
3. The value of the divisions on the outer rim of a graduated circle is $5'$ and the distance between successive graduations is 0.1 cm. Find the radius of the circle.
4. The diameter of a graduated circle is 72 cm and the graduations on its rim are $5'$ apart; find the distance from one graduation to another.
5. Find the radius of a globe which is such that the distance between two places on the same meridian whose latitude differs by $1°10'$ may be 0.5 cm.
6. Taking the radius of the earth as 6400 km, find the difference in latitude of two places, one of which is 100 km north of the other.
7. Assuming the earth to be a sphere and the distance between two parallels of latitude, which subtends an angle of $1°$ at the earth's centre, to be $69\frac{1}{9}$ km, find the radius of the earth.
8. The radius of certain circle is 30 cm; find the approximately the length of an arc of this circle, if the length of the chord of the arc be 30 cm. also.
9. What is the ratio of the radii of two circles at the centre of which two arcs of the same length subtend angles of $60°$ and $75°$?

10. If an arc, of length 10 cm, on a circle of 8 cm diameter subtend at the centre an angle of 143°14′22″, find the value of π to 4 places of decimals.

11. If the circumference of a circle be divided into 5 parts which are in A.P., and if the greatest part be 6 times the least, find in radians the magnitudes of the angles that the parts subtend at the centre of the circle.

12. The perimeter of a certain sector of a circle is equal to the length of the arc of a semicircle having the same radius; express the angle of the sector in degrees, minutes and seconds.

13. At what distance does a man, whose height is 2 m subtend an angle of 10′?

14. Find the length which at a distance of 5280 m will subtend an angle of 1′ at the eye.

15. Find approximately the distance at which a globe, $5\frac{1}{2}$ cm in diameter, will subtend an angle of 6′.

16. Find approximately the distance of a tower whose height is 51 metres and which subtends at the eye an angle of $5\frac{5}{11}''$.

17. A church spire, whose height is known to be 10 metres, subtends an angle of 9′ at the eye; find approximately its distance.

18. Find approximately in minutes the inclination to the horizon of an incline which rises $1\frac{1}{6}$ metres in 210 metres.

19. The radius of the earth being taken to be 6400 km., and the distance of the moon from the earth being 60 times the radius of the earth, find approximately the radius of the moon which subtends at the earth an angle of 16′

20. When the moon is setting at any given place, the angle that is subtended at its centre by the radius of the earth passing through the given place is 57′. If the earth's radius be 6400 km, find approximately the distance of the moon.

2

TRIGONOMETRICAL RATIOS FOR ANGLES LESS THAN A RIGHT ANGLE

➤ **23.** In the present chapter we shall only consider angles which are less than a right angle.

Let a revolving line OP start from OA and revolve into the position OP, thus tracing out the angle AOP.

In the revolving line take any point P and draw PM perpendicular to the initial line OA.

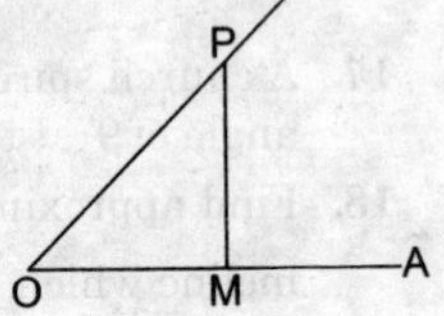

In the triangle MOP, OP is the hypotenuse, PM is the perpendicular, and OM is the base.

The trigonometrical ratios, or functions, of the angle AOP are defined as follows:

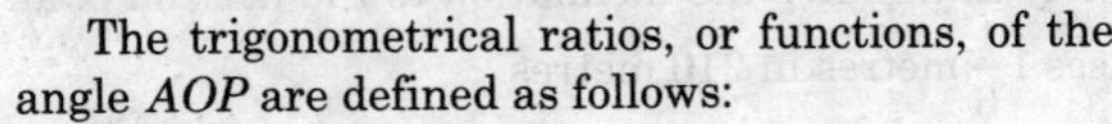

$\frac{MP}{OP}$, *i.e.*, $\frac{\text{Perp.}}{\text{Hyp.}}$, **Sine**

$\frac{OM}{OP}$, *i.e.*, $\frac{\text{Base}}{\text{Hyp.}}$, **Cosine**

$\frac{MP}{OM}$, *i.e.*, $\frac{\text{Perp.}}{\text{Base}}$, **Tangent**

$\frac{OM}{MP}$, *i.e.*, $\frac{\text{Base.}}{\text{Perp.}}$, **Cotangent**

$\frac{OP}{OM}$, *i.e.*, $\frac{\text{Hyp.}}{\text{Base}}$, **Secant**

$\frac{OP}{MP}$, *i.e.*, $\frac{\text{Hyp.}}{\text{Perp.}}$, **Cosecant**

The quantity by which the cosine falls short of unity, *i.e.*, $1 - \cos AOP$, is called the **Versed Sine** of AOP; also the quantity $1 - \sin AOP$, by which the sine falls short of unity, is called the **Coversed Sine** of AOP.

➤ **24.** It will be noted that the trigonometrical ratios are all **numbers**.

The names of these eight ratios are written, for brevity, sin *AOP*, cos *AOP*, tan *AOP*, cot *AOP*, cosec *AOP*, sec *AOP*, vers *AOP*, and covers *AOP* respectively.

The two latter ratios are seldom used.

➤ **25.** It will be noticed, from the definitions, that the cosecant is the reciprocal of the sine, so that

$$\text{cosec } AOP = \frac{1}{\sin AOP}$$

So the secant is the reciprocal of the cosine, *i.e.*,

$$\sec AOP = \frac{1}{\cos AOP}$$

and the cotangent is the reciprocal of the tangent, *i.e.*,

$$\cot AOP = \frac{1}{\tan AOP}$$

➤ **26.** *To show that the trigonometrical ratios are always the same for the same angle.*

We have to show that, if in the revolving line *OP* any other point *P′* be taken and *P′ M′* be drawn perpendicular to *OA*, the ratios derived from the triangle *OP′ M′* are the same as those derived from the triangle *OPM*.

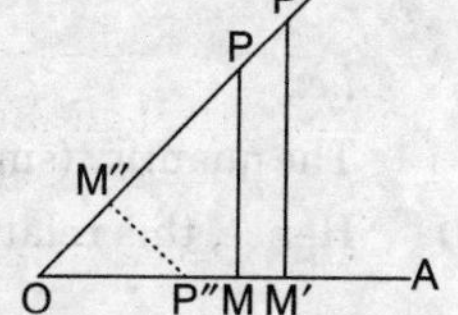

In the two triangles, the angle at *O* is common, and the angles at *M* and *M′* are both right angles and therefore equal.

Hence, the two triangles are equiangular and therefore, by Geometry, we have $\frac{MP}{OP} = \frac{M'P'}{OP'}$, *i.e.*, the sine of the angle *AOP* is the same whatever point we take on the revolving line.

Since, by the same proposition, we have

$$\frac{OM}{OP} = \frac{OM'}{OP'}$$

and

$$\frac{MP}{OM} = \frac{M'P'}{OM'}$$

It follows that the cosine and tangent are the same whatever point be taken on the revolving line. Similarly, for the other ratios.

If OA be considered as the revolving line, and in it be taken any point P'' and $P''M''$ be drawn perpendicular to OP, the functions as derived from the triangle $OP''M''$ will have the same values as before.

For, since in the two triangles OPM and $OP''M''$ the two angles $P''OM''$ and $OM''P''$ are respectively equal to POM and OMP, these two triangles are equiangular and therefore similar, and we have

$$\frac{M''P''}{OP''} = \frac{MP}{OP} \text{ and } \frac{OM''}{OP''} = \frac{OM}{OP}.$$

➤ **27.** *Fundamental relations between the trigonometrical ratios of an angle.*

We shall find that if one of the trigonometrical ratios of an angle be known, the numerical magnitude of each of the others is known also.

Let the angle AOP (Fig., Art. 23) be denoted by θ [pronounced "Theta"].

In the right-angled triangle MOP we have

$$MP^2 + OM^2 = OP^2 \qquad ...(1)$$

Hence, dividing by OP^2, we have

$$\left(\frac{MP}{OP}\right)^2 + \left(\frac{OM}{OP}\right)^2 = 1,$$

i.e., $$(\sin\theta)^2 + (\cos\theta)^2 = 1.$$

The quantity $(\sin\theta)^2$ is always written $\sin^2\theta$, and so for the other ratios.

Hence, this relation is

$$\mathbf{\sin^2\theta + \cos^2\theta = 1} \qquad ...(2)$$

Again, dividing both sides of Eq. (1) by OM^2, we have

$$\left(\frac{MP}{OM}\right)^2 + 1 = \left(\frac{OP}{OM}\right)^2$$

i.e., $$(\tan\theta)^2 + 1 = (\sec\theta)^2,$$

so that $$\mathbf{\sec^2\theta = 1 + \tan^2\theta} \qquad ...(3)$$

Again, dividing Eq. (1) by MP^2, we have

$$1 + \left(\frac{OM}{MP}\right)^2 = \left(\frac{OP}{MP}\right)^2,$$

i.e., $$1 + (\cot\theta)^2 = (\operatorname{cosec}\theta)^2,$$

so that $$\mathbf{\operatorname{cosec}^2\theta = 1 + \cot^2\theta} \qquad ...(4)$$

Also, since $$\sin\theta = \frac{MP}{OP} \text{ and } \cos\theta = \frac{OM}{OP}$$

We have $\dfrac{\sin\theta}{\cos\theta} = \dfrac{MP}{OP} \div \dfrac{OM}{OP} = \dfrac{MP}{OM} = \tan\theta$

Hence, $$\boldsymbol{\tan\theta = \frac{\sin\theta}{\cos\theta}} \qquad \text{...(5)}$$

Similarly $$\boldsymbol{\cot\theta = \frac{\cos\theta}{\sin\theta}} \qquad \text{...(6)}$$

➤ **28.**

EXAMPLE 1 *Prove that* $\sqrt{\dfrac{1-\cos A}{1+\cos A}} = \operatorname{cosec} A - \cot A.$

We have $$\sqrt{\frac{1-\cos A}{1+\cos A}} = \sqrt{\frac{(1-\cos A)^2}{1-\cos^2 A}}$$
$$= \frac{1-\cos A}{\sqrt{1-\cos^2 A}} = \frac{1-\cos A}{\sin A},$$

by relation (2) of the last article,
$$= \frac{1}{\sin A} - \frac{\cos A}{\sin A} = \operatorname{cosec} A - \cot A.$$

EXAMPLE 2 *Prove that*
$$\sqrt{\sec^2 A + \operatorname{cosec}^2 A} = \tan A + \cot A.$$

We have seen that $\sec^2 A = 1 + \tan^2 A$

and $\operatorname{cosec}^2 A = 1 + \cot^2 A.$

$\therefore$ $$\sec^2 A + \operatorname{cosec}^2 A = \tan^2 A + 2 + \cot^2 A$$
$$= \tan^2 A + 2\tan A \cot A + \cot^2 A$$
$$= (\tan A + \cot A)^2$$

So that $$\sqrt{\sec^2 A + \operatorname{cosec}^2 A} = \tan A + \cot A.$$

EXAMPLE 3 *Prove that*
$$(\operatorname{cosec} A - \sin A)(\sec A - \cos A)(\tan A + \cot A) = 1.$$

The given expression
$$= \left(\frac{1}{\sin A} - \sin A\right)\left(\frac{1}{\cos A} - \cos A\right)\left(\frac{\sin A}{\cos A} + \frac{\cos A}{\sin A}\right)$$
$$= \frac{1-\sin^2 A}{\sin A} \cdot \frac{1-\cos^2 A}{\cos A} \cdot \frac{\sin^2 A + \cos^2 A}{\sin A \cos A}$$
$$= \frac{\cos^2 A}{\sin A} \cdot \frac{\sin^2 A}{\cos A} \cdot \frac{1}{\sin A \cos A}$$

EXAMPLES V

Prove the following statements:

1. $\cos^4 A - \sin^4 A + 1 = 2\cos^2 A.$
2. $(\sin A + \cos A)(1 - \sin A \cos A) = \sin^3 A + \cos^3 A.$
3. $\dfrac{\sin A}{1 + \cos A} + \dfrac{1 + \cos A}{\sin A} = 2\operatorname{cosec} A.$
4. $\cos^6 A + \sin^6 A = 1 - 3\sin^2 A \cos^2 A.$
5. $\sqrt{\dfrac{1 - \sin A}{1 + \sin A}} = \sec A - \tan A.$
6. $\dfrac{\operatorname{cosec} A}{\operatorname{cosec} A - 1} + \dfrac{\operatorname{cosec} A}{\operatorname{cosec} A + 1} = 2\sec^2 A.$
7. $\dfrac{\operatorname{cosec} A}{\cot A + \tan A} = \cos A.$
8. $(\sec A + \cos A)(\sec A - \cos A) = \tan^2 A + \sin^2 A.$
9. $\dfrac{1}{\cot A + \tan A} = \sin A \cos A.$
10. $\dfrac{1}{\sec A - \tan A} = \sec A + \tan A.$
11. $\dfrac{1 - \tan A}{1 + \tan A} = \dfrac{\cot A - 1}{\cot A + 1}.$
12. $\dfrac{1 + \tan^2 A}{1 + \cot^2 A} = \dfrac{\sin^2 A}{\cos^2 A}.$
13. $\dfrac{\sec A - \tan A}{\sec A + \tan A} = 1 - 2\sec A \tan A + 2\tan^2 A.$
14. $\dfrac{\tan A}{1 - \cot A} + \dfrac{\cot A}{1 - \tan A} = \sec A \operatorname{cosec} A + 1.$
15. $\dfrac{\cos A}{1 - \tan A} + \dfrac{\sin A}{1 - \cot A} = \sin A + \cos A.$
16. $(\sin A + \cos A)(\cot A + \tan A) = \sec A + \operatorname{cosec} A.$
17. $\sec^4 A - \sec^2 A = \tan^4 A + \tan^2 A.$
18. $\cot^4 A + \cot^2 A = \operatorname{cosec}^4 A - \operatorname{cosec}^2 A.$
19. $\sqrt{\operatorname{cosec}^2 A - 1} = \cos A \operatorname{cosec} A.$
20. $\operatorname{cosec}^2 A \operatorname{cosec}^2 A = \tan^2 A + \cot^2 A + 2.$
21. $\tan^2 A - \sin^2 A = \sin^4 A \sec^2 A.$
22. $(1 + \cot A - \operatorname{cosec} A)(1 + \tan A + \sec A) = 2.$
23. $\dfrac{1}{\operatorname{cosec} A - \cot A} - \dfrac{1}{\sin A} = \dfrac{1}{\sin A} - \dfrac{1}{\operatorname{cosec} A + \cot A}.$

24. $\dfrac{\cot A \cos A}{\cot A + \cos A} = \dfrac{\cot A - \cos A}{\cot A \cos A}$.

25. $\dfrac{\cot A + \tan B}{\cot B + \tan A} = \cot A \tan B$.

26. $\left(\dfrac{1}{\sec^2\alpha - \cos^2\alpha} + \dfrac{1}{\operatorname{cosec}^2\alpha - \sin^2\alpha}\right)\cos^2\alpha \sin^2\alpha = \dfrac{1 - \cos^2\alpha \sin^2\alpha}{2 + \cos^2\alpha \sin^2\alpha}$.

27. $\sin^3 A - \cos^3 A = (\sin^2 A - \cos^2 A)(1 - 2\sin^2 A \cos^2 A)$.

28. $\dfrac{\cos A \operatorname{cosec} A - \sin A \sec A}{\cos A + \sin A} = \operatorname{cosec} A - \sec A$.

29. $\dfrac{\tan A + \sec A - 1}{\tan A - \sec A + 1} = \dfrac{1 + \sin A}{\cos A}$.

30. $(\tan\alpha + \operatorname{cosec}\beta)^2 - (\cot\beta - \sec\alpha)^2 = 2\tan\alpha \cot\beta (\operatorname{cosec}\alpha + \sec\beta)$.

31. $2\sec^2\alpha - \sec^4\alpha - 2\operatorname{cosec}^2\alpha + \operatorname{cosec}^4\alpha = \cot^4\alpha - \tan^4\alpha$.

32. $(\sin\alpha + \operatorname{cosec}\alpha)^2 + (\cos\alpha + \sec\alpha)^2 = \tan^2\alpha + \cot^2\alpha + 7$.

33. $(\operatorname{cosec} A + \cot A)\operatorname{covers} A - (\sec A + \tan A)\operatorname{vers} A$.

$= (\operatorname{cosec} A - \sec A)(2 - \operatorname{vers} A \operatorname{covers} A)$.

34. $(1 + \cot A + \tan A)(\sin A - \cos A) = \dfrac{\sec A}{\operatorname{cosec}^2 A} - \dfrac{\operatorname{cosec} A}{\sec^2 A}$.

35. $2\operatorname{versin} A + \cos^2 A = 1 + \operatorname{versin}^2 A$.

➤ **29.** *Limits to the values of the trigonometrial ratios.*

From Eq. (2) of Art. 27, we have, $\sin^2\theta + \cos^2\theta = 1$

Now, $\sin^2\theta$ and $\cos^2\theta$, being both squares, are both necessarily positive. Hence, since their sum is unity, neither of them can be greater than unity.

[For if one of them, say $\sin^2\theta$, were greater than unity, the other, $\cos^2\theta$, would have to be negative, which is impossible.]

Hence, neither the sine nor the cosine can be numerically greater than unity.

Since, $\sin\theta$ cannot be greater than unity, therefore $\operatorname{cosec}\theta$, which equals $\dfrac{1}{\sin\theta}$, cannot be numerically less than unity.

So $\sec\theta$, which equals $\dfrac{1}{\cos\theta}$, cannot be numerically less than unity.

➤ **30.** The foregoing results follow easily from the figure of Art. 23. For, whatever be the value of the angle *AOP*, neither the side *OM* nor the side *MP* is ever greater than *OP*.

Since, *MP* is never greater than *OP*, the ratio $\dfrac{MP}{OP}$ is never greater than unity, so that the sine of an angle is never greater than unity.

Also, since OM is never greater than OP, the ratio $\frac{OM}{OP}$ is never greater than unity, *i.e.*, the cosine is never greater than unity.

➤ **31.** We can express the trigonometrical ratios of an angle in terms of any one of them.

The simplest method of procedure is best shown by examples.

EXAMPLE 1 *To express all the trigonometrical ratios in terms of the sine.*

Let AOP be any angle θ.

Let the length OP be unity and let the corresponding length of MP be s.

Then $$OM = \sqrt{OP^2 - MP^2} = \sqrt{1-s^2}$$

Hence, $$\sin\theta = \frac{MP}{OP} = \frac{s}{1} = s$$

$$\cos\theta = \frac{OM}{OP} = \sqrt{1-s^2} = \sqrt{1-\sin^2\theta},$$

$$\tan\theta = \frac{MP}{OM} = \frac{s}{\sqrt{1-s^2}} = \frac{\sin\theta}{\sqrt{1-\sin^2\theta}}$$

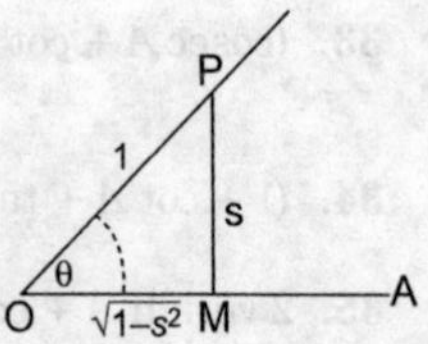

$$\cot\theta = \frac{OM}{MP} = \frac{\sqrt{1-s^2}}{s} = \frac{\sqrt{1-\sin^2\theta}}{\sin\theta}$$

$$\text{cosec}\theta = \frac{OP}{MP} = \frac{1}{s} = \frac{1}{\sin\theta},$$

and $$\sec\theta = \frac{OP}{OM} = \frac{1}{\sqrt{1-s^2}} = \frac{1}{\sqrt{1-\sin^2\theta}}$$

The last five equations give what is required.

EXAMPLE 2 *To express all the trigonometrical ratios in terms of the cotangent.*

Taking the usual figure, let the length MP be unity, and let the corresponding value of OM be x

Then, $$OP = \sqrt{OM^2 + MP^2} = \sqrt{1+x^2}$$

Hence, $$\cot\theta = \frac{OM}{MP} = \frac{x}{1} = x,$$

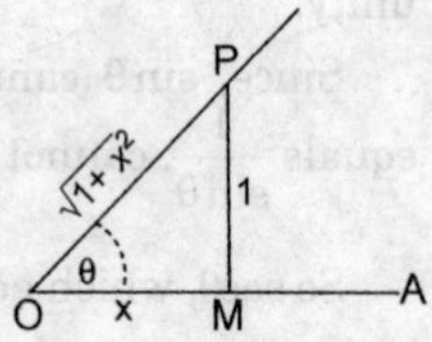

$$\sin\theta = \frac{MP}{OP} = \frac{1}{\sqrt{1+x^2}} = \frac{1}{\sqrt{1+\cot^2\theta}},$$

$$\cos\theta = \frac{OM}{OP} = \frac{x}{\sqrt{1+x^2}} = \frac{\cot\theta}{\sqrt{1+\cot^2\theta}},$$

$$\tan\theta = \frac{MP}{OM} = \frac{1}{x} = \frac{1}{\cot\theta}$$

$$\sec\theta = \frac{OP}{OM} = \frac{\sqrt{1+x^2}}{x} = \frac{\sqrt{1+\cot^2\theta}}{\cot\theta}$$

and $$\text{cosec}\theta = \frac{OP}{MP} = \frac{\sqrt{1+x^2}}{1} = \sqrt{1+\cot^2\theta}$$

The last five equations give what is required.

It will be noticed that, in each case, the denominator of the fraction which defines the trigonometrical ratio was taken equal to unity. For example, the sine is $\frac{MP}{OP}$, and hence in Ex. 1 the denominator OP is taken equal to unity.

The cotangent is $\frac{OM}{MP}$, and hence in Ex. 2 the side MP is taken equal to unity.

Similarly, suppose we had to express the other ratios in terms of the cosine, we should, since, the cosine is equal to $\frac{OM}{OP}$, put OP equal to unity and OM equal to c. The working would then be similar to that of Exs. 1 and 2.

In the following examples the sides have numerical values.

EXAMPLE 3 *If* $\cos\theta$ *equal* $\frac{3}{5}$, *find the values of the other ratios.*

Along the initial line OA take OM equal to 3, and erect a perpendicular MP.

Let a line OP, of length 5, revolve round O until its other end meets this perpendicular in the point P. Then AOP is the angle θ.

By Geometry, $$MP = \sqrt{OP^2 - OM^2} = \sqrt{5^2 - 3^3} = 4$$

Hence clearly $$\sin\theta = \frac{4}{5}, \tan\theta = \frac{4}{3}, \cot\theta = \frac{3}{4}, \text{cosec}\theta = \frac{5}{4}, \text{and} \sec\theta = \frac{5}{3}.$$

EXAMPLE 4 *Supposing* θ *to be an angle whose sine is* $\frac{1}{3}$, *to find the numerical magnitude of the other trigonometrical ratios.*

Here, $\sin\theta = \frac{1}{3}$, so that the relation (2) of Art.27 gives

$$\left(\frac{1}{3}\right)^2 + \cos^2\theta = 1,$$

i.e., $$\cos^2\theta = 1 - \frac{1}{9} = \frac{8}{9},$$

i.e., $$\cos\theta = \frac{2\sqrt{2}}{3}$$

Hence, $$\tan\theta = \frac{\sin\theta}{\cos\theta} = \frac{1}{2\sqrt{2}} = \frac{\sqrt{2}}{4},$$

$$\cot\theta = \frac{1}{\tan\theta} = 2\sqrt{2},$$

$$\text{cosec}\theta = \frac{1}{\sin\theta} = 3,$$

$$\sec\theta = \frac{1}{\cos\theta} = \frac{3}{2\sqrt{2}} = \frac{3\sqrt{2}}{4},$$

$$\text{vers}\,\theta = 1 - \cos\theta = 1 - \frac{2\sqrt{2}}{3}$$

and $$\text{covers}\theta = 1 - \sin\theta = 1 - \frac{1}{3} = \frac{2}{3}$$

➤ **32.** In the following table is given the result of expressing each trigonometrical ratio in terms of each of the others.

	$\sin\theta$	$\cos\theta$	$\tan\theta$	$\cot\theta$	$\sec\theta$	$\text{cosec}\,\theta$
$\sin\theta$	$\sin\theta$	$\sqrt{1-\cos^2\theta}$	$\frac{\tan\theta}{\sqrt{1+\tan^2\theta}}$	$\frac{1}{\sqrt{1+\cot^2\theta}}$	$\frac{\sqrt{\sec^2\theta-1}}{\sec\theta}$	$\frac{1}{\text{cosec}\theta}$
$\cos\theta$	$\sqrt{1-\sin^2\theta}$	$\cos\theta$	$\frac{1}{\sqrt{1+\tan^2\theta}}$	$\frac{\cot\theta}{\sqrt{1+\cot^2\theta}}$	$\frac{1}{\sec\theta}$	$\frac{\sqrt{\text{cosec}^2\theta-1}}{\text{cosec}\theta}$
$\tan\theta$	$\frac{\sin\theta}{\sqrt{1-\sin^2\theta}}$	$\frac{\sqrt{1-\cos^2\theta}}{\cos\theta}$	$\tan\theta$	$\frac{1}{\cot\theta}$	$\sqrt{\sec^2\theta-1}$	$\frac{1}{\sqrt{\text{cosec}^2\theta-1}}$
$\cot\theta$	$\frac{\sqrt{1-\sin^2\theta}}{\sin\theta}$	$\frac{\cos\theta}{\sqrt{1-\cos^2\theta}}$	$\frac{1}{\tan\theta}$	$\cot\theta$	$\frac{1}{\sqrt{\sec^2\theta-1}}$	$\sqrt{\text{cosec}^2\theta-1}$
$\sec\theta$	$\frac{1}{\sqrt{1-\sin^2\theta}}$	$\frac{1}{\cos\theta}$	$\sqrt{1+\tan^2\theta}$	$\frac{\sqrt{1+\cot^2\theta}}{\cot\theta}$	$\sec\theta$	$\frac{\text{cosec}\theta}{\sqrt{\text{cosec}^2\theta-1}}$
$\text{cosec}\,\theta$	$\frac{1}{\sin\theta}$	$\frac{1}{\sqrt{1-\cos^2\theta}}$	$\frac{\sqrt{1+\tan^2\theta}}{\tan\theta}$	$\sqrt{1+\cot^2\theta}$	$\frac{\sec\theta}{\sqrt{\sec^2\theta-1}}$	$\text{cosec}\theta$

EXAMPLES VI

1. Express all the other trigonometrical ratios in terms of the cosine.
2. Express all the ratios in terms of the tangent.
3. Express all the ratios in terms of the cosecant.
4. Express all the ratios in terms of the secant.
5. The sine of a certain angle is $\frac{1}{4}$; find the numerical values of the other trigonometrical ratios of this angle.
6. If $\sin\theta = \frac{12}{13}$, find $\tan\theta$ and versin θ.
7. If $\sin A = \frac{11}{61}$, find $\tan A$, $\cos A$, and $\sec A$.
8. If $\cos\theta = \frac{4}{5}$, find $\sin\theta$ and $\cot\theta$.
9. If $\cos A = \frac{9}{41}$, find $\tan A$ and $\operatorname{cosec} A$.
10. If $\tan\theta = \frac{3}{4}$, find the sine, cosine, versine, and cosecant of θ.
11. If $\tan\theta = \frac{1}{\sqrt{7}}$, find the value of $\frac{\operatorname{cosec}^2\theta - \sec^2\theta}{\operatorname{cosec}^2\theta + \sec^2\theta}$.
12. If $\cot\theta = \frac{15}{8}$, find $\cos\theta$ and $\operatorname{cosec}\theta$.
13. If $\sec A = \frac{3}{2}$, find $\tan A$ and $\operatorname{cosec} A$.
14. If $2\sin\theta = 2 - \cos\theta$, find $\sin\theta$.
15. If $8\sin\theta = 4 + \cos\theta$, find $\sin\theta$.
16. If $\tan\theta + \sec\theta = 1.5$, find $\sin\theta$.
17. If $\cot\theta + \operatorname{cosec}\theta = 5$, find $\cos\theta$.
18. If $3\sec^4\theta + 8 = 10\sec^2\theta$, find the values of $\tan\theta$.
19. If $\tan^2\theta + \sec\theta = 5$, find $\cos\theta$.
20. If $\tan\theta + \cot\theta = 2$, find $\sin\theta$.
21. If $\sec^2\theta = 2 + 2\tan\theta$, find $\tan\theta$.
22. If $\tan\theta = \frac{2x(x+1)}{2x+1}$, find $\sin\theta$ and $\cos\theta$.

Values of the Trigonometrical Ratios in Some Useful Cases

➤ **33.** *Angle of* 45°.

Let the angle *AOP* traced out be 45°.

Then, since the three angles of a triangle are together equal to two right angles,

$$\angle OPM = 180° - \angle POM - \angle PMO$$
$$= 180° - 45° - 90°$$
$$= 45° = \angle POM$$

$\therefore$ $OM = MP$

If $OP = 2a$, we have

$$4a^2 = OP^2 = OM^2 + MP^2 = 2\,OM^2,$$

so that $OM = a\sqrt{2}$

$\therefore$ $$\sin 45° = \frac{MP}{OP} = \frac{a\sqrt{2}}{2a} = \frac{1}{\sqrt{2}}$$

$$\cos 45° = \frac{OM}{OP} = \frac{a\sqrt{2}}{2a} = \frac{1}{\sqrt{2}}$$

and $\tan 45° = 1$

➤ **34.** *Angle of* 30°.

Let the angle *AOP* traced out be 30°.

Produce *PM* to *P′* making *MP′* equal to *PM*.

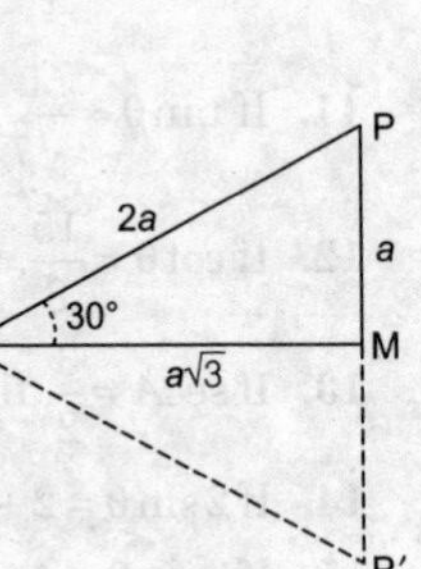

The two triangles *OMP* and *OMP′* have their sides *OM* and *MP* equal to *OM* and *MP′* and also the contained angles equal.

Therefore $OP' = OP$, and $\angle OP'P = \angle OPP' = 60°$, so that the triangle *P′OP* is equilateral.

Hence, if $OP = 2a$, we have

$$MP = \frac{1}{2}P'P = \frac{1}{2}OP = a$$

Also, $$OM = \sqrt{OP^2 - MP^2}$$
$$= \sqrt{4a^2 - a^2} = a\sqrt{3}$$

$\therefore$ $$\sin 30° = \frac{MP}{OP} = \frac{1}{2}$$

$$\cos 30° = \frac{OM}{OP} = \frac{a\sqrt{3}}{2a} = \frac{\sqrt{3}}{2}.$$

and $$\tan 30° = \frac{\sin 30°}{\cos 30°} = \frac{1}{\sqrt{3}}.$$

➤ **35.** *Angle of* 60°.

Let the angle AOP traced out be 60°.

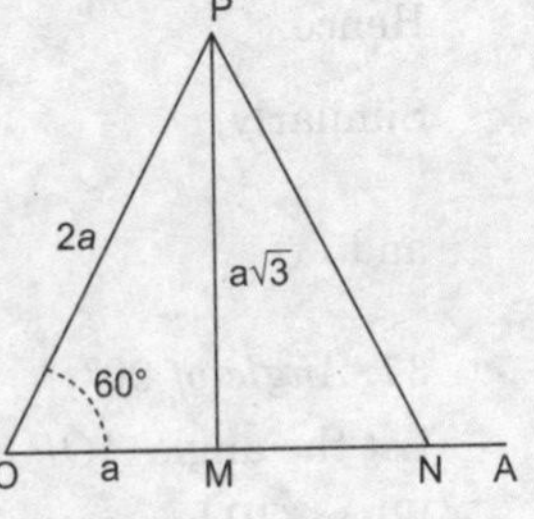

Take a point N on OA, so that

$$MN = OM = a \text{ (say)}.$$

The two triangles OMP and NMP have now the sides OM and MP equal to NM and MP respectively, and the included angles equal, so that the triangles are equal.

$\therefore \quad PN = OP$ and $\angle PNM = \angle POM = 60°$

The triangle OPN is therefore, equilateral, and hence,

$$OP = ON = 2\,OM = 2a$$

$$\therefore \qquad MP = \sqrt{OP^2 - OM^2} = \sqrt{4a^2 - a^2} = a\sqrt{3}$$

Hence, $\quad \sin 60° = \dfrac{MP}{OP} = \dfrac{a\sqrt{3}}{2a} = \dfrac{\sqrt{3}}{2}$

$$\cos 60° = \frac{OM}{OP} = \frac{a}{2a} = \frac{1}{2}$$

and $\quad \tan 60° = \dfrac{\sin 60°}{\cos 60°} = \sqrt{3}$

➤ **36.** *Angle of* 0°.

Let the revolving line OP have turned through a very small angle, so that the angle MOP is very small.

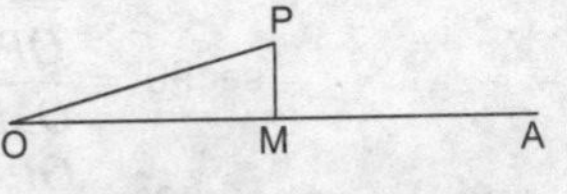

The magnitude of MP is then very small, and initially, before OP had turned through an angle large enough to be perceived, the quantity MP was smaller than any quantity we could assign, *i.e.* was what we denote by 0.

Also in this case, the two points M and P very nearly coincide, and the smaller the angle AOP the more nearly do they coincide.

Hence, when the angle AOP is actually zero, the two lengths OM and OP are equal and MP is zero.

Hence, $\quad \sin 0° = \dfrac{MP}{OP} = \dfrac{0}{OP} = 0,$

$$\cos 0° = \frac{OM}{OP} = \frac{OP}{OP} = 1$$

and $\quad \tan 0° = \dfrac{0}{1} = 0.$

Also, $\cot 0° =$ the value of $\dfrac{OM}{MP}$ when M and P coincide.

= the ratio of a finite quantity to something infinitely small

= a quantity which is infinitely great.

Such a quantity is usually denoted by the symbol ∞.

Hence, $\cot 0° = \infty$

Similarly, $\operatorname{cosec} 0° = \frac{OP}{MP} = \infty$ also

and $\sec 0° = \frac{OP}{OM} = 1$

➤ **37.** *Angle of* 90°

Let the angle *AOP* be very nearly, but not quite, a right angle.

When *OP* has actually described a right angle, the point *M* coincides with *O*, so that then *OM* is zero and *OP* and *MP* are equal.

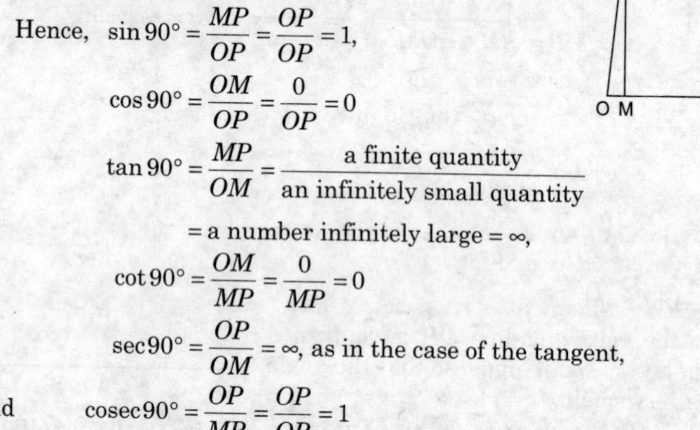

Hence, $\sin 90° = \frac{MP}{OP} = \frac{OP}{OP} = 1,$

$$\cos 90° = \frac{OM}{OP} = \frac{0}{OP} = 0$$

$$\tan 90° = \frac{MP}{OM} = \frac{\text{a finite quantity}}{\text{an infinitely small quantity}}$$

$$= \text{a number infinitely large} = \infty,$$

$$\cot 90° = \frac{OM}{MP} = \frac{0}{MP} = 0$$

$$\sec 90° = \frac{OP}{OM} = \infty, \text{ as in the case of the tangent,}$$

and $\operatorname{cosec} 90° = \frac{OP}{MP} = \frac{OP}{OP} = 1$

➤ **38. Complementary Angles. Def :** Two angles are said to be complementary when their sum is equal to a right angle. Thus any angle θ and the angle 90° – θ are complementary.

➤ **39.** *To find the relations between the trigonometrical ratios of two complementary angles.*

Let the revolving line, starting from *OA*, trace out any acute angle *AOP*, equal to θ. From any point *P* on it draw *PM* perpendicular to *OA*.

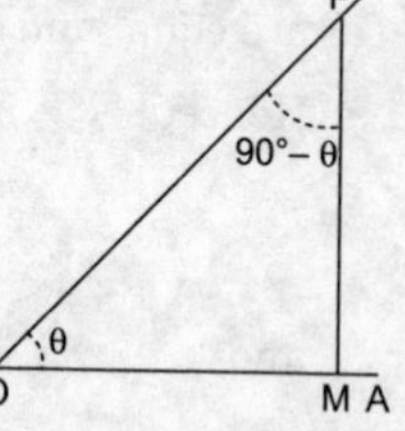

Since the three angles of a triangle are together equal to two right angles, and since *OMP* is a right angle, the sum of the two angles *MOP* and *OPM* is a right angle.

They are therefore complementary and $\angle OPM = 90° - \theta$.

[When the angle *OPM* is considered, the line *PM* is the "base" and *MO* is the "perpendicular".]

We then have

$$\mathbf{sin(90° - \theta)} = \sin MPO = \frac{MO}{PO} = \cos AOP = \mathbf{cos\theta},$$

$$\mathbf{cos(90° - \theta)} = \cos MPO = \frac{PM}{PO} = \sin AOP = \mathbf{sin\theta},$$

$$\tan(90° - \theta) = \tan MPO = \frac{MO}{PM} = \cot AOP = \cot\theta,$$

$$\cot(90° - \theta) = \cot MPO = \frac{PM}{MO} = \tan AOP = \tan\theta,$$

$$\text{cosec}\,(90° - \theta) = \text{cosec}\,MPO = \frac{PO}{MO} = \sec AOP = \sec\theta,$$

and $$\sec(90° - \theta) = \sec MPO = \frac{PO}{PM} = \text{cosec}\,AOP = \text{cosec}\,\theta$$

Hence, we observe that

The **Sine** of any angle = the **Cosine** of its complement,

The **Tangent** of any angle = the **Cotangent** of its complement,

and the **Secant** of any angle = the **Cosecant** of its complement.

From this is apparent what is the derivation of the names **Co**sine, **Co**tangent, and **Co**secant.

➤ **40.** The student is advised before proceeding any further to make himself quite familiar with the following table. [For an extension of this table, see Art. 76.]

Angle	0°	30°	45°	60°	90°
Sine	0	$\frac{1}{2}$	$\frac{1}{\sqrt{2}}$	$\frac{\sqrt{3}}{2}$	1
Cosine	1	$\frac{\sqrt{3}}{2}$	$\frac{1}{\sqrt{2}}$	$\frac{1}{2}$	0
Tangent	0	$\frac{1}{\sqrt{3}}$	1	$\sqrt{3}$	∞
Cotangent	∞	$\sqrt{3}$	1	$\frac{1}{\sqrt{3}}$	0
Cosecant	∞	2	$\sqrt{2}$	$\frac{2}{\sqrt{3}}$	1
Secant	1	$\frac{2}{\sqrt{3}}$	$\sqrt{2}$	2	∞

If the student commits accurately to memory the portion of the above table included between the thick lines, he should be able to easily reproduce the rest.

For

(1) The sines of 60° and 90° are respectively the cosines of 30° and 0°, and (Art. 39)

(2) The cosines of 60° and 90° are respectively the sines of 30° and 0°. (Art. 39)

Hence the second and third lines are known.

(3) The tangent of any angle is the result of dividing the sine by the cosine.

Hence any quantity in the fourth line is obtained by dividing the corresponding quantity in the second line by the corresponding quantity in the third line.

(4) The cotangent of any angle is the reciprocal of the tangent, so that the quantities in the fifth row are the reciprocals of the quantities in the fourth row.

(5) Since, $\operatorname{cosec}\theta = \frac{1}{\sin\theta}$, the sixth row is obtained by inverting the corresponding quantities in, the second row.

(6) Since, $\sec\theta = \frac{1}{\cos\theta}$, the seventh row is similarly obtained from the third row.

EXAMPLES VII

1. If $A = 30°$, verify that

(a) $\cos 2A = \cos^2 A - \sin^2 A = 2\cos^2 A - 1$,

(b) $\sin 2A = 2\sin A\cos A$,

(c) $\cos 3A = 4\cos^3 A - 3\cos A$,

(d) $\sin 3A = 3\sin A - 4\sin^3 A$, and

(e) $\tan 2A = \frac{2\tan A}{1 - \tan^2 A}$.

2. If $A = 45°$, verify that

(a) $\sin 2A = 2\sin A\cos A$

(b) $\cos 2A = 1 - 2\sin^2 A$ and

(c) $\tan 2A = \frac{2\tan A}{1 - \tan^2 A}$

Verify that

3. $\sin^2 30° + \sin^2 45° + \sin^2 60° = \frac{3}{2}$.

4. $\tan^2 30° + \tan^2 45° + \tan^2 60° = 4\frac{1}{3}$.

5. $\sin 30° \cos 60° + \cos 30° \sin 60° = 1$.

6. $\cos 45° \cos 60° - \sin 45° \sin 60° = \frac{\sqrt{3}-1}{2\sqrt{2}}$.

7. $\frac{4}{3}\cot^2 30° + 3\sin^2 60° - 2\operatorname{cosec}^2 60° - \frac{3}{4}\tan^2 30° = 3\frac{1}{3}$.

8. $\operatorname{cosec}^2 45° \sec^2 30° \cdot \sin^3 90° \cdot \cos 60° = 1\frac{1}{3}$.

9. $4\cot^2 45° - \sec^2 60° + \sin^3 30° = \frac{1}{8}$.

3

SIMPLE PROBLEMS IN HEIGHTS AND DISTANCES

➤ **41.** One of the objects of Trigonometry is to find the distances between points, or the heights of objects, without actually measuring these distances or these heights.

➤ **42.** Supposed O and P to be two points, P being at a higher level than O.

Let OM be a horizontal line drawn through O to meet in M the vertical line drawn through P.

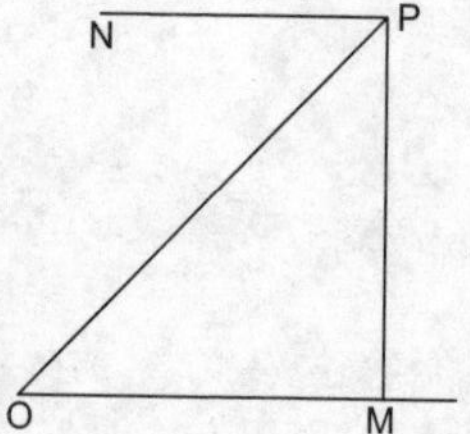

The angle MOP is called the **Angle of Elevation** of the point P as seen from O.

Draw PN parallel to MO, so that PN is the horizontal line passing through P. The angle NPO is the **Angle of Depression** of the point O as seen from P.

➤ **43.** Two of the instruments used in practical work are the Theodolite and the Sextant.

The Theodolite is used to measure angles in a vertical plane.

In its simple form it consists of a telescope attached to a flat piece of wood. This piece of wood is supported by three legs and can be arranged so as to be accurately horizontal.

This table being at O and horizontal, and the telescope being initially pointing in the direction OM, the latter can be made to rotate in a vertical plane until it points accurately towards P. A graduated scale shows the angle through which it has been turned from the horizontal, *i.e.*, gives us the angle of elevation MOP.

Similarly, if the instrument were at P, the angle NPO through which the telescope would have to be turned, downward from the horizontal would give us the angle NPO.

The instrument can also be used to measure angles in a horizontal plane.

➤ **44.** The Sextant is used to find the angle subtended by any two points D and E at a third point F. It is an instrument much used on board ships.

Its construction and application are too complicated to be here considered.

➤ **45.** We shall now solve a few simple examples in heights and distances.

EXAMPLE 1 *A vertical flagstaff stands on a horizontal plane from a point distant* 60 *metres from its foot, the angle of elevation of its top is found to be* 30°*; find the height of the flagstaff.*

Let MP (fig., Art. 42) represent the flagstaff and O the point from which the angle of elevation is taken.

Then $OM = 60$ metres, and $\angle MOP = 30°$

Since PMO is a right angle, we have

$$\frac{MP}{OM} = \tan MOP = \tan 30° = \frac{1}{\sqrt{3}} \qquad \text{(Art. 34.)}$$

$$\therefore \qquad MP = \frac{OM}{\sqrt{3}} = \frac{60}{\sqrt{3}} = \frac{60\sqrt{3}}{3} = 20\sqrt{3}$$

Now, by extraction of the square root, we have

$$\sqrt{3} = 1.73205\ldots$$

Hence, $\quad MP = 20 \times 1.73205\ldots$ metres $= 34.641\ldots$ metres

EXAMPLE 2 *A man wishes to find the height of a church spire which stands on a horizontal plane; at a point on this plane he finds the angle of elevation of the top of the spire to be* 45°*; on walking* 30 *metres toward the tower he finds the corresponding angle of elevation to be* 60°*; deduce the height of the tower and also his original distance from the foot of the spire.*

Let P be the top of the spire and A and B the two points at which the angles of elevation are taken. Draw PM perpendicular to AB produced and let MP be x.

We are given $AB = 30$ metres,

$$\angle MAP = 45°$$

and

$$\angle MBP = 60°$$

We then have

$$\frac{AM}{x} = \cot 45° = 1$$

and

$$\frac{BM}{x} = \cot 60° = \frac{1}{\sqrt{3}}$$

Hence, $\quad AM = x$, and $BM = \dfrac{x}{\sqrt{3}}$

$$\therefore \qquad 30 = AM - BM = x - \frac{x}{\sqrt{3}} = x\left[\frac{\sqrt{3}-1}{\sqrt{3}}\right]$$

$$\therefore \qquad x = \frac{30\sqrt{3}}{\sqrt{3}-1} = \frac{30\sqrt{3}(\sqrt{3}+1)}{3-1} = 15(3+\sqrt{3})$$

$$= 15\,[3 + 1.73205\ldots] = 71 \text{ metres}$$

Also $AM = x$, so that both of the required distances are equal to 71 metres.

EXAMPLE 3 *From the top of a cliff, 60 metres high, the angles of depression of the top and bottom of a tower are observed to be 30° and 60°; find the height of the tower.*

Let A be the point of observation and BA the height of the cliff, and let CD be the tower.

Draw AE horizontally, so that $\angle EAC = 30°$ and $\angle EAD = 60°$

Let x metres be the height of the tower and produce DC to meet AE in E, so that

$$CE = AB - x = 60 - x$$

Since $\qquad \angle ADB = \angle DAE = 60°$

$$\therefore \qquad DB = AB \cot ADB = 60 \cot 60° = \frac{60}{\sqrt{3}}$$

Also, $\qquad \dfrac{60-x}{DB} = \dfrac{CE}{EA} = \tan 30° = \dfrac{1}{\sqrt{3}}$

$$\therefore \qquad 60 - x = \frac{DB}{\sqrt{3}} = \frac{60}{3}$$

so that $\qquad x = 60 - \dfrac{60}{3} = 40$ metres

EXAMPLE 4 *A man observes that at a point due south of a certain tower its angle of elevation is 60°; he then walks 100 metres due west on a horizontal plane and finds that the angle of elevation is 30°; find the height of the tower and his original distance from it.*

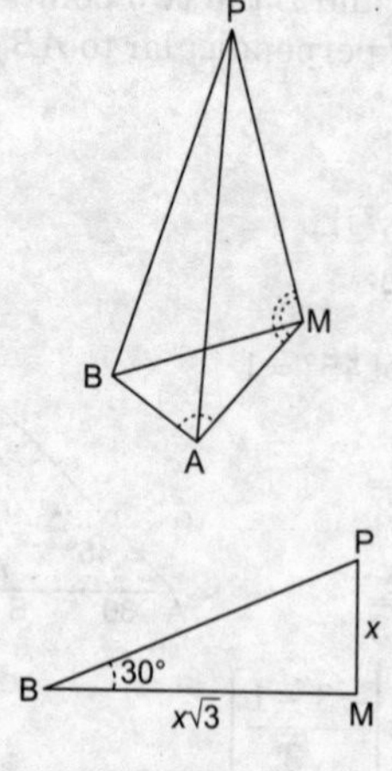

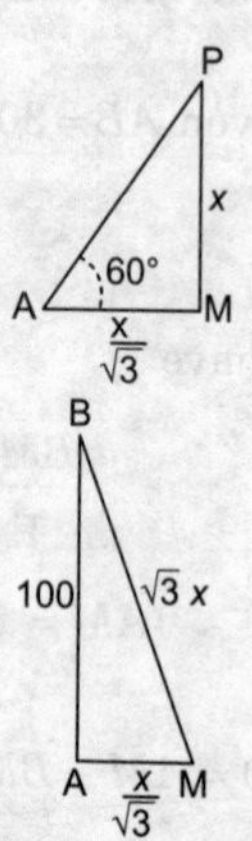

Let P be the top, and PM the height of the tower, A the point due south of the tower and B the point due west of A.

The angles PMA, PMB, and MAB are therefore all right angles.

For simplicity, since the triangles $PAM, PBM,$ and ABM are in different planes, they are reproduced in the second, third, and fourth figures and drawn to scale.

We are given $AB = 100$ metres, $\angle PAM = 60°$, and $\angle PBM = 30°$.

Let the height of the tower be x metres.

From the second figure,

$$\frac{AM}{x} = \cot 60° = \frac{1}{\sqrt{3}}$$

so that $$AM = \frac{x}{\sqrt{3}}$$

From the third figure,

$$\frac{BM}{x} = \cot 30° = \sqrt{3}$$

so that $$BM = x\sqrt{3}$$

From the last figure, we have

$$BM^2 = AM^2 + AB^2$$

i.e., $$3x^2 = \frac{1}{3}x^2 + (100)^2$$

$\therefore$ $$8x^2 = 3 \times (100)^2$$

$\therefore$ $$x = \frac{100\sqrt{3}}{2\sqrt{2}} = \frac{50\sqrt{6}}{2} = 25\sqrt{6}$$

$$= 25 \times 2.44949\ldots = 61.24 \text{ metres}$$

Also his original distance from the tower

$$= x \cot 60° = \frac{x}{\sqrt{3}} = 25 \times \sqrt{2}$$

$$= 25 \times (1.4142\ldots) = 35.35 \text{ metres}$$

EXAMPLES VIII

1. A person, standing on the bank of a river, observes that the angle subtended by a tree on the opposite bank is 60°; when he retires 20 m from the bank he finds the angle to be 30°; find the height of the tree and the breadth of the river.
2. At a certain point the angle of elevation of a tower is found to be such that its cotangent is $\frac{3}{5}$; on walking 32 m directly toward the tower its angle of elevation is an angle whose cotangent is $\frac{2}{3}$. Find the height of the tower.

3. At a point A, the angle of elevation of a tower is found to be such that its tangent is $\frac{5}{12}$; on walking 240 m nearer the tower the tangent of the angle of elevation is found to be $\frac{3}{4}$; what is the height of the tower?
4. Find the height of a chimney when it is found that, on walking towards it 50 m in a horizontal line through its base, the angular elevation of its top changes from 30° to 45°.
5. An observer on the top of a cliff, 200 m above the sea-level, observes the angles of depression of two ships at anchor to be 45° and 30° respectively; find the distances between the ships if the line joining them points to the base of the cliff.
6. From the top of a cliff an observer finds that the angles of depression of two buoys in the sea are 39° and 26° respectively; the buoys are 300 metres apart and the line joining them points straight at the foot of the cliff; find the height of the cliff and the distance of the nearest buoy from the foot of the cliff, given that $\cot 26° = 2.0503$, and $\cot 39° = 1.2349$.
7. The upper part of a tree broken over by the wind makes an angle of 30° with the ground, and the distance from the root to the point where the top of the tree touches the ground is 10 m; what was the height of the tree?
8. The horizontal distance between two towers is 60 m and the angular depression of the top of the first as seen from the top of the second, which is 150 m high, is 30°; find the height of the first.
9. The angle of elevation of the top of an unfinished tower at a point distant 120 m from its base is 45°; how much higher must the tower be raised so that its angle of elevation at the same point may be 60°?
10. Two towers of equal height stand on either side of a wide road which is 100 m wide; at a point in the road between the pillars the elevations of the tops of the pillars are 60° and 30°; find their height and the position of the point.
11. The angle of elevation of the top of a tower is observed to be 60°; at a point 40 m above the first point of observation the elevation is found to be 45°; find the height of the tower and its horizontal distance from the points of observation.
12. At the foot of a mountain the elevation of its summit is found to be 45°; after ascending 1000 m towards the mountain up a slope of 30° inclination the elevation is found to be 60°. Find the height of the mountain.
13. What is the angle of elevation of the sun when the length of the shadow of a pole is $\sqrt{3}$ times the height of the pole?

14. The shadow of a tower standing on a level plane is found to be 60 m longer when the sun's altitude is 30° than when it is 45°. Prove that the height of the tower is $30(1 + \sqrt{3})$ metres.

15. On a straight coast there are three objects A, B and C, such that $AB = BC = 2$ km. A vessel approaches B in a line perpendicular to the coast, and at a certain point AC is found to subtend an angle of 60°; after sailing in the same direction for ten minutes AC is found to subtend an angle of 120°; find the rate at which the ship is going.

16. Two flagstaffs stand on a horizontal plane. A and B are two points on the line joining the bases of the flagstaffs and between them. The angles of elevation of the tops of the flagstaffs as seen from A are 30° and 60° and, as seen from B, they are 60° and 45°. If the length AB be 10 metres, find the heights of the flagstaffs and the distance between them.

17. P is the top and Q the foot of a tower standing on a horizontal plane. A and B are two points on this plane such that AB is 32 m and QAB is a right angle. It is found that

$$\cot PAQ = \frac{2}{5} \text{ and } \cot PBQ = \frac{3}{5};$$

find the height of the tower.

18. A square tower stands upon a horizontal plane. From a point in this plane, from which three of its upper corners are visible, their angular elevations are respectively 45°, 60°, and 45°. Show that the height of the tower is to the breadth of one of its sides as $\sqrt{6}(\sqrt{5} + 1)$ to 4.

19. A lighthouse, facing north, sends out a fan-shaped beam of light extending from north-east to north-west. An observer on a steamer, sailing due west, first sees the light when he is 5 km away from the lighthouse and continues to see it for $30\sqrt{2}$ minutes. What is the speed of the steamer?

20. A man stands at a point X on the bank XY of a river with straight and parallel banks, and observes that the line joining X to a point Z on the opposite bank makes an angle of 30° with XY. He then goes along the bank a distance of 200 metres to Y and finds that the angle ZYX is 60°. Find the breadth of the river.

21. A man, walking due north, observes that the elevation of a balloon, which is due east of him and is sailing toward the north-west, is then 60°; after he has walked 400 metres the balloon is vertically over his head; find its height supposing it to have always remained the same.

4

APPLICATION OF ALGEBRAIC SIGNS TO TRIGONOMETRY

46. Positive and Negative Angles. In Art. 6, in treating of angles of any size, we spoke of the revolving line as if it always revolved in a direction opposite to that in which the hands of a watch revolve, when the watch is held with its face uppermost.

This direction is called counter-clockwise.

When the revolving line turns in this manner it is said to revolve in the positive direction and to trace out a positive angle.

When the line OP revolves in the opposite direction, *i.e.*, in the same direction as the hands of the watch, it is said to revolve in the negative direction and to trace out a negative angle. This negative direction is clockwise.

47. Let the revolving line start from OA and revolve until it reaches a position OP, which lies between OA' and OB' and which bisects the angle $A'OB'$.

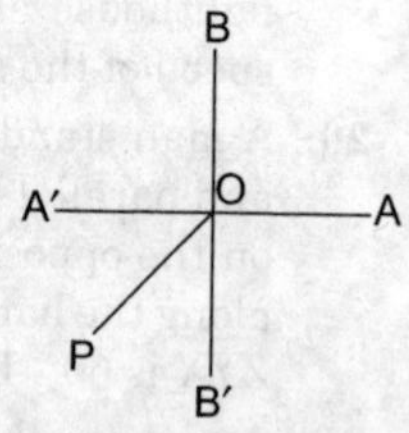

If it has revolved in the positive direction, it has traced out the positive angle whose measure is $+225°$.

If it has revolved in the negative direction, it has traced out the negative angle $-135°$.

Again, suppose we only know that the revolving line is in the above position. It may have made one, two, three ... complete revolutions and then have described the positive angle $+225°$. Or again, it may have made one, two, three... complete revolutions in the negative direction and then have described the negative angle $-135°$.

In the first case, the angle it has described is either $225°$, or $360° + 225°$, or $2 \times 360° + 225°$, or $3 \times 360° + 225°$,... *i.e.*, $225°$ or $585°$, or $945°$, or $1305°$...

In the second case, the angle it has described is $-135°$, or $-360° - 135°$, or $-2 \times 360° - 135°$, or $-3 \times 360° - 135°$..., *i.e.*, $-135°$, or $-495°$, or $-855°$, or $-1215°$...

48. Positive and Negative Lines. Suppose that a man is told to start from a given milestone on a straight road and to walk 1000 yards along the road and then to stop. Unless we are told the *direction* in which he started, we do not know his position when he stops. All we know is that he is either at a distance 1000 yards on one side of the milestone or at the same distance on the other side.

In measuring distances along a straight line it is therefore convenient to have a standard direction; this direction is called the positive direction and all distances measured along it are said to be positive. The opposite direction is called the negative direction; and all distances measured along it are said to be negative.

The standard, or positive, direction for lines drawn parallel to the foot of the page is towards the right.

The length OA is in the positive direction. The length OA' is in the negative direction. If the magnitude of the distance OA or OA' be a, the point A is at a distance $+a$ from O and the point A' is at a distance $-a$ from O.

All lines measured to the right have then the positive sign prefixed; all lines to the left have the negative sign prefixed.

If a point start from O and describe a positive distance OA, and then a distance AB back again toward O, equal numerically to b, the total distance it has described measured in the positive direction is $OA + AB$,

i.e., $$a + (-b), \text{ i.e., } a - b$$

49. For lines at right angles to AA', the positive direction is from O towards the top of the page, *i.e.*, the direction of OB (fig., Art. 47). All lines measured from O towards the foot of the page, *i.e.*, in the direction OB', are negative.

50. *Trigonometrical ratios for an angle of any magnitude.*

Let OA be the initial line (drawn in the positive direction) and let OA' be drawn in the opposite direction to OA.

Let BOB' be a line at right angles to OA, its positive direction being OB.

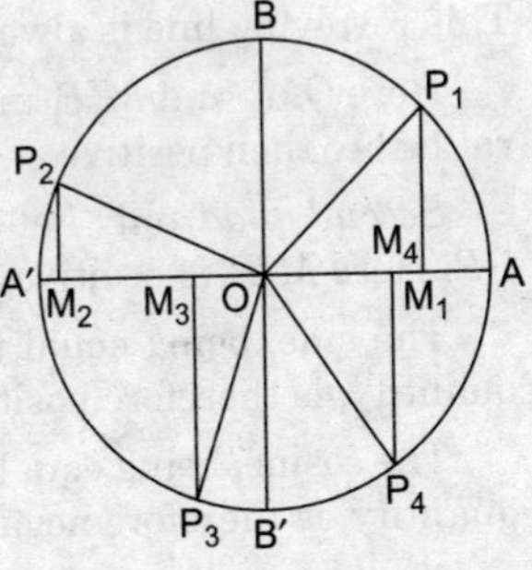

Let a revolving line OP start from OA and revolving in either direction, positive or negative, trace out an angle of any magnitude whatever. From a point P in the revolving line draw PM perpendicular to AOA'.

[Four positions of the revolving line are given in the figure, one in each of the four quadrants, and the suffixes 1, 2, 3 and 4 are attached to P for the purpose of distinction.]

We then have the following definitions, which are the same as those given in Art. 23 for the simple case of an acute angle :

$\frac{MP}{OP}$ is called the **sine** of the angle AOP,

$\frac{OM}{OP}$ " " " **Cosine** " " " AOP,

$\frac{MP}{OM}$ " " " **Tangent** " " " AOP,

$\frac{OM}{MP}$ " " " **Cotangent** " " " AOP,

$\frac{OP}{OM}$ " " " **Secant** " " " AOP,

$\frac{OP}{MP}$ " " " **Cosecant** " " " AOP.

The quantities $1 - \cos AOP$ and $1 - \sin AOP$ are respectively called the **Versed Sine** and the **Coversed Sine** of AOP.

➤ **51.** In exactly the same manner as in Art. 27 it may be shown that, for all values of the angle AOP $(= \theta)$, we have

$$\sin^2\theta + \cos^2\theta = 1$$

$$\frac{\sin\theta}{\cos\theta} = \tan\theta$$

$$\sec^2\theta = 1 + \tan^2\theta$$

and
$$\operatorname{cosec}^2\theta = 1 + \cot^2\theta$$

➤ 52. Signs of the trigonometrical ratios.

First quadrant : Let the revolving line be in the first quadrant, as OP_1. This revolving line is always positive.

Here OM_1 and M_1P_1 are both positive, so that all the trigonometrical ratios are then positive.

Second quadrant : Let the revolving line be in the second quadrant, as OP_2. Here M_2P_2 is positive and OM_2 is negative.

The sine, being equal to the ratio of a positive quantity to a positive quantity, is therefore positive.

The cosine, being equal to the ratio of a negative quantity to a positive quantity, is therefore negative.

The tangent, being equal to the ratio of a positive quantity to a negative quantity, is therefore negative.

The cotangent is negative.

The secant is negative.

The cosecant is positive.

Third quadrant : If the revolving line be, as OP_3, in the third quadrant, we have both M_3P_3 and OM_3 negative.

The sine is therefore negative.

The cosine is negative.

The tangent is positive.

The cotangent is positive.

The secant is negative.

The cosecant is negative.

Fourth quadrant : Let the revolving line be in the fourth quadrant, as OP_4. Here M_4P_4 is negative and OM_4 is positive.

The sine is therefore negative.

The cosine is positive.

The tangent is negative.

The cotangent is negative.

The secant is positive.

The cosecant is negative.

The annexed table shows the signs of the trigonometrical ratios according to the quadrant in which lies the revolving line which bounds the angle considered.

Ratio	Second quadrant (between OB and OA′)	First quadrant (between OA and OB)	Third quadrant (between OA′ and OB′)	Fourth quadrant (between OB′ and OA)
sin	+	+	–	–
cos	–	+	–	+
tan	–	+	+	–
cot	–	+	+	–
sec	–	+	–	+
cosec	+	+	–	–

➤ **53.** *Tracing of the changes in the sign and magnitude of the trigonometrical ratios of an angle, as the angle increases from* 0° *to* 360°.

Let the revolving line OP be of constant length a.

When it coincides with OA, the length OM_1 is equal to a; and, when it coincides with OB, the point M_1 coincides with O and OM_1 vanishes. Also, as the revolving line turns from OA to OB, the distance OM_1 decreases from a to zero.

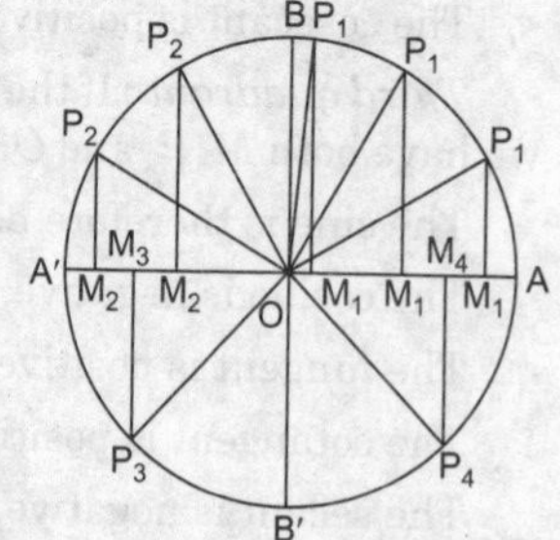

Whilst the revolving line is in the second quadrant and is revolving from OB to OA', the distance OM_2 is negative and increases numerically from 0 to a [*i.e.*, it decreases algebraically from 0 to $-a$].

In the third quadrant, the distance OM_3 increases algebraically from $-a$ to 0; and, in the fourth quadrant the distance OM_4 increases from 0 to a.

In the first quadrant, the length M_1P_1 increases from 0 to a; in the second quadrant, M_2P_2 decreases from a to 0; in the third quadrant, M_3P_3 decreases algebraically from 0 to $-a$; whilst in the fourth quadrant M_4P_4 increases algebraically from $-a$ to 0.

➤ **54. Sine :** In the first quadrant, as the angle increases from 0 to 90°, the sine, i.e. $\frac{M_1P_1}{a}$, increases from $\frac{0}{a}$ to $\frac{a}{a'}$ *i.e.*, from 0 to 1.

In the second quadrant, as the angle increases from 90° to 180°, the sine decreases from $\frac{a}{a}$ to $\frac{0}{a'}$ *i.e.*, from 1 to 0.

In the third quadrant, as the angle increases from 180° to 270°, the sine *decreases* from $\frac{0}{a}$ to $\frac{-a}{a}$, *i.e.*, from 0 to −1.

In the fourth quadrant, as the angle increases from 270° to 360°, the sine *increases* from $\frac{-a}{a}$ to $\frac{0}{a}$, *i.e.*, from −1 to 0.

➤ **55. Cosine :** In the first quadrant the cosine, which is equal to $\frac{OM_1}{a}$, decreases from $\frac{a}{a}$ to $\frac{0}{a}$, *i.e.*, from 1 to 0.

In the second quadrant, it decreases from $\frac{0}{a}$ to $\frac{-a}{a}$, *i.e.*, from 0 to −1.

In the third quadrant, it increases from $\frac{-a}{a}$ to $\frac{0}{a'}$ *i.e.*, from −1 to 0.

In the fourth quadrant, it increases from $\frac{0}{a}$ to $\frac{a}{a'}$ *i.e.*, from 0 to 1.

➤ **56. Tangent :** In the first quadrant, M_1P_1 increases from 0 to a and OM_1 decreases from a to 0, so that $\frac{M_1P_1}{OM_1}$ continually increases (for its numerator continually increases and its denominator continually decreases).

When OP_1 coincides with OA, the tangent is 0; when the revolving line has turned through an angle which is slightly less than a right angle, so that OP_1 nearly coincides with OB, then M_1P_1 is very nearly equal to a and OM_1 is very small. The ratio $\frac{M_1P_1}{OM_1}$ is therefore very large, and the nearer OP_1 gets to OB the larger does the ratio become, so that, by taking the revolving line near enough to OB, we can make the tangent as large as we please. This is expressed by saying that, when the angle is equal to 90°, its tangent is infinite.

The symbol ∞ is used to denote an infinitely great quantity.

Hence in the first quadrant the tangent increases from 0 to ∞.

In the second quadrant, when the revolving line has described an angle AOP_2 slightly greater than a right angle, M_2P_2 is very nearly equal to a and OM_2 is very small and negative, so that the corresponding tangent is very large and negative.

Also, as the revolving line turns from OB to OA', M_2P_2 decreases from a to 0 and OM_2 is negative and decreases from 0 to $-a$, so that when the revolving line coincides with OA' the tangent is zero.

Hence, in the second quadrant, the tangent increases from $-\infty$ to 0.

In the third quadrant, both M_3P_3 and OM_3 are negative, and hence their ratio is positive. Also, when the revolving line coincides with OB', the tangent is infinite.

Hence, in the third quadrant, the tangent increases from 0 to ∞.

In the fourth quadrant, M_4P_4 is negative and OM_4 is positive, so that their ratio is negative. Also, as the revolving line passes through OB' the tangent changes from $+\infty$ to $-\infty$. [Just as in passing through OB].

Hence, in the fourth quadrant, the tangent increases from $-\infty$ to 0.

➤ **57. Cotangent**. When the revolving line coincides with OA, M_1P_1 is very small and OM_1 is very nearly equal to a, so that the cotangent, *i.e.*, the ratio $\frac{OM_1}{M_1P_1}$ is infinite to start with. Also, as the revolving line rotates from OA to OB, the quantity M_1P_1 increases from 0 to a and OM_1 decreases from a to 0.

Hence, in the first quadrant, the cotangent decreases from ∞ to 0.

In the second quadrant, M_2P_2 is positive and OM_2 negative, so that the cotangent decreases from 0 to $\frac{-a}{0}$, *i.e.*, from 0 to $-\infty$.

In the third quadrant, it is positive and decreases from ∞ to 0 [for as the revolving line crosses OA' the cotangent changes from $-\infty$ to ∞].

In the fourth quadrant, it is negative and decreases from 0 to $-\infty$.

➤ **58. Secant :** When the revolving line coincides with OA the value of OM_1 is a, so that the value of the secant is then unity.

As the revolving line turns from OA to OB, OM_1 decreases from a to 0, and when the revolving line coincides with OB the value of the secant is $\frac{a}{0}$, *i.e.*, ∞.

Hence, in the first quadrant, the secant increases from 1 to ∞.

In the second quadrant, OM_2 is negative and decreases from 0 to $-a$. Hence, in this quadrant, the secant increases from $-\infty$ to -1 [for as the revolving line crosses OB the quantity OM_1 changes sign and therefore the secant changes from $+\infty$ to $-\infty$].

In the third quadrant, OM_2 is always negative and increases from $-a$ to 0; therefore the secant decreases from -1 to $-\infty$.

In the fourth quadrant, OM_4 is always positive and increases from 0 to a. Hence, in this quadrant, the secant decreases from ∞ to + 1.

➤ **59. Cosecant :** The change in the cosecant may be traced in a similar manner to that in the secant.

In the third quadrant, it increases from $-\infty$ to -1.

In the fourth quadrant, it decreases from -1 to $-\infty$.

➤ **60.** The foregoing results are collected in the annexed table.

B

In the second quadrant, the			In the first quadrant, the		
sine	decreases from	1 to 0	sine	increases from	0 to 1
cosine	decreases from	0 to –1	cosine	decreases from	1 to 0
tangent	increases from	–∞ to 0	tangent	increases from	0 to ∞
cotangent	decreases from	0 to –∞	cotangent	decreases from	∞ to 0
secant	increases from	–∞ to –1	secant	increases from	1 to ∞
cosecant	increases from	1 to ∞	cosecant	decreases from	∞ to 1

A′ O A

In the third quadrant, the			In the fourth quadrant, the		
sine	decreases from	0 to –1	sine	increases from	–1 to 0
cosine	increases from	–1 to 0	cosine	increases from	0 to 1
tangent	increases from	0 to ∞	tangent	increases from	–∞ to 0
cotangent	decreases from	∞ to –0	cotangent	decreases from	0 to –∞
secant	decreases from	–1 to ∞	secant	decreases from	∞ to 1
cosecant	increases from	–∞ to –1	cosecant	decreases from	–1 to –∞

B′

➤ **61. Periods of the trigonometrical functions :** As an angle increases from 0 to 2π radians, *i.e.*, whilst the revolving line makes a complete revolution, its sine first increases from 0 to 1, then decreases from 1 to -1, and finally increases from -1 to 0, and thus the sine goes through all its changes, returning to its original value. Similarly, as the angle increases from 2π radians to 4π radians, the sine goes through the same series of changes.

Also, the sines of any two angles which differ by four right angles, *i.e.*, 2π radians, are the same.

This is expressed by saying that the **period of the sine is 2π.**

Similarly, the cosine, secant, and cosecant go through all their changes as the angle increases by 2π.

The tangent, however, goes through all its changes as the angle increases from 0 to π radians, *i.e.*, whilst the revolving line turns through two right angles. Similarly, for the cotangent.

The period of the sine, cosine, secant, and cosecant is therefore 2π radians; the period of the tangent and cotangent is π radians.

Since the values of the trigonometrical functions repeat over and over again as the angle increases, they are called **periodic functions**.

➤ ***62.** The variations in the values of the trigonometrical ratios may be graphically represented to the eye by means of curves constructed in the following manner.

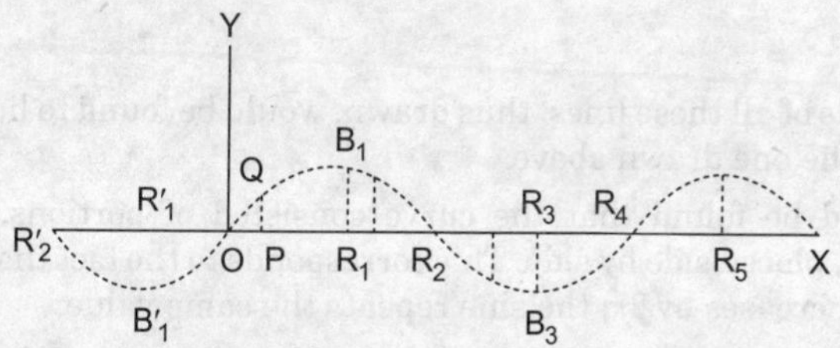

Sine-Graph

Let OX and OY be two straight lines at right angles and let the magnitudes of **angles** be represented by **lengths** measured along OX.

Let $R_1, R_2, R_3, \ldots$ be points such that the distances $OR_1, R_1R_2, R_2R_3, \ldots$ are equal. If then the distance OR_1 represent a right angle, the distances $OR_2, OR_3, OR_4, \ldots$ must represent two, three, four, ... right angles.

Also, if P be any point on the line OX, then OP represents an angle which bears the same ratio to a right angle that OP bears to OR_1.

[For example, if OP be equal to $\frac{1}{3}OR_1$, then OP would represent one-third of a right angle; if P bisected R_3R_4, then OP would represent $3\frac{1}{2}$ right angles.]

Let also OR_1 be so chosen that one unit of length represents one radian; since OR_2 represents two right angles, *i.e.*, π radians, the length OR_2 must be π units of length, *i.e.*, about $3\frac{1}{7}$ units of length.

In a similar manner, negative angles are represented by distances OR_1', OR_2',... measured from O in a negative direction.

At each point P erect a perpendicular PQ to represent the sine of the angle which is represented by OP; if the sine be positive, the perpendicular is to be drawn parallel to OY in the positive direction; if the sine be negative, the line is to be drawn in the negative direction.

[For example, since, OR_1 represents a right angle, the sine of which is 1, we erect a perpendicular R_1B_1 equal to one unit of length; since OR_2 represents an angle equal to two right angles, the sine of which is zero, we erect a perpendicular of length zero; since, OR_3 represents three right angles, the sine of which is -1, we erect a perpendicular equal to -1 *i.e.*, we draw R_2B_3 downward and equal to a unit of length; if OP were equal to one-third of OR_1, it would represent $\frac{1}{3}$ of a right angle, *i.e.*, 30°, the sine of which is $\frac{1}{2}$, and so we should erect a perpendicular PQ equal to one-half the unit of length.]

The ends of all these lines, thus drawn, would be found to lie on a curve similar to the one drawn above.

It would be found that the curve consisted of portions, similar to $OB_1R_2B_3R_4$, placed side by side. This corresponds to the fact that each time the angle increases by 2π, the sine repeats the same value.

➤ ***63. Cosine-Graph:** The Cosine-Graph is obtained in the same manner as the Sine-Graph, except that in this case the perpendicular PQ represents the cosine of the angle represented by OP.

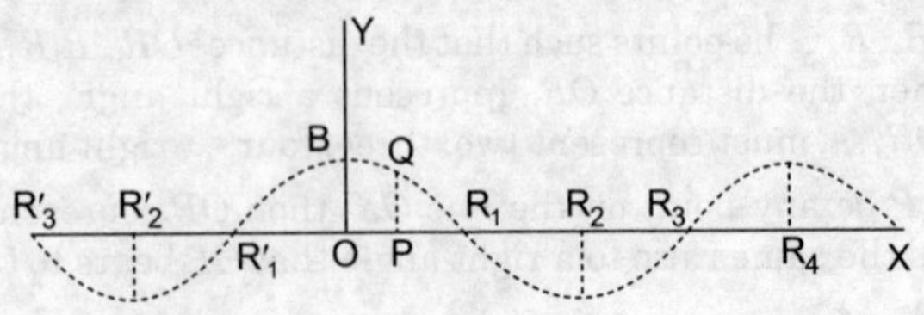

The curve obtained is the same as that of Art. 62 if in that curve we move O to R_1 and let OY be drawn along R_1B_1.

➤ ***64. Tangent-Graph :** In this case, since the tangent of a right angle is infinite and since OR_1 represents a right angle, the perpendicular drawn at R_1 must be of infinite length and the dotted curve will only meet the line R_1L at an infinite distance.

Since the tangent of an angle slightly greater than a right angle is negative and almost infinitely great, the dotted curve immediately beyond LR_1L' commences at an infinite distance on the negative side of, *i.e.*, below OX.

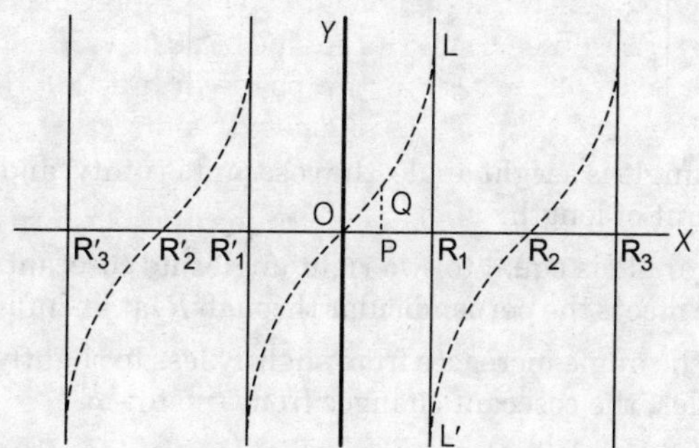

The Tangent-Graph will clearly consist of an infinite number of similar but disconnected portions, all ranged parallel to one another.

Such a curve is called a Discontinuous Curve. Both the Sine-Graph and the Cosine-Graph are, on the other hand, Continuous Curves.

➤ ***65. Cotangent-Graph:** If the curve to represent the cotangent be drawn in similar manner, it will be found to meet OY at an infinite distance above O; it will pass through the point R_1 and touch the vertical line through R_2 at an infinite distance on the negative side of OX. Just beyond R_2 it will start at an infinite distance above R_2, and proceed as before.

The curve is therefore discontinuous and will consist of an infinite number of portions all ranged side by side.

➤ ***66. Cosecant-Graph:** When the angle is zero, the sine is zero, and the cosecant is therefore infinite.

Hence, the curve meets OY at infinity.

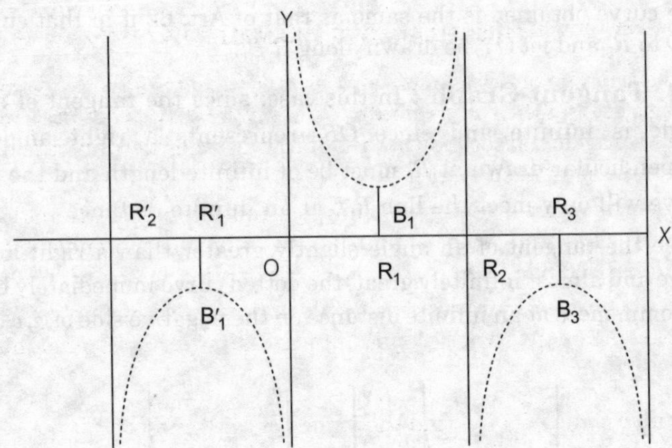

When the angle is a right angle, the cosecant is unity, and hence R_1B_1 is equal to the unit of length.

When the angle is equal to two right angles its cosecant is infinity, so that the curve meets the perpendicular through R_2 at an infinite distance.

Again, as the angle increases from slightly less to slightly greater than two right angles, the cosecant changes from $+\infty$ to $-\infty$.

Hence just beyond R_2 the curve commences at an infinite distance on the negative side of, *i.e.*, below, OX.

➤ ***67. Secant-Graph :** If, similarly, the Secant-Graph be traced, it will be found to be the same as the Cosecant-Graph would be if we moved OY to R_1B_1.

[Some further examples of graphs will be found on pages 115, 116, 117, 128 and 229.]

MISCELLANEOUS EXAMPLES IX

1. In a triangle one angle contains as many grades as another contains degrees, and the third contains as many centesimal seconds as there are sexagesimal seconds in the sum of the other two; find the number of radians in each angle.

2. Find the number of degrees, minutes and seconds in the angle at the centre of a circle, whose radius is 5 m., which is subtended by an arc of length 6 m.

3. To turn radians into seconds, prove that we must multiply by 206265 nearly, and to turn seconds into radians the multiplier must be 0.0000048.

4. If $\sin\theta$ equal $\dfrac{x^2-y^2}{x^2+y^2}$ find the values of $\cos\theta$ and $\cot\theta$.

5. If
$$\sin\theta = \frac{m^2+2mn}{m^2+2mn+2n^2}$$
prove that
$$\tan\theta = \frac{m^2+2mn}{2mn+2n^2}.$$

6. If
$$\cos\theta - \sin\theta = \sqrt{2}\sin\theta$$
prove that
$$\cos\theta + \sin\theta = \sqrt{2}\cos\theta,$$

7. Prove that
$$\text{cosec}^6 a - \cot^6 a = 3\,\text{cosec}^2 a \cot^2 a + 1.$$

8. Express $2\sec^2 A - \sec^4 A - 2\text{cosec}^2 A + \text{cosec}^4 A$ in terms of $\tan A$.

9. Solve the equation $3\ \text{cosec}^2\theta = 2\sec\theta$.s

10. A man on a cliff observes a boat at an angle of depression of 30°, which is making for the shore immediately beneath him. Three minutes later the angle of depression of the boat is 60°. How soon will it reach the shore?

11. Prove that the equation $\sin\theta = x + \dfrac{1}{x}$ is impossible if x be real.

12. Show that the equation $\sec^2\theta = \dfrac{4xy}{(x+y)^2}$ is only possible when $x = y$.

5

TRIGONOMETRICAL FUNCTIONS OF ANGLES OF ANY SIZE AND SIGN

[On a first reading of the subject, the student is recommended to confine his attention to the first of the four figures given in Arts. 68, 69, 70 and 72.]

➤ **68.** *To find the trigonometrical ratios of an angle* $(-\theta)$ *in terms of those of* θ, *for all values of* θ.

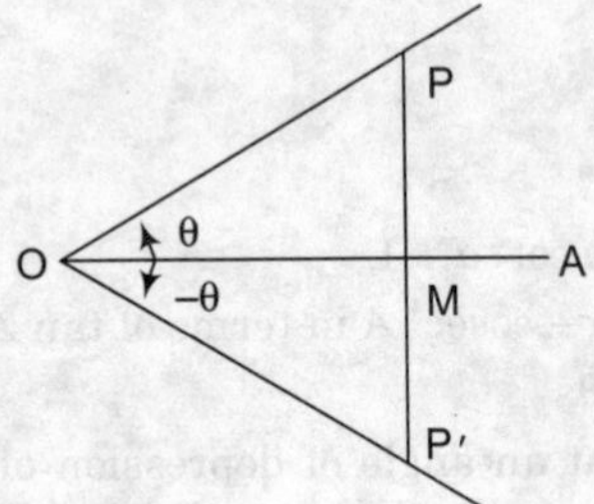

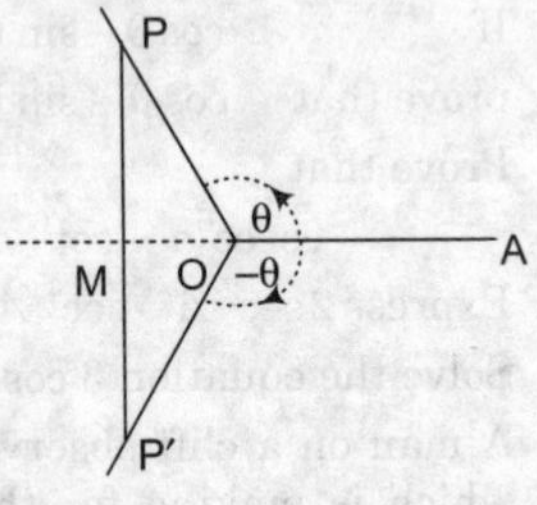

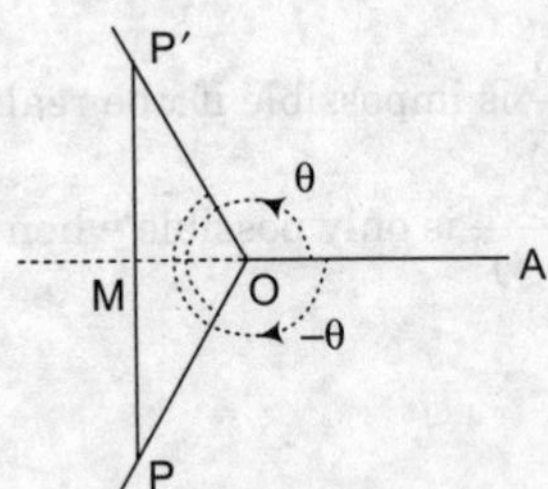

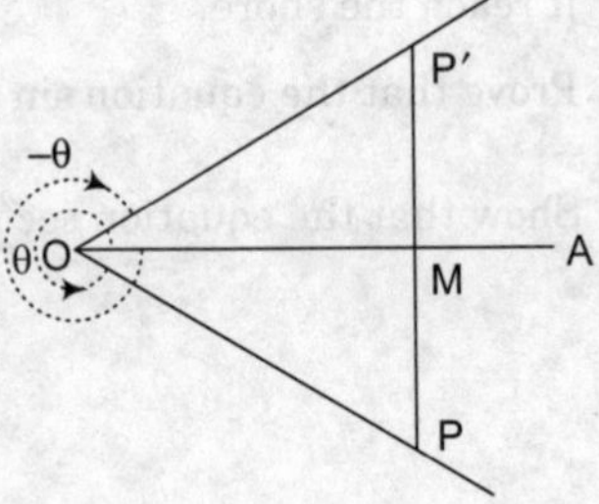

Let the revolving line, starting from OA, revolve through any angle θ and stop in the position OP.

Draw PM perpendicular to OA (or OA produced) and produce it to P', so that the lengths of PM and MP' are equal.

In the geometrical triangles MOP and MOP' we have the two sides OM and MP equal to the two sides OM and MP', and the included angles OMP and OMP' are right angles.

Hence, the magnitudes of the angles MOP and MOP' are the same, and OP is equal to OP'.

In each of the four figures, the magnitudes of the angle AOP (measured counter-clockwise) and of the angle AOP' (measured clockwise) are the same.

Hence, the angle AOP' (measured clockwise) is denoted by $-\theta$. Also MP and MP' are equal in magnitude but are opposite in sign. (Art. 49.) We have therefore,

$$\sin(-\theta) = \frac{MP'}{OP'} = \frac{-MP}{OP} = -\sin\theta,$$

$$\cos(-\theta) = \frac{OM}{OP'} = \frac{OM}{OP} = \cos\theta,$$

$$\tan(-\theta) = \frac{MP'}{OM} = \frac{-MP}{OM} = -\tan\theta,$$

$$\cot(-\theta) = \frac{OM}{MP'} = \frac{OM}{-MP} = -\cot\theta,$$

$$\operatorname{cosec}(-\theta) = \frac{OP'}{MP'} = \frac{OP}{-MP} = -\operatorname{cosec}\theta,$$

and $$\sec(-\theta) = \frac{OP'}{OM} = \frac{OP}{OM} = \sec\theta.$$

[In this article, and the following articles, the values of the last four trigonometrical ratios may be found, without reference to the figure, from the values of the first two ratios.

Thus, $$\tan(-\theta) = \frac{\sin(-\theta)}{\cos(-\theta)} = \frac{-\sin\theta}{\cos\theta} = -\tan\theta,$$

$$\cot(-\theta) = \frac{\cos(-\theta)}{\sin(-\theta)} = \frac{\cos\theta}{-\sin\theta} = -\cot\theta,$$

$$\operatorname{cosec}(-\theta) = \frac{1}{\sin(-\theta)} = \frac{1}{-\sin\theta} = -\operatorname{cosec}\theta,$$

and $$\sec(-\theta) = \frac{1}{\cos(-\theta)} = \frac{1}{\cos\theta} = \sec\theta.]$$

EXAMPLE $$\sin(-30^\circ) = -\sin 30^\circ = -\frac{1}{2},$$

$$\tan(-60^\circ) = -\tan 60^\circ = -\sqrt{3},$$

and $$\cos(-45^\circ) = \cos 45^\circ = \frac{1}{\sqrt{2}}.$$

➤ **69.** *To find the trigonometrical ratios of the angle* $(90° - \theta)$ *in terms of those of* θ, *for all values of* θ.

The relations have already been discussed in Art. 39, for values of θ less than a right angle.

Let the revolving line, starting from *OA*, trace out any angle *AOP* denoted by θ.

To obtain the angle $90° - \theta$, let the revolving line rotate to *B* and then rotate from *B* in the opposite direction through the angle θ, and let the position of the revolving line be then *OP′*.

The angle *AOP′* is then $90° - \theta$.

Take *OP′* equal to *OP*, and draw *P′ M′* and *PM* perpendicular to *OA*, produced if necessary. Also draw *P′ N′* perpendicular to *OB*, produced if necessary.

In each figure, the angles *AOP* and *BOP′* are numerically equal, by construction.

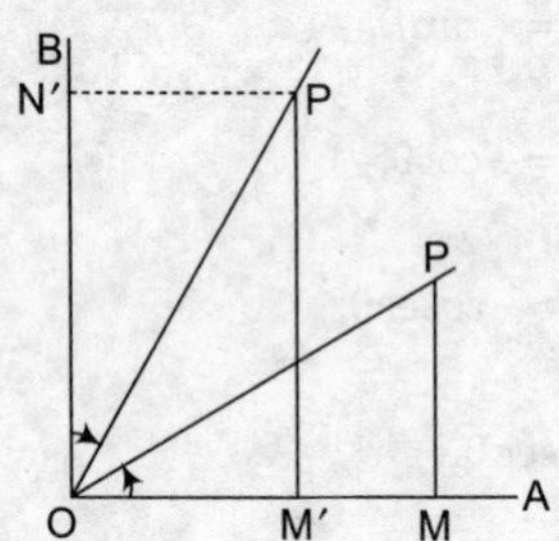

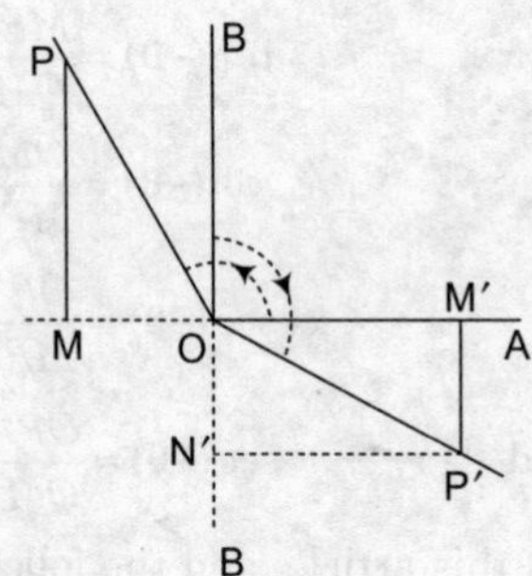

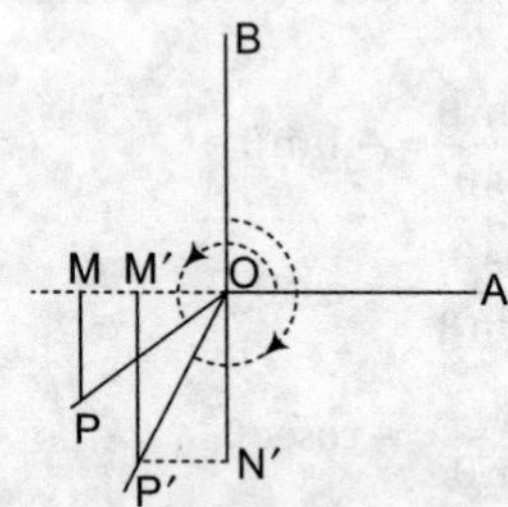

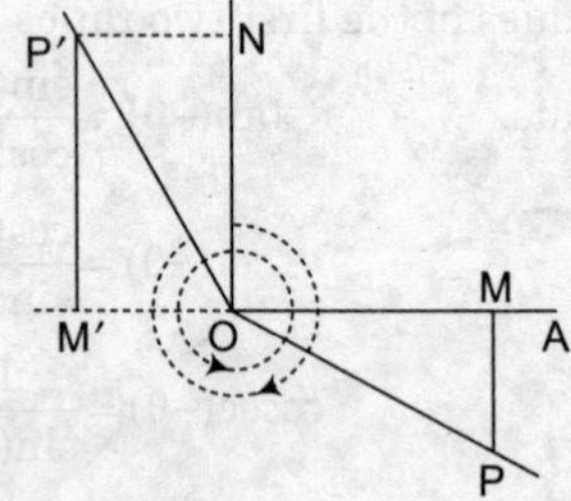

Hence, in each figure,

$$\angle MOP = \angle N'OP' = \angle OP'M'$$

Since, *ON′* and *M′ P′* are parallel.

Hence, the triangles *MOP* and *M′ P′ O* are equal in all respects, and therefore,

OM = *M′ P′* numerically, and *OM′* = *MP* numerically.

Also, in each figure, OM and $M'P'$ are of the same sign, and so also are MP and OM',

i.e., $\quad OM + M'P'$, and $OM' = +MP$.

Hence, $\quad \mathbf{sin(90°-\theta)} = \sin AOP' = \dfrac{M'P'}{OP'} = \dfrac{OM}{OP} = \mathbf{cos\,\theta},$

$$\mathbf{cos(90°-\theta)} = \cos AOP' = \frac{M'P'}{OP'} = \frac{MP}{OP} = \mathbf{sin\,\theta}$$

$$\tan(90° - \theta) = \tan AOP' = \frac{OM'}{OM'} = \frac{OM}{MP} = \cot\theta,$$

$$\cot(90° - \theta) = \cot AOP' = \frac{OM'}{M'P'} = \frac{MP}{OM} = \tan\theta,$$

$$\sec(90° - \theta) = \sec AOP' = \frac{OP'}{OM'} = \frac{OP}{MP} = \text{cosec}\theta,$$

$$\text{cosec}\,(90° - \theta) = \text{cosec}\,AOP' = \frac{OP'}{M'P'} = \frac{OP}{OM} = \sec\theta,$$

➤ **70.** *To find the trigonometrical ratios of the angle* $(90° + \theta)$ *in terms of those of* θ*, for all values of* θ.

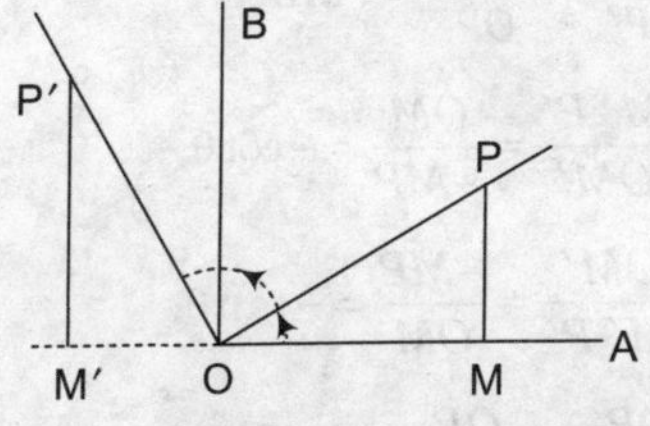

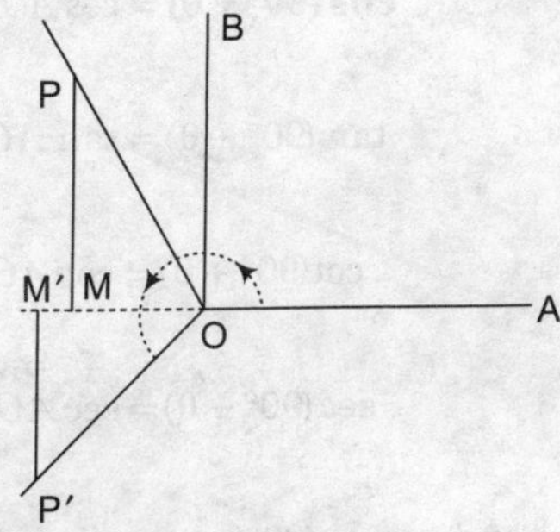

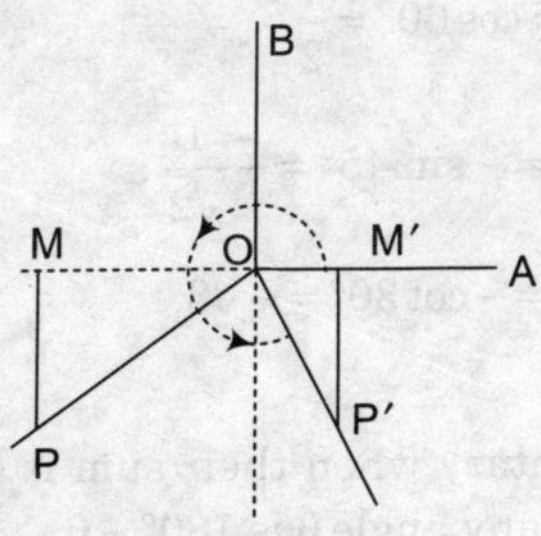

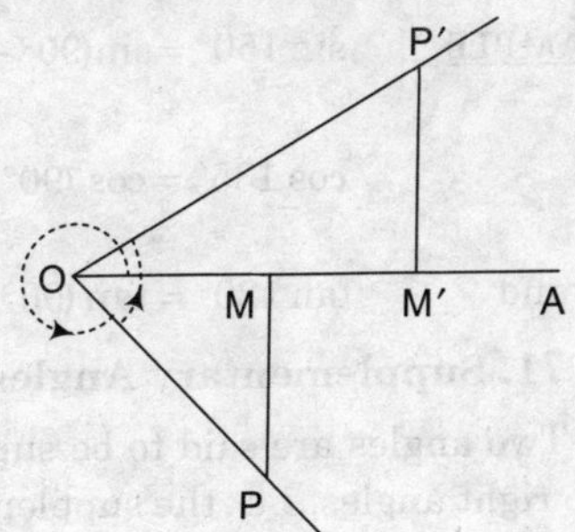

Let the revolving line, starting from OA, trace out any angle θ and let OP be the position of the revolving line then, so that the angle AOP is θ.

Let the revolving line turn through a right angle from OP in the positive direction to the position OP', so that the angle AOP' is $(90^\circ + \theta)$.

Take OP' equal to OP and draw PM and $P'M'$ perpendicular to AO, produced if necessary. In each figure, since POP' is a right angle, the sum of the angles MOP and $P'OM'$ is always a right angle.

Hence, $\angle MOP = 90^\circ - \angle P'OM' = \angle OP'M'$.

The two triangles MOP and $M'P'O$ are therefore, equal in all respects.

Hence, OM and $M'P'$ are numerically equal, as also MP and OM' are numerically equal.

In each figure, OM and $M'P'$ have the same sign, while MP and OM' have the opposite sign, so that

$$M'P' = +OM, \text{ and } OM' = -MP$$

We therefore, have

$$\mathbf{\sin(90^\circ + \theta)} = \sin AOP' = \frac{M'P'}{OP} = \frac{OM}{OP} = \mathbf{\cos\theta},$$

$$\mathbf{\cos(90^\circ + \theta)} = \cos AOP' = \frac{OM'}{OP'} = \frac{-MP}{OP} = -\mathbf{\sin\theta},$$

$$\tan(90^\circ + \theta) = \tan AOP' = \frac{M'P'}{OM'} = \frac{OM}{-MP} = -\cot\theta,$$

$$\cot(90^\circ + \theta) = \cot AOP' = \frac{OM'}{M'P'} = \frac{-MP}{OM} = -\tan\theta,$$

$$\sec(90^\circ + \theta) = \sec AOP' = \frac{OP'}{OM'} = \frac{OP}{-MP} = -\operatorname{cosec}\theta,$$

and $$\operatorname{cosec}(90^\circ + \theta) = \operatorname{cosec} AOP' = \frac{OP'}{M'P'} = \frac{OP}{OM} = \sec\theta.$$

<u>EXAMPLE</u> $\sin 150^\circ = \sin(90^\circ + 60^\circ) = \cos 60^\circ = \frac{1}{2}$,

$\cos 135^\circ = \cos(90^\circ + 45^\circ) = -\sin 45^\circ = -\frac{1}{\sqrt{2}}$,

and $\tan 120^\circ = \tan(90^\circ + 30^\circ) = -\cot 30^\circ = -\sqrt{3}$

➤ 71. Supplementary Angles.

Two angles are said to be supplementary when their sum is equal to two right angles, *i.e.*, the supplement of any angle θ is $180^\circ - \theta$.

EXAMPLE The supplement of $30° = 180° - 30° = 150°$

The supplement of $120° = 180° - 120° = 60°$

The supplement of $275° = 180° - 275° = -95°$

The supplement of $-126° = 180° - (-126°) = 306°$.

➤ **72.** *To find the values of the trigonometrical ratios of the angle* $(180° - \theta)$ *in terms of those of the angle* θ, *for all values of* θ.

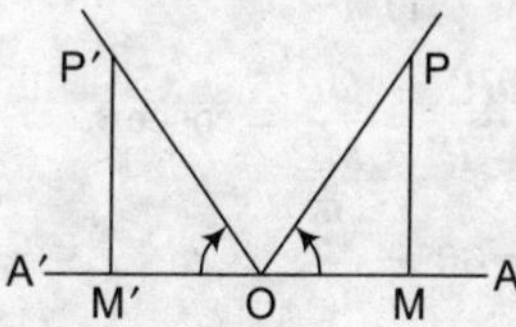

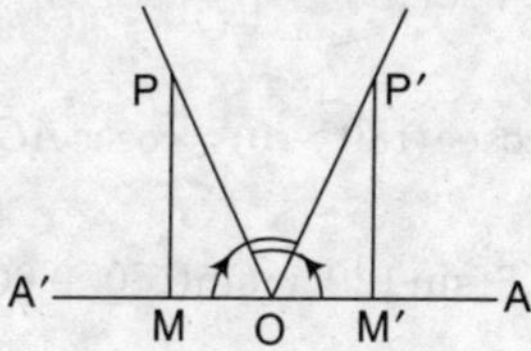

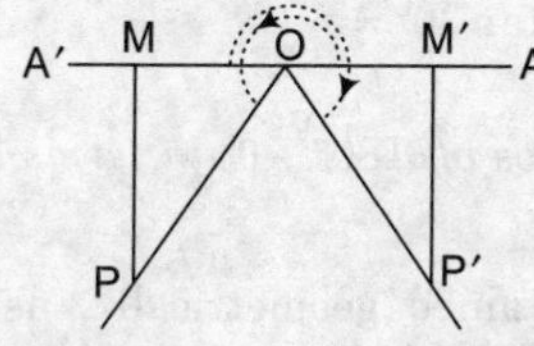

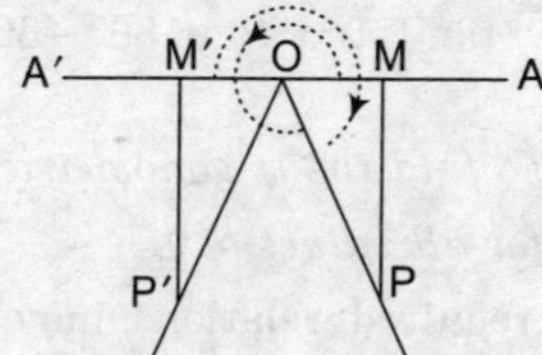

Let the revolving line start from OA and describe any angle $AOP (= \theta)$.

To obtain the angle $180° - \theta$, let the revolving line start from OA and, after revolving through two right angles (*i.e.*, into the position OA'), then revolve back through an angle θ into the position OP', so that the angle $A'OP'$ is equal in magnitude but opposite in sign to the angle AOP.

The angle AOP' is then $180° - \theta$.

Take OP' equal to OP, and draw $P'M'$ and PM perpendicular to AOA'.

The angles MOP and $M'OP'$ are equal, and hence the triangles MOP and $M'OP'$ are equal in all respects.

Hence OM and OM' are equal in magnitude, and so also are MP and $M'P'$.

In each figure, OM and OM' are drawn in opposite directions, while MP and $M'P'$ are drawn in the same directions, so that

$$OM' = -OM, \text{ and } M'P' = +MP$$

Hence, we have

$$\mathbf{\sin (180° - \theta)} = \sin AOP' = \frac{M'P'}{OP'} = \frac{MP}{OP} = \mathbf{\sin\theta},$$

$$\textbf{cos}\ \mathbf{(180° - \theta)} = \cos AOP' = \frac{OM'}{OP'} = \frac{-OM}{OP} = -\,\mathbf{cos\theta},$$

$$\tan (180° - \theta) = \tan AOP' = \frac{M'P'}{OM'} = \frac{MP}{-OM} = -\tan\theta,$$

$$\cot(180° - \theta) = \cot AOP' = \frac{OM'}{M'P'} = \frac{-OM}{MP} = -\cot\theta,$$

$$\sec (180° - \theta) = \sec AOP' = \frac{OP'}{OM'} = \frac{OP}{-OM} = -\sec\theta,$$

$$\operatorname{cosec} (180° - \theta) = \operatorname{cosec} AOP' = \frac{OP'}{M'P'} = \frac{OP}{MP} = \operatorname{cosec}\theta.$$

<u>EXAMPLE</u> $\sin 120° = \sin(180° - 60°) = \sin 60° = \dfrac{\sqrt{3}}{2}$,

$$\cos 135° = \cos(180° - 45°) = -\cos 45° = -\frac{1}{\sqrt{2}},$$

and $\tan 150° = \tan(180° - 30°) = -\tan 30° = \dfrac{-1}{\sqrt{3}}$.

➤ **73.** *To find the trigonometrical ratios of* $(180° + \theta)$ *in terms of those of* θ, *for all values of* θ.

The required relations may be obtained geometrically, as in the previous articles. The figures for this proposition are easily obtained and are left as an example for the student.

They may also be deduced from the results of Art. 70, which have been proved true for all angles. For, putting $90° + \theta = B$, we have

$$\mathbf{sin(180° + \theta)} = \sin(90° + B) = \cos B \qquad \text{(Art. 70)}$$
$$= \cos(90° + \theta) = -\,\mathbf{sin}\,\theta \qquad \text{(Art. 70)}$$

and $$\mathbf{cos(180° + \theta)} = \cos(90° + B) = -\sin B \qquad \text{(Art. 70)}$$
$$= -\sin(90° + \theta) = -\,\mathbf{cos}\,\theta, \qquad \text{(Art. 70)}$$

So, $$\tan(180° + \theta) = \tan(90° + B) = -\cot B$$
$$= -\cot(90° + \theta) = \tan\theta,$$

and similarly, $\cot(180° + \theta) = \cot\theta$

$$\sec(180° + \theta) = -\sec\theta,$$

and $$\operatorname{cosec}(180° + \theta) = -\operatorname{cosec}\theta.$$

➤ **74.** *To find the trigonometrical ratios of an angle* $(360° + \theta)$ *in terms of those of* θ, *for all values of* θ.

In whatever position the revolving line may be when it has described any angle θ, it will be in exactly the same position when it has made one more complete revolution in the positive direction, *i.e.*, when it has described an angle $360° + \theta$.

Hence the trigonometrical ratios for an angle $360° + \theta$ are the same as those for θ.

It follows that the addition or subtraction of 360°, or any multiple of 360°, to or from any angle does not alter its trigonometrical ratios.

➤ **75.** From the theorems of this chapter it follows that the trigonometrical ratios of any angle whatever can be reduced to the determination of the trigonometrical ratios of an angle which lies between 0° and 45°.

For example

$$\sin 1765° = \sin [4 \times 360° + 325°] = \sin 325° \qquad \text{(Art. 74)}$$
$$= \sin (180° + 145°) = -\sin 145° \qquad \text{(Art. 73)}$$
$$= -\sin (180° - 35°) = -\sin 35° \qquad \text{(Art. 72);}$$
$$\tan 1190° = \tan (3 \times 360° + 110°) = \tan 110° \qquad \text{(Art. 74)}$$
$$= \tan (90° + 20°) = -\cot 20° \qquad \text{(Art. 70);}$$
$$\text{and } \operatorname{cosec}(-1465°) = -\operatorname{cosec} 1465° \qquad \text{(Art. 68)}$$
$$= -\operatorname{cosec} (4 \times 360° + 25°) = -\operatorname{cosec} 25° \qquad \text{(Art. 74)}$$

Similarly, any other such large angles may be treated. First, multiples of 360° should be subtracted until the angle lies between 0° and 360°; if it be then greater than 180°, it should be reduced by 180°, if then greater than 90°, the formulae of Art. 70 should be used, and finally if necessary, the formulae of Art. 69 applied.

➤ **76.** The table of Art. 40 may now be extended to some important angles greater than a right angle.

Angle	0°	30°	45°	60°	90°	120°	135°	150°	180°
Sine	**0**	$\frac{1}{2}$	$\frac{1}{\sqrt{2}}$	$\frac{\sqrt{3}}{2}$	**1**	$\frac{\sqrt{3}}{2}$	$\frac{1}{\sqrt{2}}$	$\frac{1}{2}$	0
Cosine	**1**	$\frac{\sqrt{3}}{2}$	$\frac{1}{\sqrt{2}}$	$\frac{1}{2}$	**0**	$-\frac{1}{2}$	$-\frac{1}{\sqrt{2}}$	$-\frac{\sqrt{3}}{2}$	-1
Tangent	0	$\frac{1}{\sqrt{3}}$	1	$\sqrt{3}$	∞	$-\sqrt{3}$	-1	$-\frac{1}{\sqrt{3}}$	0
Cotangent	∞	$\sqrt{3}$	1	$\frac{1}{\sqrt{3}}$	0	$-\frac{1}{\sqrt{3}}$	-1	$-\sqrt{3}$	∞
Cosecant	∞	2	$\sqrt{2}$	$\frac{2}{\sqrt{3}}$	1	$\frac{2}{\sqrt{3}}$	$\sqrt{2}$	2	∞
Secant	1	$\frac{2}{\sqrt{3}}$	$\sqrt{2}$	2	∞	-2	$-\sqrt{2}$	$-\frac{2}{\sqrt{3}}$	-1

EXAMPLES X

Prove that

1. $\sin 420° \cos 390° + \cos(-300°) \sin(-330°) = 1$
2. $\cos 570° \sin 510° - \sin 330° \cos 390° = 0$ and
3. $\tan 225° \cot 405° + \tan 765° \cot 675° = 0$

What are the values of $\cos A - \sin A$ and $\tan A + \cot A$ when A has the values

4. $\frac{\pi}{3}$ 5. $\frac{2\pi}{3}$ 6. $\frac{5\pi}{4}$
7. $\frac{7\pi}{4}$ 8. $\frac{11\pi}{3}$

What values between 0° and 360° may A have when

9. $\sin A = \frac{1}{\sqrt{2}}$ 10. $\cos A = -\frac{1}{2}$ 11. $\tan A = -1$
12. $\cot A = -\sqrt{3}$ 13. $\sec A = -\frac{2}{\sqrt{3}}$ 14. $\text{cosec}\, A = -2$

Express in terms of the ratios of a positive angle, which is less than 45°, the quantities

15. $\sin(-65°)$ 16. $\cos(-84°)$
17. $\tan 137°$ 18. $\sin 168°$
19. $\cos 287°$ 20. $\tan(-246°)$
21. $\sin 843°$ 22. $\cos(-928°)$
23. $\tan 1145°$ 24. $\cos 1410°$
25. $\cot(-1054°)$ 26. $\sec 1327°$
27. $\text{cosec}(-756°)$

What sign has $\sin A + \cos A$ for the following values of A?

28. 140° 29. 278°
30. $-356°$ 31. $-1125°$

What sign has $\sin A - \cos A$ for the following values of A?

32. 215° 33. 825°
34. $-634°$ 35. $-457°$

36. Find the sines and cosines of all angles in the first four quadrants whose tangents are equal to cos 135°.

Prove that

37. $\sin(270° + A) = -\cos A$, and $\tan(270° + A) = -\cot A$
38. $\cos(270° - A) = -\sin A$, and $\cot(270° - A) = \tan A$
39. $\cos A + \sin(270° + A) - \sin(270° - A) + \cos(180° + A) = 0$
40. $\sec(270° - A)\sec(90° - A) - \tan(270° - A)\tan(90° + A) + 1 = 0$
41. $\cot A + \tan(180° + A) + \tan(90° + A) + \tan(360° - A) = 0$

6

GENERAL EXPRESSIONS FOR ALL ANGLES HAVING A GIVEN TRIGONOMETRICAL RATIO

➤ **77.** *To construct the least positive angle whose sine is equal to a, where a is a proper fraction.*

Let OA be the initial line, and let OB be drawn in the positive direction perpendicular to OA.

Measure off along OB a distance ON which is equal to a units of length. [If a be negative, the point N will lie in BO produced.]

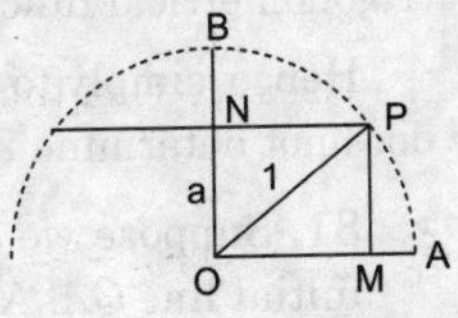

Through N draw NP parallel to OA. With centre O, and radius equal to the unit of length, describe a circle and let it meet NP in P.

Then AOP will be the required angle.

Draw PM perpendicular to OA, so that

$$\sin AOP = \frac{MP}{OP} = \frac{ON}{OP} = \frac{a}{1} = a$$

The sine of AOP is therefore equal to the given quantity, and hence AOP is the angle required.

➤ **78.** *To construct the least positive angle whose cosine is equal to b, where b is a proper fraction.*

Along the initial line measure-off a distance OM equal to b and draw MP perpendicular to OA. [If b be negative, M will lie on the other side of O in the line AO produced.]

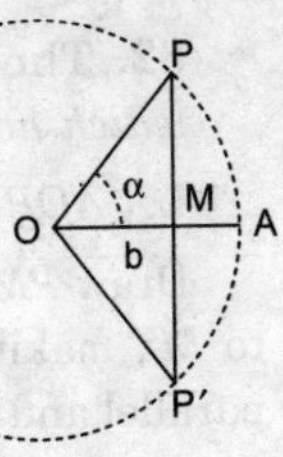

With centre O, and radius equal to unity, describe a circle and let it meet MP in P.

Then AOP is the angle required. For

$$\cos AOP = \frac{OM}{OP} = \frac{b}{1} = b$$

➤ **79.** *To construct the least positive angle whose tangent is equal to c.*

Along the initial line measure off *OM* equal to unity, and erect a perpendicular *MP*. Measure off *MP* equal to *c*.

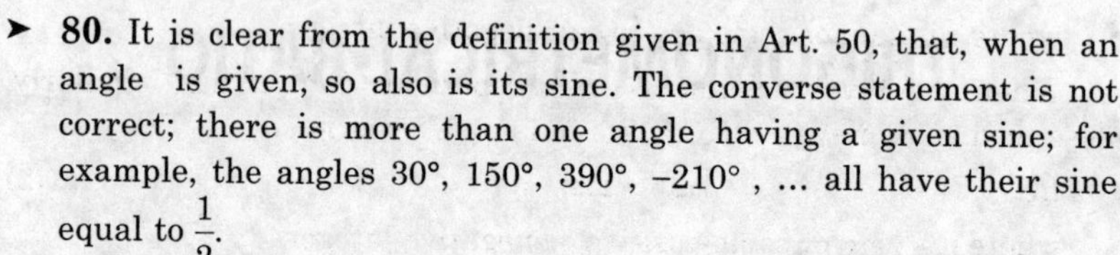

Then $$\tan AOP = \frac{MP}{OM} = c$$

so that *AOP* is the required angle.

➤ **80.** It is clear from the definition given in Art. 50, that, when an angle is given, so also is its sine. The converse statement is not correct; there is more than one angle having a given sine; for example, the angles 30°, 150°, 390°, −210° , ... all have their sine equal to $\frac{1}{2}$.

Hence, when the sine of an angle is given, we do not definitely know the angle; all we know is that the angle is one out of a large number of angles.

Similar statements are true if the cosine, tangent, or any other trigonometrical function of the angle be given.

Hence, simply to given one of the trigonometrical functions of an angle does not determine it without ambiguity.

➤ **81.** Suppose we know that the revolving line *OP* coincides with the initial line *OA*. All we know is that the revolving line has made 0, or 1, or 2, or 3, ... complete revolutions, either positive or negative.

But when the revolving line has made one complete revolution, the angle it has described is (Art. 17) equal to 2π radians.

Hence, when the revolving line *OP* coincides with the initial line *OA*, the angle that it has described is 0, or 1, or 2, or 3, ... times 2π radians, in either the positive or negative directions, *i.e.*, either 0, or $\pm 2\pi$, or $\pm 4\pi$, or $\pm 6\pi$, ... radians.

This is expressed by saying that when the revolving line coincides with the initial line the angle it has described is $2n\pi$, where *n* is some positive or negative integer.

➤ **82. Theorem** : *To find a general expression to include all angles which have the same sine.* [See also Art. 102.]

Let *AOP* be any angle having the given sine, and let it be denoted by α.

Draw *PM* perpendicular to *OA* and produce *MO* to *M′*, making *OM′* equal to *MO*, and draw *M′P′* parallel and equal to *MP*.

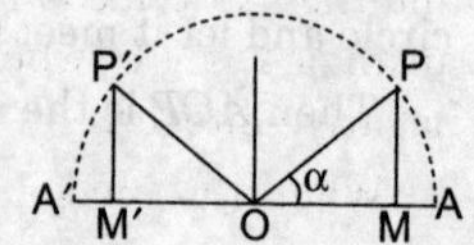

As in Art. 72, the angle AOP' is equal to $\pi - \alpha$.

When the revolving line is in either of the positions OP or OP', and in no other position, the sine of the angle traced out is equal to the given sine.

When the revolving line is in the position OP, it has made a whole number of complete revolutions and then described an angle α, *i.e.*, by the previous article, it has described an angle equal to

$$2r\pi + \alpha \qquad \ldots(1)$$

where r is zero or some positive or negative integer.

When the revolving line is in the position OP', it has, similarly, described an angle $2r\pi + AOP'$, *i.e.*, an angle $2r\pi + \pi - \alpha$,

i.e.,
$$(2r + 1)\pi - \alpha \qquad \ldots(2)$$

where r is zero or some positive or negative integer.

All these angles will be found to be included in the expression

$$n\pi + (-1)^n\alpha \qquad \ldots(3)$$

where n is zero or a positive or negative integer.

For, when $n = 2r$, since $(-1)^{2r} = +1$, the expression (3) gives $2r\pi + \alpha$, which is the same as the expression (1)

Also, when $n = 2r + 1$, since $(-1)^{2r+1} = -1$, the expression (3) gives $(2r + 1)\pi - \alpha$, which is the same as the expression (2).

Cor. : Since, all angles which have the same sine have also the same cosecant, the expression (3) includes all angles which have the same cosecant as α.

➤ **83. Theorem** : *To find a general expression to include all angles which have the same cosine.* [See also Art. 103.]

Let AOP be any angle having the given cosine, and let it be denoted by α.

Draw PM perpendicular to OA and produce it to P', making MP' equal to PM.

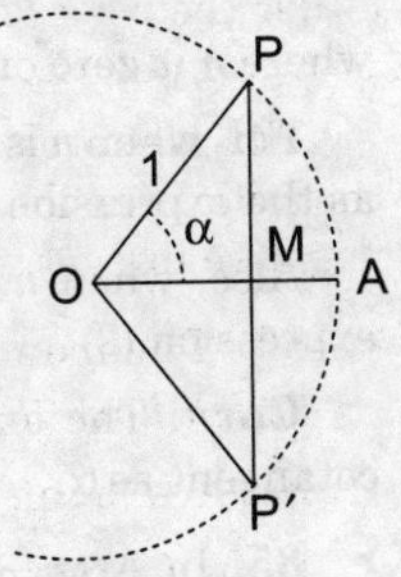

When the revolving line is in the position OP or OP', and in no other position, then, as in Art. 78, the cosine of the angle traced out is equal to the given cosine.

When the revolving line is in the position OP, it has made a whole number of complete revolutions and then described an angle α, *i.e.*, it has described an angle $2n\pi + \alpha$, where n is zero or some positive or negative integer.

When the revolving line is in the position OP', it has made a whole

When the revolving line is in the position OP', it has made a whole number of complete revolutions and then described an angle $-\alpha$, *i.e.*, it has described an angle $2n\pi - \alpha$.

All these angles are included in the expression

$$2n\pi \pm \alpha \qquad ...(1)$$

where n is zero or some positive or negative integer.

Cor. : The expression (1) includes all angles having the same secant as α.

➤ **84. Theorem.** *To find a general expression for all angles which have the same tangent.* [See also Art. 104.]

Let AOP be any angle having the given tangent, and let it be denoted by α.

Produce PO to P', making OP' equal to OP, and draw $P'M'$ perpendicular to OM'.

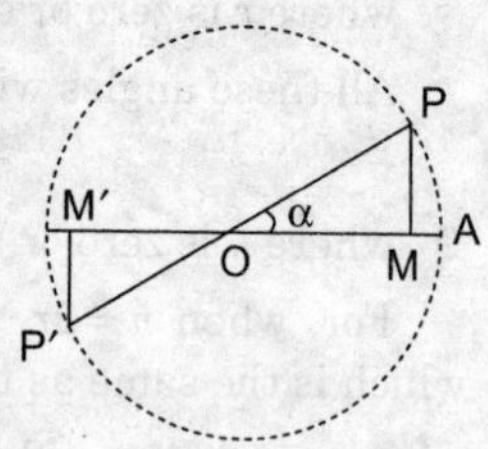

As in Art. 73, the angles AOP and AOP' have the same tangent; also the angle $AOP' = \pi + \alpha$.

When the revolving line is in the position OP it has described a whole number of complete revolutions and then turned through an angles α, *i.e.*, it has described an angle

$$2r\pi + \alpha \qquad ...(1)$$

where r is zero or some positive or negative integer.

When the revolving line is in the position OP', it has similarly described an angle $2r\pi + (\pi + \alpha)$,

i.e., $$(2r + 1)\pi + \alpha \qquad ...(2)$$

All these angles are included in the expression

$$n\pi + \alpha \qquad ...(3)$$

where n is zero or some positive or negative integer.

For, when n is even, $(= 2r$ say), the expression (3) gives the same angles as the expression (1).

Also, when n is odd, $(= 2r + 1$ say), it gives the same angles as the expression (2).

Cor. : The expression (3) includes all angles which have the same cotangent as α.

➤ **85.** In Arts. 82, 83, and 84 the angle α is any angle satisfying the given condition. In practical examples it is, in general, desirable to take α as the smallest positive angle which is suitable.

EXAMPLE 1 *Write down the general expression for all angles,*

(1) *whose sine is equal to* $\frac{\sqrt{3}}{2}$,

(2) *whose cosine is equal to* $\frac{1}{2}$, *and*

(3) *whose tangent is equal to* $\frac{1}{\sqrt{3}}$.

(1) The smallest angle, whose sine is $\frac{\sqrt{3}}{2}$, is 60°, *i.e.*, $\frac{\pi}{3}$.

Hence, by Art. 82, the general expression for all the angles which have this sine is

$$n\pi + (-1)^n \frac{\pi}{3}.$$

(2) The smallest positive angle, whose cosine is $-\frac{1}{2}$, is 120°, *i.e.*, $\frac{2\pi}{3}$.

Hence, by Art. 83, the general expression for all the angles which have this cosine is

$$2n\pi \pm \frac{2\pi}{3}.$$

(3) The smallest positive angle, whose tangent is $\frac{1}{\sqrt{3}}$, is 30° *i.e.*, $\frac{\pi}{6}$.

Hence, by Art. 84, the general expression for all the angles which have this tangent is $n\pi + \frac{\pi}{6}$.

EXAMPLE 2 *What is the most general value of* θ *satisfying the equation,*

$$\sin^2 \theta = \frac{1}{4} ?$$

Here, we have $\sin\theta = \pm\frac{1}{2}$.

Taking the upper sign,

$$\sin\theta = \frac{1}{2} = \sin\frac{\pi}{6}$$

$$\therefore \qquad \theta = n\pi + (-1)^n \frac{\pi}{6}$$

Taking the lower sign, $\sin\theta = -\frac{1}{2} = \sin\left(-\frac{\pi}{6}\right)$

$$\therefore \qquad \theta = n\pi + (-1)^n\left(-\frac{\pi}{6}\right)$$

Putting both solutions together, we have

$$\theta = n\pi \pm (-1)^n \frac{\pi}{6}$$

or, what is the same expression,

$$\theta = n\pi \pm \frac{\pi}{6}.$$

EXAMPLE 3 *What is the most general value of* θ *which satisfies both of the equations* $\sin\theta = -\frac{1}{2}$ *and* $\tan\theta = \frac{1}{\sqrt{3}}$?

Considering only angles between 0° and 360°, the only values of θ, when $\sin\theta = -\frac{1}{2}$, are 210° and 330°. Similarly, the only values of θ, when $\tan\theta = \frac{1}{\sqrt{3}}$, are 30° and 210°.

The only value of θ, between 0° and 360°, satisfying both conditions is therefore 210°, *i.e.*, $\frac{7\pi}{6}$.

The most general value is hence obtained by adding any multiple of four right angles to this angle, and hence is $2n\pi + \frac{7\pi}{6}$, where n is any positive or negative integer.

EXAMPLES XI

What are the most general values of θ which satisfy the equations,

1. $\sin\theta = \frac{1}{2}$

2. $\sin\theta = -\frac{\sqrt{3}}{2}$

3. $\sin\theta = \frac{1}{\sqrt{2}}$

4. $\cos\theta = -\frac{1}{2}$

5. $\cos\theta = \frac{\sqrt{3}}{2}$

6. $\cos\theta = -\frac{1}{\sqrt{2}}$

7. $\tan\theta = \sqrt{3}$

8. $\tan\theta = -1$

9. $\cot\theta = 1$

10. $\sec\theta = 2$

11. $\operatorname{cosec}\theta = \frac{2}{\sqrt{3}}$

12. $\sin^2\theta = 1$

13. $\cos^2\theta = \frac{1}{4}$

14. $\tan^2\theta = \frac{1}{3}$

15. $4\sin^2\theta = 3$

16. $2\cot^2\theta = \operatorname{cosec}^2\theta$

17. $\sec^2\theta = \frac{4}{3}$

18. What is the most general value of θ that satisfies both of the equations $\cos\theta = -\frac{1}{\sqrt{2}}$ and $\tan\theta = 1$?

19. What is the most general value of θ that satisfies both of the equations $\cot\theta = -\sqrt{3}$ and $\operatorname{cosec}\theta = -2$?

20. If $\cos(A-B)=\frac{1}{2}$, and $\sin(A+B)=\frac{1}{2}$, find the smallest positive values of A and B and also their most general values.

21. If $\tan(A-B)=1$, and $\sec(A+B)=\frac{2}{\sqrt{3}}$, find the smallest positive values of A and B and also their most general values.

22. Find the angles between 0° and 360° which have respectively

(1) their sines equal to $\frac{\sqrt{3}}{2}$,

(2) their cosines equal to $-\frac{1}{2}$, and

(3) their tangents equal to $\frac{1}{\sqrt{3}}$.

23. Taking into consideration only angles between 0° and 180°, how many values of x are there if

(1) $\sin x=\frac{5}{7}$, (2) $\cos x=\frac{1}{5}$,

(3) $\cos x=-\frac{4}{5}$, (4) $\tan x=\frac{2}{3}$, and

(5) $\cot x=-7$?

24. Given the angle x, construct the angle y if (1) $\sin y=2\sin x$, (2) $\tan y=3\tan x$, (3) $\cos y=\frac{1}{2}\cos x$, and (4) $\sec y=\operatorname{cosec} x$.

25. Show that the same angles are indicated by the two following formulae

(1) $(2n-1)\frac{\pi}{2}+(-1)^n\frac{\pi}{3}$, and (2) $2n\pi\pm\frac{\pi}{6}$, n being any integer.

26. Prove that the two formulae

(1) $\left(2n+\frac{1}{2}\right)\pi\pm\alpha$ and (2) $n\pi+(-1)^n\left(\frac{\pi}{2}-\alpha\right)$ denote the same angles, n being any integer.

Illustrate by a figure.

27. If $\theta-\alpha=n\pi+(-1)^n\beta$, prove that $\theta=2m\pi+\alpha+\beta$ or else that $\theta=(2m+1)\pi+\alpha-\beta$, where m and n are any integers.

28. If $\cos p\theta+\cos q\theta=0$, prove that the different values of θ form two arithmetical progressions in which the common differences are $\frac{2\pi}{p+q}$ and $\frac{2\pi}{p\sim q}$ respectively.

29. Construct the angle whose sine is $\frac{3}{2+\sqrt{5}}$.

➤ **86.** An equation involving the trigonometrical ratios of an unknown angle is called a trigonometrical equation.

The equation is not completely solved unless we obtain an expression for all the angles which satisfy it.

Some elementary types of equations are solved in the following article.

➤ **87.**

EXAMPLE 1 *Solve the equation* $2\sin^2 x + \sqrt{3}\cos x + 1 = 0$.

The equation may be written

$$2 - 2\cos^2 x + \sqrt{3}\cos x + 1 = 0$$

i.e., $$2\cos^2 x - \sqrt{3}\cos x - 3 = 0$$

i.e., $$(\cos x - \sqrt{3})(2\cos x + \sqrt{3}) = 0$$

The equation is therefore satisfied by,

$$\cos x = \sqrt{3} \text{ or } \cos x = -\frac{\sqrt{3}}{2}$$

Since, the cosine of an angle cannot be numerically greater than unity, the first factor gives no solution.

The smallest positive angle, whose cosine is $-\frac{\sqrt{3}}{2}$, is 150°, *i.e.*, $\frac{5\pi}{6}$.

Hence the most general value of the angle, whose cosine is $-\frac{\sqrt{3}}{2}$, is $2n\pi \pm \frac{5\pi}{6}$. (Art. 83.)

This is the general solution of the given equation.

EXAMPLE 2 *Solve the equation* $\tan 5\theta = \cot 2\theta$.

The equation may be written

$$\tan 5\theta = \tan\left(\frac{\pi}{2} - 2\theta\right)$$

Now the most general value of the angle, that has the same tangent as

$$\frac{\pi}{2} - 2\theta, \text{ is by Art. 84, } n\pi + \frac{\pi}{2} - 2\theta$$

where n is any positive or negative integer.

The most general solution of the equation is therefore

$$5\theta = n\pi + \frac{\pi}{2} - 2\theta$$

$$\therefore \qquad \theta = \frac{1}{7}\left(n\pi + \frac{\pi}{2}\right)$$

where n is any integer.

EXAMPLES XII

Solve the equations

1. $\cos^2\theta - \sin\theta - \frac{1}{4} = 0$
2. $2\sin^2\theta + 3\cos\theta = 0$
3. $2\sqrt{3}\cos^2\theta = \sin\theta$
4. $\cos\theta + \cos^2\theta = 1$
5. $4\cos\theta - 3\sec\theta = 2\tan\theta$
6. $\sin^2\theta - 2\cos\theta + \frac{1}{4} = 0$
7. $\tan^2\theta - (1+\sqrt{3})\tan\theta + \sqrt{3} = 0$
8. $\cot^2\theta + \left(\sqrt{3} + \frac{1}{\sqrt{3}}\right)\cot\theta + 1 = 0$
9. $\cot\theta - ab\tan\theta = a - b$
10. $\tan^2\theta + \cot^2\theta = 2$
11. $\sec\theta - 1 = (\sqrt{2} - 1)\tan\theta$
12. $3(\sec^2\theta + \tan^2\theta) = 5$
13. $\cot\theta + \tan\theta = 2\operatorname{cosec}\theta$
14. $4\cos^2\theta + \sqrt{3} = 2(\sqrt{3} + 1)\cos\theta$
15. $3\sin^2\theta - 2\sin\theta = 1$
16. $\sin 5\theta = \frac{1}{\sqrt{2}}$
17. $\sin 9\theta = \sin\theta$
18. $\sin 3\theta = \sin 2\theta$
19. $\cos m\theta = \cos n\theta$
20. $\sin 2\theta = \cos 3\theta$
21. $\cos 5\theta = \cos 4\theta$
22. $\cos m\theta = \sin n\theta$
23. $\cot\theta = \tan 8\theta$
24. $\cot\theta = \tan n\theta$
25. $\tan 2\theta = \tan\frac{2}{\theta}$
26. $\tan 2\theta\tan\theta = 1$
27. $\tan^2 3\theta = \cot^2\alpha$
28. $\tan 3\theta = \cot\theta$
29. $\tan^2 3\theta = \tan^2\alpha$
30. $3\tan^2\theta = 1$
31. $\tan mx + \cot nx = 0$
32. $\tan(\pi\cot\theta) = \cot(\pi\tan\theta)$
33. $\sin(\theta - \phi) = \frac{1}{2}$ and $\cos(\theta + \phi) = \frac{1}{2}$
34. $\cos(2x + 3y) = \frac{1}{2}$ and $\cos(3x + 2y) = \frac{\sqrt{3}}{2}$
35. Find all the angles between 0° and 90° which satisfy the equation $\sec^2\theta\operatorname{cosec}^2\theta + 2\operatorname{cosec}^2\theta = 8$
36. If $\tan^2\theta = \frac{5}{4}$, find versin θ and explain the double result.
37. If the coversin of an angle be $\frac{1}{3}$, find its cosine and cotangent.

7

TRIGONOMETRICAL RATIOS OF THE SUM AND DIFFERENCE OF TWO ANGLES

➤ **88. Theorem** : *To prove that*

$$\sin(A + B) = \sin A \cos B + \cos A \sin B$$

and

$$\cos(A + B) = \cos A \cos B - \sin A \sin B$$

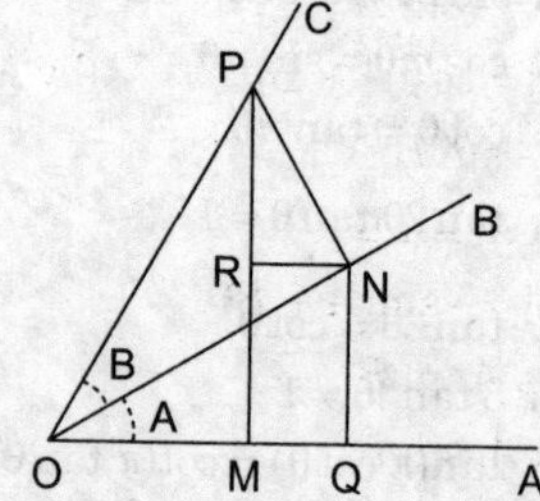

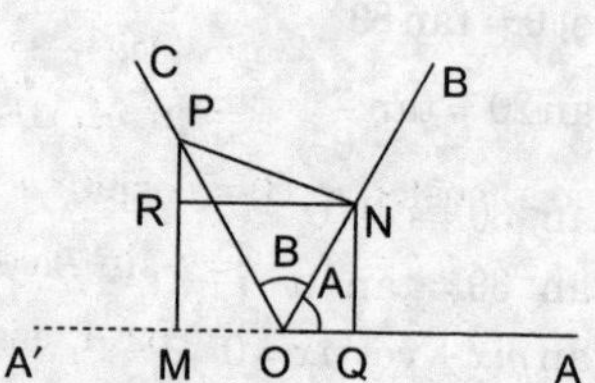

Let the revolving line start from OA and trace out the angle AOB (= A), and then trace out the further angle BOC (= B).

In the final position of the revolving line take any point P, and draw PM and PN perpendicular to OA and OB respectively; through N draw NR parallel to AO to meet MP in R, and draw NQ perpendicular to OA.

The angle, $\quad RPN = 90° - \angle PNR = \angle RNO = \angle NOQ = A$

Hence, $\quad \sin(A + B) = \sin AOP$

$$= \frac{MP}{OP} = \frac{MR + RP}{OP}$$

$$= \frac{QN}{OP} + \frac{RP}{OP} = \frac{QN}{ON}\frac{ON}{OP} + \frac{RP}{NP}\frac{NP}{OP}$$

$$= \sin A \cos B + \cos RPN \sin B$$

$\therefore \quad$ $$\mathbf{\sin(A + B) = \sin A \cos B + \cos A \sin B}$$

Again, $\cos(A+B) = \cos AOP = \dfrac{OM}{OP} = \dfrac{OQ - MQ}{OP}$

$$= \frac{OQ}{OP} - \frac{RN}{OP} = \frac{OQ}{ON}\,\frac{ON}{OP} - \frac{RN}{NP}\,\frac{NP}{OP}$$

$$= \cos A \cos B - \sin RPN \sin B$$

$\therefore$ $\mathbf{\cos(A+B) = \cos A \cos B - \sin A \sin B}$

➤ **89.** The figures in the previous article have been drawn only for the case in which A and B are acute angles.

The same proof will be found to apply to angles of any size, due attention being paid to the signs of the quantities involved.

The results may however be shown to be true of all angles, without drawing any more figures, as follows.

Let A and B be acute angles, so that, by Art. 88, we know that the theorem is true for A and B.

Let $A_1 = 90° + A$, so that, by Art. 70 we have

$$\sin A_1 = \cos A, \text{ and } \cos A_1 = -\sin A$$

Then, $\sin(A_1 + B) = \sin[90° + (A+B)] = \cos(A+B)$, (by Art. 70)

$$= \cos A \cos B - \sin A \sin B$$

$$= \sin A_1 \cos B + \cos A_1 \sin B$$

Also, $\cos(A_1 + B) = \cos[90° + (A+B)] = -\sin(A+B)$

$$= -\sin A \cos B - \cos A \sin B$$

$$= \cos A_1 \cos B - \sin A_1 \sin B$$

Similarly, we may proceed if B be increased by 90°.

Hence, the formulae of Art. 88 are true if either A or B be increased by 90°, *i.e.*, they are true if the component angles lie between 0° and 180°.

Similarly, by putting $A_2 = 90° + A_1$, we can prove the truth of the theorems when either or both of the component angles have values between 0° and 270°.

By proceeding in this way, we see that the theorems are true universally.

➤ **90. Theorem :** *To prove that*

$$\sin(A - B) = \sin A \cos B - \cos A \sin B$$

and $\cos(A - B) = \cos A \cos B + \sin A \sin B$

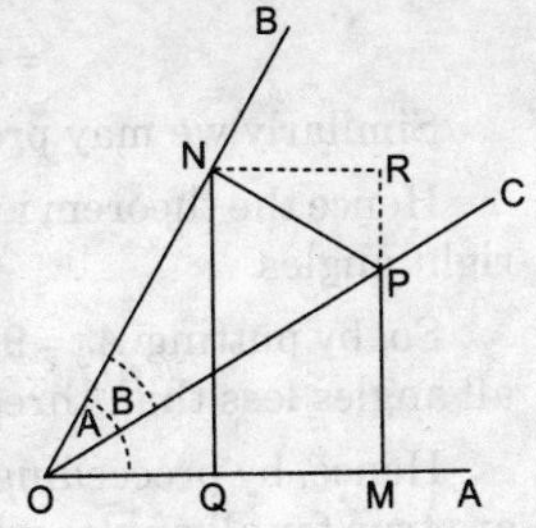

Let the revolving line starting from the initial line OA trace out the angle AOB (= A), and then, revolving in the opposite direction, trace out the angle BOC, whose magnitude is B. The angle AOC is therefore $A - B$.

Take a point P in the final position of the revolving line, and draw PM and PN perpendicular to OA and OB respectively; from N draw NQ and NR perpendicular to OA and MP respectively.

The angle

$$RPN = 90° - \angle PNR = \angle RNB = \angle QON = A$$

Hence,

$$\sin(A - B) = \sin AOC = \frac{MP}{OP} = \frac{MR - PR}{OP} = \frac{QN}{OP} - \frac{PR}{OP}$$

$$= \frac{QN}{ON}\frac{ON}{OP} - \frac{PR}{PN}\frac{PN}{OP} = \sin A \cos B - \cos RPN \sin B$$

so that $\mathbf{\sin(A - B) = \sin A \cos B - \cos A \sin B}$

Also $\cos(A - B) = \dfrac{OM}{OP} = \dfrac{OQ + QM}{OP} = \dfrac{OQ}{OP} + \dfrac{NR}{OP}$

$$= \frac{OQ}{ON}\frac{ON}{OP} + \frac{NR}{NP}\frac{NP}{OP}$$

$$= \cos A \cos B + \sin NPR \sin B$$

so that $\mathbf{\cos(A - B) = \cos A \cos B + \sin A \sin B.}$

➤ **91.** The proofs of the previous article will be found to apply to angles of any size, provided that due attention be paid to the signs of the quantities involved.

Assuming the truth of the formulae for acute angles, we can show them to be true universally without drawing any more figures.

For, putting $A_1 = 90° + A$, we have

(since $\sin A_1 = \cos A$, and $\cos A_1 = -\sin A$)

$$\sin(A_1 - B) = \sin[90° + (A - B)] = \cos(A - B) \text{ (Art. 70)}$$

$$= \cos A \cos B + \sin A \sin B$$

$$= \sin A_1 \cos B - \cos A_1 \sin B$$

Also, $\cos(A_1 - B) = \cos[90° + (A - B)] = -\sin(A - B) \text{(Art. 70)}$

$$= -\sin A \cos B + \cos A \sin B$$

$$= \cos A_1 \cos B + \sin A_1 \sin B$$

Similarly we may proceed if B be increased by 90°.

Hence the theorem is true for all angles which are not greater than two right angles.

So, by putting $A_2 = 90° + A_1$, we may show the theorems to be true for all angles less than three right angles, and so on.

Hence, by proceeding in this manner, we may show that the theorems are true for all angles whatever.

➤ **92.** The theorems of Arts. 88 and 90, which give respectively the trigonometrical functions of the sum and differences of two angles in terms of the functions of the angles themselves, are often called the **Addition and Subtraction Theorems.**

➤ **93.**

EXAMPLE 1 *Find the values of* $\sin 75°$ *and* $\cos 75°$.

$$\sin 75° = \sin(45° + 30°) = \sin 45° \cos 30° + \cos 45° \sin 30°$$
$$= \frac{1}{\sqrt{2}} \cdot \frac{\sqrt{3}}{2} + \frac{1}{\sqrt{2}} \cdot \frac{1}{2} = \frac{\sqrt{3}+1}{2\sqrt{2}}$$

and $\cos 75° = \cos(45° + 30°) = \cos 45° \cos 30° - \sin 45° \sin 30°$

$$= \frac{1}{\sqrt{2}} \cdot \frac{\sqrt{3}}{2} - \frac{1}{\sqrt{2}} \cdot \frac{1}{2} = \frac{\sqrt{3}-1}{2\sqrt{2}}$$

EXAMPLE 2 *Prove that* $\sin(A + B)\sin(A - B) = \sin^2 A - \sin^2 B$

and $\cos(A + B)\cos(A - B) = \cos^2 A - \sin^2 B$

By Arts. 88 and 90, we have

$$\sin(A + B)\sin(A - B) = (\sin A \cos B + \cos A \sin B)$$
$$\times (\sin A \cos B - \cos A \sin B)$$
$$= \sin^2 A \cos^2 B - \cos^2 A \sin^2 B$$
$$= \sin^2 A(1 - \sin^2 B) - (1 - \sin^2 A)\sin^2 B$$
$$= \sin^2 A - \sin^2 B$$

Again, by the same articles, we have

$$\cos(A + B)\cos(A - B) = (\cos A \cos B - \sin A \sin B)$$
$$\times (\cos A \cos B + \sin A \sin B)$$
$$= \cos^2 A \cos^2 B - \sin^2 A \sin^2 B$$
$$= \cos^2 A(1 - \sin^2 B) - (1 - \cos^2 A)\sin^2 B$$
$$= \cos^2 A - \sin^2 B$$

EXAMPLE 3 *Assuming the formulae for* $\sin(x + y)$ *and* $\cos(x + y)$, *deduce the formulae for* $\sin(x - y)$ *and* $\cos(x - y)$.

We have

$$\sin x = \sin\{(x - y) + y\} = \sin(x - y)\cos y + \cos(x - y)\sin y \quad \text{...(1)}$$

and $\cos x = \cos\{(x - y) + y\} = \cos(x - y)\cos y - \sin(x - y)\sin y$ ...(2)

Multiplying (1) by $\cos y$ and (2) by $\sin y$ and subtracting, we have

$$\sin x \cos y - \cos x \sin y = \sin(x - y)\{\cos^2 y + \sin^2 y\} = \sin(x - y)$$

Multiplying Eq. (1) by $\sin y$ and (2) by $\cos y$ and adding, we have

$$\sin x \sin y + \cos x \cos y = \cos(x - y)\{\cos^2 y + \sin^2 y\} = \cos(x - y)$$

Hence the two formulae required are proved.

These two formulae are true for all values of the angles, since the formulae from which they are derived are true for all values of the angles.

EXAMPLES XIII

1. If $\sin\alpha = \frac{3}{5}$ and $\cos\beta = \frac{9}{41}$, find the value of $\sin(\alpha - \beta)$ and $\cos(\alpha + \beta)$. Verify by a graph and accurate measurement.
2. If $\sin\alpha = \frac{15}{53}$ and $\sin\beta = \frac{33}{65}$, find the values of $\sin(\alpha - \beta)$ and $\sin(\alpha + \beta)$.
3. If $\sin\alpha = \frac{15}{17}$ and $\cos\beta = \frac{12}{13}$, find the values of $\sin(\alpha + \beta)$, $\cos(\alpha - \beta)$, and $\tan(\alpha + \beta)$. Verify by a graph and accurate measurement.
4. Prove that
$\cos(45° - A)\cos(45° - B) - \sin(45° - A)\sin(45° - B) = \sin(A + B)$
Prove that
5. $\sin(45° + A)\cos(45° - B) + \cos(45° + A)\sin(45° - B) = \cos(A - B)$
6. $\dfrac{\sin(A - B)}{\cos A\cos B} + \dfrac{\sin(B - C)}{\cos B\cos C} + \dfrac{\sin(C - A)}{\cos C\cos A} = 0$
7. $\sin 105° + \cos 105° = \cos 45°$
8. $\sin 75° - \sin 15° = \cos 105° + \cos 15°$
9. $\cos\alpha\cos(\gamma - \alpha) - \sin\alpha\sin(\gamma - \alpha) = \cos\gamma$
10. $\cos(\alpha + \beta)\cos\gamma - \cos(\beta + \gamma)\cos\alpha = \sin\beta\sin(\gamma - \alpha)$
11. $\sin(n + 1)A\sin(n - 1)A + \cos(n + 1)A\cos(n - 1)A = \cos 2A$
12. $\sin(n + 1)A\sin(n + 2)A + \cos(n + 1)A\cos(n + 2)A = \cos A$

➤ **94.** From Arts. 88 and 90, we have, for all values of A and B,

$$\sin(A + B) = \sin A\cos B + \cos A\sin B,$$

and

$$\sin(A - B) = \sin A\cos B - \cos A\sin B,$$

Hence, by addition and subtraction, we have

$$\sin(A + B) + \sin(A - B) = 2\sin A\cos B \quad \text{...(1)}$$

and

$$\sin(A + B) - \sin(A - B) = 2\cos A\sin B \quad \text{...(2)}$$

From the same articles we have, for all values of A and B,

$$\cos(A + B) = \cos A\cos B - \sin A\sin B$$

and

$$\cos(A - B) = \cos A\cos B + \sin A\sin B$$

Hence, by addition and subtraction, we have

$$\cos(A + B) + \cos(A - B) = 2\cos A\cos B \quad \text{...(3)}$$

and

$$\cos(A - B) - \cos(A + B) = 2\sin A\sin B \quad \text{...(4)}$$

Put $A + B = C$, and $A - B = D$, so that

$$A = \frac{C + D}{2}, \text{ and } B = \frac{C - D}{2}$$

On making these substitutions, the relations (1) to (4) become, for all values of C and D,

$$\sin C + \sin D = 2 \sin \frac{C + D}{2} \cos \frac{C - D}{2} \quad \text{...(I)}$$

$$\sin C - \sin D = 2 \cos \frac{C + D}{2} \sin \frac{C - D}{2} \quad \text{...(II)}$$

$$\cos C + \cos D = 2 \cos \frac{C + D}{2} \cos \frac{C - D}{2} \quad \text{...(III)}$$

and

$$\cos C - \cos D = 2 \sin \frac{C + D}{2} \sin \frac{D - C}{2} \quad \text{...(IV)}$$

[The student should carefully notice that the second factor of the right-hand member of IV is $\sin \frac{D - C}{2}$, and not $\sin \frac{C - D}{2}$.]

➤ **95.** These relations I to IV are extremely important and should be very carefully committed to memory.

On account of their great importance we give a geometrical proof for the case when C and D are acute angles.

Let AOC be the angle C and AOD the angle D. Bisect the angle COD by the straight line OE. On OE take a point P and draw QPR perpendicular to OP to meet OC and OD in Q and R respectively.

Draw PL, QM, and RN perpendicular to OA, and through R draw RST perpendicular to PL or QM to meet them in S and T respectively.

Since, the angle DOC is $C - D$, each of the angles DOE and EOC is $\frac{C - D}{2}$, and also

$$\angle AOE = \angle AOD + \angle DOE = D + \frac{C - D}{2} = \frac{C + D}{2}$$

Since, the two triangles POR and POQ are equal in all respects, we have $OQ = OR$, and $PR = PQ$, so that

$$RQ = 2\,RP$$

Hence, $QT = 2\,PS$, and $RT = 2\,RS$, *i.e.* $MN = 2\,ML$

Therefore

$$MQ + NR = TQ + 2\,LS = 2\,SP + 2\,LS = 2\,LP$$

Also

$$OM + ON = 2\,OM + MN = 2\,OM + 2\,ML = 2\,OL$$

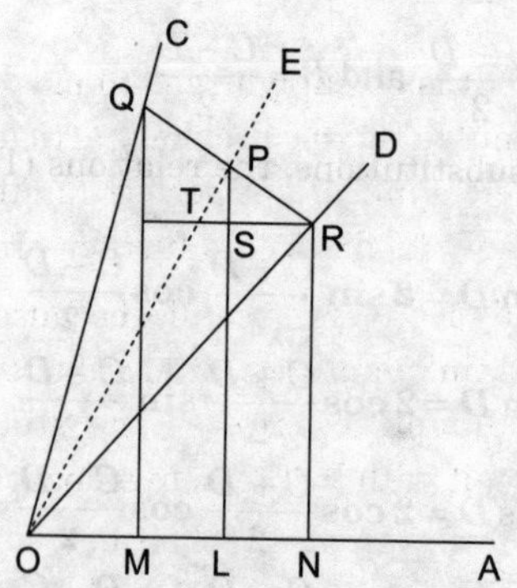

Hence, $\sin C + \sin D = \frac{MQ}{OQ} + \frac{NR}{OR} = \frac{MQ + NR}{OR}$

$= \frac{2\,LP}{OR} = 2\frac{LP}{OP}\cdot\frac{OP}{OR} = 2\sin LOP\cos POR$

$= 2\sin\frac{C+D}{2}\cos\frac{C-D}{2}$

Again, $\sin C - \sin D = \frac{MQ}{OQ} - \frac{NR}{OR} = \frac{MQ - NR}{OR} = \frac{TQ}{OR}$

$= 2\frac{SP}{OR} = 2\frac{SP}{RP}\cdot\frac{RP}{OR} = 2\cos SPR\sin ROP$

$= 2\cos\frac{C+D}{2}\sin\frac{C-D}{2}$

$\left[\text{for } \angle SPR = 90^\circ - \angle SPO = \angle LOP = \frac{C+D}{2}\right]$

Also, $\cos C + \cos D = \frac{OM}{OQ} + \frac{ON}{OR} = \frac{OM + ON}{OR}$

$= 2\frac{OL}{OR} = 2\frac{OL}{OP}\cdot\frac{OP}{OR}$

$= 2\cos LOP\cos POR$

$= 2\cos\frac{C+D}{2}\cos\frac{C-D}{2}$

Finally, $\cos D - \cos C = \frac{ON}{OR} - \frac{OM}{OQ} = \frac{ON - OM}{OR}$

$= \frac{MN}{OR} = 2\frac{SR}{OR} = \frac{2\,SR}{PR}\cdot\frac{PR}{OR}$

$= 2\sin SPR\sin POR$

$= 2\sin\frac{C+D}{2}\sin\frac{C-D}{2}$

➤ **96.** The student is strongly urged to make himself perfectly familiar with the formulae of the previous article and to carefully practise himself in their application; perfect familiarity with these formulae will considerably facilitate his further progress.

The formulae are very useful, because they change sums and differences of certain quantities into products of certain other quantities, and products of quantities are, as the student probably knows from Algebra, easily dealt with by the help of logarithms.

We subjoin a few examples of their use.

EXAMPLE 1 $\sin 6\theta + \sin 4\theta = 2\sin\frac{6\theta + 4\theta}{2}\cos\frac{6\theta - 4\theta}{2} = 2\sin 5\theta\cos\theta$

EXAMPLE 2 $\cos 3\theta - \cos 7\theta = 2\sin\frac{3\theta + 7\theta}{2}\cdot\sin\frac{7\theta - 3\theta}{2} = 2\sin 5\theta\sin 2\theta$

EXAMPLE 3 $$\frac{\sin 75^\circ - \sin 15^\circ}{\cos 75^\circ + \cos 15^\circ} = \frac{2\cos\frac{75^\circ + 15^\circ}{2}\cdot\sin\frac{75^\circ - 15^\circ}{2}}{2\cos\frac{75^\circ + 15^\circ}{2}\cos\frac{75^\circ - 15^\circ}{2}}$$

$$= \frac{2\cos 45^\circ\sin 30^\circ}{2\cos 45^\circ\cos 30^\circ} = \tan 30^\circ$$

$$= \frac{1}{\sqrt{3}} = \frac{\sqrt{3}}{3} = 0.57735\ldots$$

[This is an example of the simplification given by these formulae; it would be a very long and tiresome process to look out from the tables the values of sin 75°, sin 15°, cos 75° and cos15° and then to perform the division of one long decimal fraction by another.]

EXAMPLE 4 *Simplify the expression*

$$\frac{(\cos\theta - \cos 3\theta)(\sin 8\theta + \sin 2\theta)}{(\sin 5\theta - \sin\theta)(\cos 4\theta - \cos 6\theta)}$$

On applying the formulae of Art. 94, this expression

$$= \frac{2\sin\frac{\theta + 3\theta}{2}\cdot\sin\frac{3\theta - \theta}{2}\times 2\sin\frac{8\theta + 2\theta}{2}\cos\frac{8\theta - 2\theta}{2}}{2\cos\frac{5\theta + \theta}{2}\sin\frac{5\theta - \theta}{2}\times 2\sin\frac{4\theta + 6\theta}{2}\cdot\sin\frac{6\theta - 4\theta}{2}}$$

$$= \frac{4\cdot\sin 2\theta\sin\theta\cdot\sin 5\theta\cos 3\theta}{4\cdot\cos 3\theta\sin 2\theta\cdot\sin 5\theta\sin\theta} = 1$$

EXAMPLES XIV

Prove that

1. $\dfrac{\sin 7\theta - \sin 5\theta}{\cos 7\theta + \cos 5\theta} = \tan\theta$

2. $\dfrac{\cos 6\theta - \cos 4\theta}{\sin 6\theta + \sin 4\theta} - \tan\theta$

3. $\dfrac{\sin A + \sin 3A}{\cos A + \cos 3A} = \tan 2A$

4. $\dfrac{\sin 7A - \sin A}{\sin 8A - \sin 2A} = \cos 4A \sec 5A$

5. $\dfrac{\cos 2B + \cos 2A}{\cos 2B - \cos 2A} = \cot(A + B)\cot(A - B)$

6. $\dfrac{\sin 2A + \sin 2B}{\sin 2A - \sin 2B} = \dfrac{\tan(A + B)}{\tan(A - B)}$

7. $\dfrac{\sin A + \sin 2A}{\cos A - \cos 2A} = \cot\dfrac{A}{2}$

8. $\dfrac{\sin 5A - \sin 3A}{\cos 3A + \cos 5A} = \tan A$

9. $\dfrac{\cos 2B - \cos 2A}{\sin 2B + \sin 2A} = \tan(A - B)$

10. $\cos(A + B) + \sin(A - B) = 2\sin(45° + A)\cos(45° + B)$

11. $\dfrac{\cos 3A - \cos A}{\sin 3A - \sin A} + \dfrac{\cos 2A - \cos 4A}{\sin 4A - \sin 2A} = \dfrac{\sin A}{\cos 2A \cos 3A}$

12. $\dfrac{\sin(4A - 2B) + \sin(4B - 2A)}{\cos(4A - 2B) + \cos(4B - 2A)} = \tan(A + B)$

13. $\dfrac{\tan 5\theta + \tan 3\theta}{\tan 5\theta - \tan 3\theta} = 4\cos 2\theta \cos 4\theta$

14. $\dfrac{\cos 3\theta + 2\cos 5\theta + \cos 7\theta}{\cos\theta + 2\cos 3\theta + \cos 5\theta} = \cos 2\theta - \sin 2\theta \tan 3\theta$

15. $\dfrac{\sin A + \sin 3A + \sin 5A + \sin 7A}{\cos A + \cos 3A + \cos 5A + \cos 7A} = \tan 4A$

16. $\dfrac{\sin(\theta + \phi) - 2\sin\theta + \sin(\theta - \phi)}{\cos(\theta + \phi) - 2\cos\theta + \cos(\theta - \phi)} = \tan\theta$

17. $\dfrac{\sin A + 2\sin 3A + \sin 5A}{\sin 3A + 2\sin 5A + \sin 7A} = \dfrac{\sin 3A}{\sin 5A}$

18. $\dfrac{\sin(A - C) + 2\sin A + \sin(A + C)}{\sin(B - C) + 2\sin B + \sin(B + C)} = \dfrac{\sin A}{\sin B}$

19. $\dfrac{\sin A - \sin 5A + \sin 9A - \sin 13A}{\cos A - \cos 5A - \cos 9A + \cos 13A} = \cot 4A$

20. $\dfrac{\sin A + \sin B}{\sin A - \sin B} = \tan\dfrac{A+B}{2}\cot\dfrac{A-B}{2}$

21. $\dfrac{\cos A + \cos B}{\cos B - \cos A} = \cot\dfrac{A+B}{2}\cot\dfrac{A-B}{2}$

22. $\dfrac{\sin A + \sin B}{\cos A + \cos B} = \tan\dfrac{A+B}{2}$

23. $\dfrac{\sin A - \sin B}{\cos B - \cos A} = \cot\dfrac{A+B}{2}$

24. $\dfrac{\cos(A+B+C)+\cos(-A+B+C)+\cos(A-B+C)+\cos(A+B-C)}{\sin(A+B+C)+\sin(-A+B+C)-\sin(A-B+C)+\sin(A+B-C)}$
$= \cot B$

25. $\cos 3A + \cos 5A + \cos 7A + \cos 15A = 4\cos 4A\cos 5A\cos 6A$

26. $\cos(-A+B+C) + \cos(A-B+C) + \cos(A+B-C)$
$+ \cos(A+B+C) = 4\cos A\cos B\cos C$

27. $\sin 50° - \sin 70° + \sin 10° = 0$

28. $\sin 10° + \sin 20° + \sin 40° + \sin 50° = \sin 70° + \sin 80°$

29. $\sin\alpha + \sin 2\alpha + \sin 4\alpha + \sin 5\alpha = 4\cos\dfrac{\alpha}{2}\cos\dfrac{3\alpha}{2}\sin 3\alpha$

Simplify :

30. $\cos\left\{\theta + \left(n - \dfrac{3}{2}\right)\phi\right\} - \cos\left\{\theta + \left(n + \dfrac{3}{2}\right)\phi\right\}$

31. $\sin\left\{\theta + \left(n - \dfrac{1}{2}\right)\phi\right\} + \sin\left\{\theta + \left(n + \dfrac{1}{2}\right)\phi\right\}$

➤ **97.** The formulae (1), (2), (3) and (4) of Art. 94 are also very important. They should be remembered in the form.

$$\mathbf{2\sin A\cos B = \sin(A+B) + \sin(A-B)} \quad ...(1)$$
$$\mathbf{2\cos A\sin B = \sin(A+B) - \sin(A-B)} \quad ...(2)$$
$$\mathbf{2\cos A\cos B = \cos(A+B) + \cos(A-B)} \quad ...(3)$$
$$\mathbf{2\sin A\sin B = \cos(A-B) - \cos(A+B)} \quad ...(4)$$

They may be looked upon as the converse of the formulae I-IV of Art. 94.

EXAMPLE 1 $2\sin 3\theta\cos\theta = \sin 4\theta + \sin 2\theta$

EXAMPLE 2 $2\sin 5\theta\sin 3\theta = \cos 2\theta - \cos 8\theta$

EXAMPLE 3 $2\cos 11\theta\cos 2\theta = \cos 13\theta + \cos 9\theta$

EXAMPLE 4 Simplify, $\dfrac{\sin 8\theta\cos\theta - \sin 6\theta\cos 3\theta}{\cos 2\theta\cos\theta - \sin 3\theta\sin 4\theta}$

By the above formulae, the expression

$$=\frac{\frac{1}{2}(\sin 9\theta+\sin 7\theta)-\frac{1}{2}(\sin 9\theta+\sin 3\theta)}{\frac{1}{2}(\cos 3\theta+\cos\theta)-\frac{1}{2}(\cos\theta-\cos 7\theta)}$$

$$=\frac{\sin 7\theta-\sin 3\theta}{\cos 3\theta+\cos 7\theta}$$

$$=\frac{2\cos 5\theta\sin 2\theta}{2\cos 5\theta\cos 2\theta} \qquad \text{(by the formulae of Art. 94.)}$$

$$=\tan 2\theta$$

[The student should carefully notice the artifice of first employing the formulae of this article and then, to obtain a further simplification, employing the converse formulae of Art. 94. This artifice is often successful in simplifications.]

EXAMPLES XV

Express as a sum or difference the following :

1. $2\sin 5\theta\sin 7\theta$ **2.** $2\cos 7\theta\sin 5\theta$

3. $2\cos 11\theta\cos 3\theta$ **4.** $2\sin 54°\sin 66°$

Prove that

5. $\sin\frac{\theta}{2}\sin\frac{7\theta}{2}+\sin\frac{3\theta}{2}\sin\frac{11\theta}{2}=\sin 2\theta\sin 5\theta$

6. $\cos 2\theta\cos\frac{\theta}{2}-\cos 3\theta\cos\frac{9\theta}{2}=\sin 5\theta\sin\frac{5\theta}{2}$

7. $\sin A\sin(A+2B)-\sin B\sin(B+2A)=\sin(A-B)\sin(A+B)$

8. $(\sin 3A+\sin A)\sin A+(\cos 3A-\cos A)\cos A=0$

9. $\frac{2\sin(A-C)\cos C-\sin(A-2C)}{2\sin(B-C)\cos C-\sin(B-2C)}=\frac{\sin A}{\sin B}$

10. $\frac{\sin A\sin 2A+\sin 3A\sin 6A+\sin 4A\sin 13A}{\sin A\cos 2A+\sin 3A\cos 6A+\sin 4A\cos 13A}=\tan 9A$

11. $\frac{\cos 2A\cos 3A-\cos 2A\cos 7A+\cos A\cos 10A}{\sin 4A\sin 3A-\sin 2A\sin 5A+\sin 4A\sin 7A}=\cot 6A\cot 5A$

12. $\cos(36°-A)\cos(36°+A)+\cos(54°+A)\cos(54°-A)=\cos 2A$

13. $\cos A\sin(B-C)+\cos B\sin(C-A)+\cos C\sin(A-B)=0$

14. $\sin(45°+A)\sin(45°-A)=1/2\cos 2A$

15. $\text{versin}(A+B)\,\text{versin}(A-B)=(\cos A-\cos B)^2$

16. $\sin(\beta-\gamma)\cos(\alpha-\delta)+\sin(\gamma-\alpha)\cos(\beta-\delta)+\sin(\alpha-\beta)\cos(\gamma-\delta)=0$

17. $2\cos\frac{\pi}{13}\cos\frac{9\pi}{13}+\cos\frac{3\pi}{13}+\cos\frac{5\pi}{13}=0$

➤ **98.** *To prove that* $\tan(A+B) = \dfrac{\tan A + \tan B}{1 - \tan A \tan B}$ *and that*

$$\tan(A-B) = \frac{\tan A - \tan B}{1 + \tan A \tan B}.$$

By Art. 88, we have, for all values of A and B

$$\tan(A+B) = \frac{\sin(A+B)}{\cos(A+B)} = \frac{\sin A \cos B + \cos A \sin B}{\cos A \cos B - \sin A \sin B}$$

$$= \frac{\dfrac{\sin A}{\cos A} + \dfrac{\sin B}{\cos B}}{1 - \dfrac{\sin A \sin B}{\cos A \cos B}}$$

by dividing both numerator and denominator by $\cos A \cos B$.

$$\therefore \quad \mathbf{\tan(A+B) = \frac{\tan A + \tan B}{1 - \tan A \tan B}}$$

Again, by Art. 90,

$$\tan(A-B) = \frac{\sin(A-B)}{\cos(A-B)} = \frac{\sin A \cos B - \cos A \sin B}{\cos A \cos B + \sin A \sin B}$$

$$= \frac{\dfrac{\sin A}{\cos A} - \dfrac{\sin B}{\cos B}}{1 + \dfrac{\sin A \sin B}{\cos A \cos B}} \quad \text{by dividing as before.}$$

$$\therefore \quad \mathbf{\tan(A-B) = \frac{\tan A - \tan B}{1 + \tan A \tan B}}$$

➤ **99.** The formulae of the preceding article may be obtained geometrically from the figures of Arts. 88 and 90.

(1) Taking the figure of Art. 88, we have

$$\tan(A+B) = \frac{MP}{OM} = \frac{QN + RP}{OQ - RN}$$

$$= \frac{\dfrac{QN}{OQ} + \dfrac{RP}{OQ}}{1 - \dfrac{RN}{OQ}} = \frac{\tan A + \dfrac{RP}{OQ}}{1 - \dfrac{RN}{RP}\dfrac{RP}{OQ}}$$

But, since the angle RPN and QON are equal the triangles RPN and QON are similar so that

$$\frac{RP}{PN} = \frac{OQ}{ON}$$

and therefore $\dfrac{RP}{OQ} = \dfrac{PN}{ON} = \tan B$

Hence, $\tan(A+B) = \dfrac{\tan A + \tan B}{1 - \tan RPN \tan B} = \dfrac{\tan A + \tan B}{1 - \tan A \tan B}$

(2) Taking the figure of Art. 90, we have

$$\tan(A-B) = \frac{MP}{OM} = \frac{QN - PR}{OQ + NR}$$

$$= \frac{\frac{QN}{OQ} - \frac{PR}{OQ}}{1 + \frac{NR}{OQ}} = \frac{\tan A - \frac{PR}{OQ}}{1 + \frac{NR}{PR}\frac{PR}{OQ}}$$

But, since the angles RPN and NOQ are equal, we have

$$\frac{RP}{PN} = \frac{OQ}{ON}$$

and therefore, $$\frac{PR}{OQ} = \frac{PN}{ON} = \tan B$$

Hence, $$\tan(A-B) = \frac{\tan A - \tan B}{1 + \tan RPN \tan B} = \frac{\tan A - \tan B}{1 + \tan A \tan B}$$

➤ **100.** As particular cases of the preceding formulae, we have, by putting B equal to 45°,

$$\tan(A + 45°) = \frac{\tan A + 1}{1 - \tan A} = \frac{1 + \tan A}{1 - \tan A}$$

and $$\tan(A - 45°) = \frac{\tan A - 1}{1 + \tan A}$$

Similarly, as in Art. 98, we may prove that

$$\cot(A+B) = \frac{\cot A \cot B - 1}{\cot A + \cot B}$$

and $$\cot(A-B) = \frac{\cot A \cot B + 1}{\cot B - \cot A}$$

➤ **101.**

<u>EXAMPLE 1</u> $\tan 75° = \tan(45° + 30°) = \dfrac{\tan 45° + \tan 30°}{1 - \tan 45° \tan 30°}$

$$= \frac{1 + \frac{1}{\sqrt{3}}}{1 - \frac{1}{\sqrt{3}}} = \frac{\sqrt{3}+1}{\sqrt{3}-1} = \frac{(\sqrt{3}+1)^2}{3-1} = \frac{4 + 2\sqrt{3}}{2} = 2 + \sqrt{3}$$

$$= 2 + 1.73205\ldots = 3.73205\ldots$$

<u>EXAMPLE 2</u> $\tan 15° = \tan(45° - 30°) = \dfrac{\tan 45° - \tan 30°}{1 + \tan 45° \tan 30°}$

$$= \frac{1 - \frac{1}{\sqrt{3}}}{1 + \frac{1}{\sqrt{3}}} = \frac{\sqrt{3}-1}{\sqrt{3}+1} = \frac{(\sqrt{3}-1)^2}{3-1} = \frac{4 - 2\sqrt{3}}{2} = 2 - \sqrt{3}$$

$$= 2 - 1.73205\ldots = 0.26795\ldots$$

EXAMPLES XVI

1. If $\tan A = \frac{1}{2}$ and $\tan B = \frac{1}{3}$, find the values of $\tan(2A + B)$ and $\tan(2A - B)$. Verify by a graph and accurate measurement.

2. If $\tan A = \frac{\sqrt{3}}{4 - \sqrt{3}}$ and $\tan B = \frac{\sqrt{3}}{4 + \sqrt{3}}$, prove that

$$\tan(A - B) = 0.375$$

3. If $\tan A = \frac{n}{n+1}$ and $\tan B = \frac{1}{2n+1}$, find $\tan(A + B)$.

4. If $\tan\alpha = \frac{5}{6}$ and $\tan\beta = \frac{1}{11'}$ prove that $\alpha + \beta = \frac{\pi}{4}$. Verify by a graph and accurate measurement.

Prove that

5. $\tan\left(\frac{\pi}{4} + \theta\right) \times \tan\left(\frac{3\pi}{4} + \theta\right) = -1.$

6. $\cot\left(\frac{\pi}{4} + \theta\right) \times \cot\left(\frac{\pi}{4} - \theta\right) = 1.$

7. $1 + \tan A \tan\frac{A}{2} = \tan A \cot\frac{A}{2} - 1 = \sec A.$

8. Construct the acute angles whose tangents are $\frac{1}{3}$ and $\frac{1}{2}$, and verify by measurement that their sum is 45°.

9. The tangents of two acute angles are respectively 3 and 2; show by a graph that the tangent of their difference is $\frac{1}{7}$.

10. The sine of one acute angle is 0.6 and cosine of another is 0.5. Show graphically, and also by calculation, that the sine of their difference is 0.39 nearly.

11. Draw the positive angle whose cosine is 0.4 and show both by measurement and calculation, that the sine and cosine of an angle which exceeds it by 45° are 0.93 and – 0.365 nearly.

12. Draw the acute angle whose tangent is 7 and the acute angle whose sine is 0.7; and show, both by measurement and calculation, that the sine of their difference is approximately 0.61.

➤ **102.** As further example of the use of the formulae of the present chapter we shall find the general value of the angle which has a given sine, cosine or tangent. This has been already found in Arts. 82-84.

Find the general value of all angles having a given sine.

Let α be any angle having the given sine, and θ any other angle having the same sine.

We have then to find the most general value of θ which satisfies the equation.

$$\sin\theta = \sin\alpha, \text{ i.e. } \sin\theta - \sin\alpha = 0$$

This may be written

$$2\cos\frac{\theta+\alpha}{2}\sin\frac{\theta-\alpha}{2} = 0$$

and it is therefore satisfied by

$$\cos\frac{\theta+\alpha}{2} = 0, \text{ and by } \sin\frac{\theta-\alpha}{2} = 0$$

i.e., by $\frac{\theta+\alpha}{2}$ = any odd multiple of $\frac{\pi}{2}$

and by $\frac{\theta-\alpha}{2}$ = any multiple of π

i.e., by $\theta = -\alpha$ + any odd multiple of π ...(1)

and $\theta = \alpha$ + any even multiple of π ...(2)

i.e., θ must $= (-1)^n \alpha + n\pi$, where n is zero or any positive or negative integer.

For, when n is odd, this expression agrees with (1), and, when n is even, it agrees with (2).

➤ **103.** *Find the general value of all angles having the same cosine.*

The equation we have now to solve is

$$\cos\theta = \cos\alpha$$

i.e., $\cos\alpha - \cos\theta = 0$

i.e., $2\sin\frac{\theta+\alpha}{2}\sin\frac{\theta-\alpha}{2} = 0$

and it is therefore satisfied by

$$\sin\frac{\theta+\alpha}{2} = 0, \text{ and by } \sin\frac{\theta-\alpha}{2} = 0$$

i.e., $\frac{\theta+\alpha}{2}$ = any multiple of π

and by $\frac{\theta-\alpha}{2}$ = any multiple of π

i.e., by $\theta = -\alpha$ + any multiple of 2π

and by $\theta = \alpha$ + any multiple of 2π

Both these sets of values are inclined in the solution $\theta = 2n\pi \pm \alpha$, where n is zero or any positive or negative integer.

➤ **104.** *Find the general value of all angles having the same tangent.*

The equation we have now to solve is

$$\tan\theta - \tan\alpha = 0$$

i.e., $$\sin\theta\cos\alpha - \cos\theta\sin\alpha = 0$$

i.e., $$\sin(\theta - \alpha) = 0$$

$\therefore$ $$\theta - \alpha = \text{any multiple of } \pi$$

$$= n\pi$$

where n is zero or any positive or negative integer, so that the most general solution is $\theta = n\pi + \alpha$.

8

TRIGONOMETRICAL RATIOS OF MULTIPLE AND SUBMULTIPLE OF ANGLES

➤ **105.** *To find the trigonometrical ratios of an angle 2A in terms of those of the angle A.*

If in the formulae of Art. 88 we put $B = A$, we have

$$\mathbf{sin2}\boldsymbol{A} = \sin A \cos A + \cos A \sin A = \mathbf{2sin}\boldsymbol{A}\ \mathbf{cos}\boldsymbol{A},$$

$$\mathbf{cos2}\boldsymbol{A} = \cos A \cos A - \sin A \sin A = \mathbf{cos^2}\boldsymbol{A} - \mathbf{sin^2}\boldsymbol{A},$$

$$= (1 - \sin^2 A) - \sin^2 A = \mathbf{1 - 2sin^2}\boldsymbol{A},$$

and also $$= \cos^2 A - (1 - \cos^2 A) = \mathbf{2cos^2}\boldsymbol{A} - \mathbf{1};$$

and $$\mathbf{tan2}\boldsymbol{A} = \frac{\tan A + \tan A}{1 - \tan A \cdot \tan A} = \frac{\mathbf{2\,tan}\boldsymbol{A}}{\mathbf{1 - tan^2}\boldsymbol{A}}.$$

Now, the formulae of Art. 88 are true for all values of A and B; hence any formulae derived from them are true for all values of the angles.

In particular the above formulae are true for all values of A.

➤ **106.** An independent geometrical proof of the formulae of the preceding article may be given for values of A which are less than a right angle.

Let QCP be the angle $2A$

With centre C and radius CP describe a circle, and let QC meet it again in O.

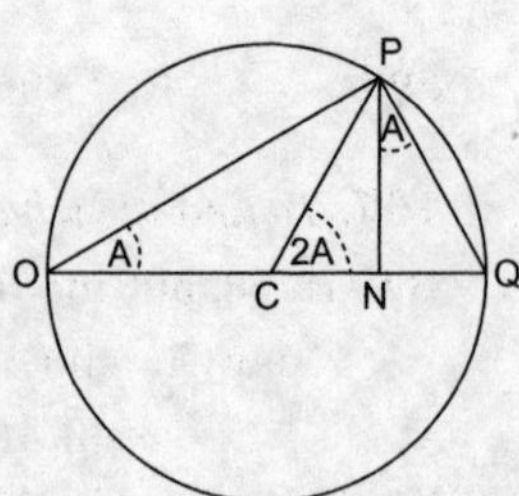

Join OP and PQ, and draw PN perpendicular to OQ.

By Geometry, the angle

$$QOP = \frac{1}{2} \angle QCP = A,$$

and the angle $NPQ = \angle QOP = A$

Hence, $\sin 2A = \dfrac{NP}{CP} = \dfrac{2\,NP}{2\,CQ} = 2\dfrac{NP}{OQ} = 2\dfrac{NP}{OP}\cdot\dfrac{OP}{OQ}$

$= 2\sin NOP \cos POQ$, since OPQ is a right angle.

$= 2\sin A \cos A;$

Also, $\cos 2A = \dfrac{CN}{CP} = \dfrac{2\,CN}{OQ} = \dfrac{(OC + CN) - (OC - CN)}{OQ}$

$= \dfrac{ON - NQ}{OQ} = \dfrac{ON}{OP}\cdot\dfrac{OP}{OQ} - \dfrac{NQ}{PQ}\cdot\dfrac{PQ}{OQ}$

$= \cos^2 A - \sin^2 A;$

and $\tan 2A = \dfrac{NP}{CN} = \dfrac{2NP}{ON - NQ} = \dfrac{2\dfrac{NP}{ON}}{1 - \dfrac{NQ}{PN}\cdot\dfrac{PN}{ON}}$

$= \dfrac{2\tan A}{1 - \tan^2 A}.$

<u>**EXAMPLE**</u> *To find the values of* $\sin 15°$ *and* $\cos 15°$.

Let the angle $2A$ be 30°, so that A is 15°.

Let the radius CP be $2a$, so that we have

$$CN = 2a\cos 30° = a\sqrt{3},$$

and $NP = 2a\sin 30° = a$

Hence, $ON = OC + CN = a(2 + \sqrt{3}),$

and $NQ = CQ - CN = a(2 - \sqrt{3})$

$\therefore$ $OP^2 = ON \cdot OQ = a(2 + \sqrt{3}) \times 4a$

so that $OP = a\sqrt{2}(\sqrt{3} + 1)$

and $PQ^2 = QN \cdot QO = a(2 - \sqrt{3}) \times 4a$

so that $PQ = a\sqrt{2}(\sqrt{3} - 1)$

Hence, $\sin 15° = \dfrac{PQ}{OQ} = \dfrac{\sqrt{2}(\sqrt{3} - 1)}{4} = \dfrac{\sqrt{3} - 1}{2\sqrt{2}}$

and $\cos 15° = \dfrac{OP}{OQ} = \dfrac{\sqrt{2}(\sqrt{3} + 1)}{4} = \dfrac{\sqrt{3} + 1}{2\sqrt{2}}.$

➤ **107.** *To find the trigonometrical functions of* $3A$ *in terms of those of* A.

By Art. 88, putting B equal to $2A$, we have

$$\sin 3A = \sin(A + 2A) = \sin A \cos 2A + \cos A \sin 2A$$

$$= \sin A(1 - 2\sin^2 A) + \cos A \cdot 2\sin A \cos A,$$

by Art. 105., $= \sin A(1 - 2\sin^2 A) + 2\sin A(1 - \sin^2 A)$

Hence, $\mathbf{\sin 3A = 3\sin A - 4\sin^3 A}$ ...(1)

So, $$\cos 3A = \cos(A + 2A) = \cos A \cos 2A - \sin A \sin 2A$$
$$= \cos A(2\cos^2 A - 1) - \sin A \cdot 2\sin A \cos A$$
$$= \cos A(2\cos^2 A - 1) - 2\cos A(1 - \cos^2 A)$$

Hence, $$\mathbf{\cos 3A = 4\cos^3 A - 3\cos A} \qquad ...(2)$$

Also, $$\tan 3A = \tan(A + 2A) = \frac{\tan A + \tan 2A}{1 - \tan A \tan 2A}$$
$$= \frac{\tan A + \dfrac{2\tan A}{1 - \tan^2 A}}{1 - \tan A \cdot \dfrac{2\tan A}{1 - \tan^2 A}}$$
$$= \frac{\tan A(1 - \tan^2 A) + 2\tan A}{(1 - \tan^2 A) - 2\tan^2 A}$$

Hence, $$\mathbf{\tan 3A = \frac{3\tan A - \tan^3 A}{1 - 3\tan^2 A}} \qquad ...(3)$$

[The student may find it difficult to remember, and distinguish between the formulae (1) and (2), which bear a general resemblance to one another, but have their signs in a different order. If in doubt, he may always verify his formula by testing it for a particular case, *e.g.*, by putting $A = 30°$ for formula (1), and by putting $A = 0°$ for formula (2).]

➤ **108.** By a process similar to that of the previous article, the trigonometrical ratios of any higher multiples of θ may be expressed in terms of those of θ. The method is however long and tedious. In a later chapter better methods will be pointed out.

As an example, let us express $\cos 5\theta$ in terms of $\cos\theta$. We have

$$\cos 5\theta = \cos(3\theta + 2\theta)$$
$$= \cos 3\theta \cos 2\theta - \sin 3\theta \sin 2\theta$$
$$= (4\cos^3\theta - 3\cos\theta)(2\cos^2\theta - 1)$$
$$- (3\sin\theta - 4\sin^3\theta) \cdot 2\sin\theta\cos\theta$$
$$= (8\cos^5\theta - 10\cos^3\theta + 3\cos\theta)$$
$$- 2\cos\theta \cdot \sin^2\theta(3 - 4\sin^2\theta)$$
$$= (8\cos^5 - 10\cos^3\theta + 3\cos\theta)$$
$$- 2\cos\theta(1 - \cos^2\theta)(4\cos^2\theta - 1)$$
$$= (8\cos^5\theta - 10\cos^3\theta + 3\cos\theta)$$
$$- 2\cos\theta(5\cos^2\theta - 4\cos^4\theta - 1)$$
$$= 16\cos^5\theta - 20\cos^3\theta + 5\cos\theta.$$

EXAMPLES XVII

1. Find the value of $\sin 2a$ when

(1) $\cos a = \frac{3}{5}$, (2) $\sin a = \frac{12}{13}$, and (3) $\tan a = \frac{16}{63}$

2. Find the value of $\cos 2a$ when

(1) $\cos a = \frac{15}{17}$, (2) $\sin a = \frac{4}{5}$, and (3) $\tan a = \frac{5}{12}$

Verify by a graph and accurate measurement.

3. If $\tan\theta = \frac{b}{a}$, find the value of $a\cos 2\theta + b\sin 2\theta$

Prove that

4. $\frac{\sin 2A}{1+\cos 2A} = \tan A$

5. $\frac{\sin 2A}{1-\cos 2A} = \cot A$

6. $\frac{1-\cos 2A}{1+\cos 2A} = \tan^2 A$

7. $\tan A + \cot A = 2\operatorname{cosec} 2A$

8. $\tan A - \cot A = -2\cot 2A$

9. $\operatorname{cosec} 2A + \cot 2A = \cot A$

10. $\frac{1-\cos A+\cos B-\cos(A+B)}{1+\cos A-\cos B-\cos(A+B)} = \tan\frac{A}{2}\cot\frac{B}{2}$

11. $\frac{\cos A}{1\mp\sin A} = \tan\left(45^\circ \pm \frac{A}{2}\right)$

12. $\frac{\sec 8A-1}{\sec 4A-1} = \frac{\tan 8A}{\tan 2A}$

13. $\frac{1+\tan^2(45^\circ-A)}{1-\tan^2(45^\circ-A)} = \operatorname{cosec} 2A$

14. $\frac{\sin\alpha+\sin\beta}{\sin\alpha-\sin\beta} = \frac{\tan\frac{\alpha+\beta}{2}}{\tan\frac{\alpha-\beta}{2}}$

15. $\frac{\sin^2 A-\sin^2 B}{\sin A\cos A-\sin B\cos B} = \tan(A+B)$

16. $\tan\left(\frac{\pi}{4}+\theta\right) - \tan\left(\frac{\pi}{4}-\theta\right) = 2\tan 2\theta$

17. $\frac{\cos A+\sin A}{\cos A-\sin A} - \frac{\cos A-\sin A}{\cos A+\sin A} = 2\tan 2A$

18. $\cot(A+15^\circ)-\tan(A-15^\circ)=\dfrac{4\cos 2A}{1+2\sin 2A}$

19. $\dfrac{\sin\theta+\sin 2\theta}{1+\cos\theta+\cos 2\theta}=\tan\theta$

20. $\dfrac{1+\sin\theta-\cos\theta}{1+\sin\theta+\cos\theta}=\tan\dfrac{\theta}{2}$

21. $\dfrac{\sin(n+1)A-\sin(n-1)A}{\cos(n+1)A+2\cos nA+\cos(n-1)A}=\tan\dfrac{A}{2}$

22. $\dfrac{\sin(n+1)A+2\sin nA+\sin(n-1)A}{\cos(n-1)A-\cos(n+1)A}=\cot\dfrac{A}{2}$

23. $\sin(2n+1)A\sin A=\sin^2(n+1)A-\sin^2 nA.$

24. $\dfrac{\sin(A+3B)+\sin(3A+B)}{\sin 2A+\sin 2B}=2\cos(A+B)$

Prove that,

25. $\sin 3A+\sin 2A-\sin A=4\sin A\cos\dfrac{A}{2}\cos\dfrac{3A}{2}$

26. $\tan 2A=(\sec 2A+1)\sqrt{\sec^2 A-1}$

27. $\cos^3 2\theta+3\cos 2\theta=4(\cos^6\theta-\sin^6\theta)$

28. $1+\cos^2 2\theta=2(\cos^4\theta+\sin^4\theta)$

29. $\sec^2 A(1+\sec 2A)=2\sec 2A$

30. $\operatorname{cosec} A-2\cot 2A\cos A=2\sin A$

31. $\cot A=\dfrac{1}{2}\left(\cot\dfrac{A}{2}-\tan\dfrac{A}{2}\right)$

32. $\sin\alpha\sin(60^\circ-\alpha)\sin(60^\circ+\alpha)=\dfrac{1}{4}\sin 3\alpha$

33. $\cos\alpha\cos(60^\circ-\alpha)\cos(60^\circ+\alpha)=\dfrac{1}{4}\cos 3\alpha$

34. $\cot\alpha+\cot(60^\circ+\alpha)-\cot(60^\circ-\alpha)=3\cot 3\alpha$

35. $\cos 20^\circ\cos 40^\circ\cos 60^\circ\cos 80^\circ=\dfrac{1}{16}$

36. $\sin 20^\circ\sin 40^\circ\sin 60^\circ\sin 80^\circ=\dfrac{3}{16}$

37. $\cos 4\alpha=1-8\cos^2\alpha+8\cos^4\alpha$

38. $\sin 4A=4\sin A\cos^3 A-4\cos A\sin^3 A$

39. $\cos 6\alpha=32\cos^6\alpha-48\cos^4\alpha+18\cos^2\alpha-1$

40. $\tan 3A\tan 2A\tan A=\tan 3A-\tan 2A-\tan A$

41. $\dfrac{2\cos 2^n\theta+1}{2\cos\theta+1}=(2\cos\theta-1)(2\cos 2\theta-1)(2\cos 2^2\theta-1)$

$\qquad\ldots(2\cos 2^{n-1}\theta-1)$

SUBMULTIPLE ANGLES

➤ **109.** Since the relations of Art. 105 are true for all values of the angle A, they will be true if instead of A we substitute $\frac{A}{2}$, and therefore if instead of $2A$ we put $2 \cdot \frac{A}{2}$ *i.e.*, A.

Hence, we have the relations

$$\sin A = 2\sin\frac{A}{2}\cos\frac{A}{2} \qquad \text{...(1)}$$

$$\cos A = \cos^2\frac{A}{2} - \sin^2\frac{A}{2}$$

$$= 2\cos^2\frac{A}{2} - 1 = 1 - 2\sin^2\frac{A}{2} \qquad \text{...(2)}$$

and $$\tan A = \frac{2\tan\frac{A}{2}}{1-\tan^2\frac{A}{2}} \qquad \text{...(3)}$$

From (1), we also have

$$\sin A = \frac{2\sin\frac{A}{2}\cos\frac{A}{2}}{\cos^2\frac{A}{2}+\sin^2\frac{A}{2}}$$

$$= \frac{2\tan\frac{A}{2}}{1+\tan^2\frac{A}{2}}$$

by dividing both numerator and denominator by $\cos^2\frac{A}{2}$

So, $$\cos A = \frac{\cos^2\frac{A}{2}-\sin^2\frac{A}{2}}{\cos^2\frac{A}{2}+\sin^2\frac{A}{2}} = \frac{1-\tan^2\frac{A}{2}}{1+\tan^2\frac{A}{2}}.$$

➤ **110.** *To express the trigonometrical ratios of the angle* $\frac{A}{2}$ *in terms of* $\cos A$.

From (2) of the previous article, we have

$$\cos A = 1 - 2\sin^2\frac{A}{2},$$

so that $$2\sin^2\frac{A}{2} = 1 - \cos A$$

and therefore, $$\sin\frac{A}{2} = \pm\sqrt{\frac{1-\cos A}{2}} \qquad ...(1)$$

Again, $$\cos A = 2\cos^2\frac{A}{2} - 1$$

So that, $$2\cos^2\frac{A}{2} = 1 + \cos A,$$

and therefore, $$\cos\frac{A}{2} = \pm\sqrt{\frac{1+\cos A}{2}} \qquad ...(2)$$

Hence, $$\tan\frac{A}{2} = \frac{\sin\frac{A}{2}}{\cos\frac{A}{2}} = \pm\sqrt{\frac{1-\cos A}{1+\cos A}} \qquad ...(3)$$

➤ **111.** In each of the preceding formulae it will be noted that there is an ambiguous sign. In any particular case the proper sign can be determined as the following examples will show.

EXAMPLE 1 *Given* $\cos 45° = \frac{1}{\sqrt{2}}$, *find the values of* $\sin 22\frac{1}{2}°$ *and* $\cos 22\frac{1}{2}°$.

The Eq. (1) of the previous article gives, by putting A equal to 45°,

$$\sin 22\frac{1}{2}° = \pm\sqrt{\frac{1-\cos 45°}{2}} = \pm\sqrt{\frac{1-\frac{1}{\sqrt{2}}}{2}} = \pm\sqrt{\frac{2-\sqrt{2}}{4}}$$
$$= \pm\frac{1}{2}\sqrt{2-\sqrt{2}}$$

Now, $\sin 22\frac{1}{2}°$ is necessarily positive, so that the upper sign must be taken.

Hence, $$\sin 22\frac{1}{2}° = \frac{1}{2}\sqrt{2-\sqrt{2}}$$

So, $\cos 22\frac{1}{2}° = \pm\sqrt{\frac{1-\cos 45°}{2}} = \pm\sqrt{\frac{2+\sqrt{2}}{4}} = \pm\frac{1}{2}\sqrt{2+\sqrt{2}}$; also $\cos 22\frac{1}{2}°$ is positive;

$$\therefore \quad \cos 22\frac{1}{2}° = \frac{\sqrt{2+\sqrt{2}}}{2}$$

EXAMPLE 2 *Given* $\cos 330° = \frac{\sqrt{3}}{2}$, *find the values of* $\sin 165°$ *and* $\cos 165°$.

The Eq. (1) gives

$$\sin 165° = \pm\sqrt{\frac{1-\cos 330°}{2}} = \pm\sqrt{\frac{1-\frac{\sqrt{3}}{2}}{2}} = \pm\sqrt{\frac{4-2\sqrt{3}}{8}}$$

$$= \pm\frac{\sqrt{3}-1}{2\sqrt{2}}$$

Also, $$\cos 165° = \pm\sqrt{\frac{1+\cos 330°}{2}} = \pm\sqrt{\frac{1+\frac{\sqrt{3}}{2}}{2}} = \pm\sqrt{\frac{4+2\sqrt{3}}{8}}$$

$$= \pm\frac{\sqrt{3}+1}{2\sqrt{2}}$$

Now, 165° lies between 90° and 180°, so that, by Art. 52, its sine is positive and its cosine is negative.

Hence, $$\sin 165° = \frac{\sqrt{3}-1}{2\sqrt{2}}$$

and $$\cos 165° = -\frac{\sqrt{3}+1}{2\sqrt{2}}$$

From the above examples it will be seen that, when the angle A and its cosine are given, the ratios for the angle $A/2$ may be determined without any ambiguity of sign.

When, however, only $\cos A$ is given, there is an ambiguity in finding $\sin\frac{A}{2}$ and $\cos\frac{A}{2}$. The explanation of this ambiguity is given in the next article.

➤ ****112.** *To explain why there is ambiguity when* $\cos\frac{A}{2}$ *and* $\sin\frac{A}{2}$ *are found from the value of* $\cos A$.

We know that, if n be any integer,

$$\cos A = \cos(2n\pi \pm A) = k \text{ (say)}$$

Hence, any formula which gives us $\cos\frac{A}{2}$ in terms of k should give us also the cosine of $\frac{2n\pi \pm A}{2}$

Now $$\cos\frac{2n\pi \pm A}{2} = \cos\left(n\pi \pm \frac{A}{2}\right)$$

$$= \cos n\pi \cos\frac{A}{2} \mp \sin n\pi \sin\frac{A}{2} = \cos n\pi \cos\frac{A}{2}$$

$$= \pm\cos\frac{A}{2}$$

according as n is even or odd.

Similarly, any formula,giving us sin sin $\frac{A}{2}$ in term of k, should gives us also the sine of $\frac{2n\pi \pm A}{2}$

Also, $\sin \frac{2n\pi \pm A}{2} = \sin\left(n\pi \pm \frac{A}{2}\right)$

$$= \sin n\pi \cos \frac{A}{2} \pm \cos n\pi \sin \frac{A}{2} = \pm \cos n\pi \sin \frac{A}{2}$$

$$= \pm \sin \frac{A}{2}$$

Hence, in each case, we should expect to obtain two values for $\cos \frac{A}{2}$ and $\sin \frac{A}{2}$, and this is the number which the formulae of Art. 110 give.

[The student may illustrate this article geometrically by drawing the angles $\frac{2n\pi \pm A}{2}$, *i.e.*, $n\pi \pm \frac{A}{2}$. The bounding line for these angles will have four positions, two inclined to the positive direction of the initial line at angles $\frac{A}{2}$ and $-\frac{A}{2}$, and two inclined at $\frac{A}{2}$ and $-\frac{A}{2}$ to the negative direction of the initial line. It will be clear from the figure that there are two values for $\cos \frac{A}{2}$ and two for $\sin \frac{A}{2}$.]

➤ **113.** *To express the trigonometrical ratios of the angle $\frac{A}{2}$ in terms of* $\sin A$.

From Eq. (1) of Art. 109, we have

$$2 \sin \frac{A}{2} \cos \frac{A}{2} = \sin A \qquad \ldots(1)$$

Also, $$\sin^2 \frac{A}{2} + \cos^2 \frac{A}{2} = 1, \text{ always} \qquad \ldots(2)$$

First adding these equations, and then subtracting Eq. (1) from Eq. (2), we have

$$\sin^2 \frac{A}{2} + 2 \sin \frac{A}{2} \cos \frac{A}{2} + \cos^2 \frac{A}{2} = 1 + \sin A,$$

and $$\sin^2 \frac{A}{2} - 2 \sin \frac{A}{2} \cos \frac{A}{2} + \cos^2 \frac{A}{2} = 1 - \sin A;$$

i.e., $$\left(\sin \frac{A}{2} + \cos \frac{A}{2}\right)^2 = 1 + \sin A$$

and $$\left(\sin \frac{A}{2} - \cos \frac{A}{2}\right)^2 = 1 - \sin A$$

so that $$\sin\frac{A}{2} + \cos\frac{A}{2} = \pm\sqrt{1 + \sin A} \quad ...(3)$$

and $$\sin\frac{A}{2} - \cos\frac{A}{2} = \pm\sqrt{1 - \sin A} \quad ...(4)$$

By adding, and then subtracting, we have

$$\mathbf{2\sin\frac{A}{2} = \pm\sqrt{1 + \sin A} \pm \sqrt{1 - \sin A}} \quad ...(5)$$

and $$\mathbf{2\cos\frac{A}{2} = \pm\sqrt{1 + \sin A} \mp \sqrt{1 - \sin A}} \quad ...(6)$$

The other ratios of $\frac{A}{2}$ are then easily obtained.

➤ **114.** In each of the formulae (5) and (6) there are two ambiguous signs. In the following examples it is shown how to determine the ambiguity in any particular case.

EXAMPLE 1 *Given that* $\sin 30°$ *is* $\frac{1}{2}$, *find the values of* $\sin 15°$ *and* $\cos 15°$.

Putting $A = 30°$, we have from relations (3) and (4)

$$\sin 15° + \cos 15° = \pm\sqrt{1 + \sin 30°} = \pm\frac{\sqrt{3}}{\sqrt{2}}$$

$$\sin 15° - \cos 15° = \pm\sqrt{1 - \sin 30°} = \pm\frac{1}{\sqrt{2}}$$

Now, $\sin 15°$ and $\cos 15°$ are both positive, and $\cos 15°$ is greater than $\sin 15°$. Hence the expressions $\sin 15° + \cos 15°$ and $\sin 15° - \cos 15°$ are respectively positive and negative.

Hence, the above two relations should be

$$\sin 15° + \cos 15° = +\frac{\sqrt{3}}{\sqrt{2}}$$

and $$\sin 15° - \cos 15° = -\frac{1}{\sqrt{2}}$$

Hence, $\sin 15° = \frac{\sqrt{3} - 1}{2\sqrt{2}}$, and $\cos 15° = \frac{\sqrt{3} + 1}{2\sqrt{2}}$

EXAMPLE 2 *Given that* $\sin 570°$ *is equal to* $\frac{-1}{2}$, *find the values of* $\sin 285°$ *and* $\cos 285°$.

Putting A equal to $570°$, we have

$$\sin 285° + \cos 285° = \pm\sqrt{1 + \sin 570°} = \pm\frac{1}{\sqrt{2}}$$

and $$\sin 285° - \cos 285° = \pm\sqrt{1 - \sin 570°} = \pm\sqrt{\frac{3}{2}}$$

Now, $\sin 285°$ is negative, $\cos 285°$ is positive, and the former is numerically greater than the latter, as may be seen by a figure.

Hence, $\sin 285° + \cos 285°$ is negative, and $\sin 285° - \cos 285°$ is also negative.

$$\therefore \qquad \sin 285° + \cos 285° = -\frac{1}{\sqrt{2}}$$

$$\text{and} \qquad \sin 285° - \cos 285° = -\frac{\sqrt{3}}{\sqrt{2}}$$

$$\text{Hence,} \qquad \sin 285° = -\frac{\sqrt{3}+1}{2\sqrt{2}}$$

$$\text{and} \qquad \cos 285° = \frac{\sqrt{3}-1}{2\sqrt{2}}.$$

➤ ****115.** *To explain why there is ambiguity when* $\sin\frac{A}{2}$ *and* $\cos\frac{A}{2}$ *are found the value of* $\sin A$.

We know that, if n be any integer,

$\sin\{n\pi + (-1)^n A\} = \sin A = k$ (say). (Art. 82.)

Hence, any formula which gives us $\sin\frac{A}{2}$ in terms of k should give us also the sine of $\frac{n\pi + (-1)^n A}{2}$.

First, let n be even and equal to $2m$. Then

$$\sin\frac{n\pi + (-1)^n A}{2} = \sin\left(m\pi + \frac{A}{2}\right)$$

$$= \sin m\pi \cos\frac{A}{2} + \cos m\pi \sin\frac{A}{2} = \cos m\pi \sin\frac{A}{2}$$

$$= \pm \sin\frac{A}{2}$$

according as m is even or odd.

Secondly, let n be odd and equal to $2p + 1$

$$\text{Then,} \quad \sin\frac{n\pi + (-1)^n A}{2} = \sin\frac{2p\pi + \pi - A}{2}$$

$$= \sin\left[p\pi + \frac{\pi - A}{2}\right]$$

$$= \sin p\pi \cos\frac{\pi - A}{2} + \cos p\pi \sin\frac{\pi - A}{2}$$

$$= \cos p\pi \cos\frac{A}{2}$$

$$= \pm \cos \frac{A}{2}$$

according as p is even or odd,

Hence, any formula which gives us $\sin \frac{A}{2}$ in terms of $\sin A$ should be expected to give us, in addition, the values of

$$-\sin \frac{A}{2}, \cos \frac{A}{2} \text{ and } -\cos \frac{A}{2}$$

i.e. four values of all. This is the number of values which we get from the formulae of Art. 113, by giving all possible values to the ambiguities.

In a similar manner it may be shown that when $\cos \frac{A}{2}$ is found from $\sin A$, we should expect four values.

[If the angles $\frac{n\pi + (-1)^n A}{2}$, *i.e.* $n \frac{\pi}{2} + (-1)^n \frac{A}{2}$, be drawn geometrically for the case when $\frac{A}{2}$ is an acute angle, it will be found that there one four positions of the bounding line, two in the first quadrant inclined at angles $\frac{A}{2}$ and $\frac{\pi}{2} - \frac{A}{2}$ to the initial line, and two in the third quadrant inclined at $\frac{A}{2}$ and $\frac{\pi}{2} - \frac{A}{2}$ to the negative direction of the initial line. It will be clear from the figure that we should then expect four values for $\sin \frac{A}{2}$ and four for $\cos \frac{A}{2}$. Similarly for any other value of $\frac{A}{2}$.]

➤ **116.** In any general case we can show how the ambiguities in relations (3) and (4) of Art. 113 may be found.

We have

$$\sin \frac{A}{2} + \cos \frac{A}{2} = \sqrt{2}\left(\frac{1}{\sqrt{2}} \sin \frac{A}{2} + \frac{1}{\sqrt{2}} \cos \frac{A}{2}\right)$$

$$= \sqrt{2}\left[\sin \frac{A}{2} \cos \frac{\pi}{4} + \cos \frac{A}{2} \sin \frac{\pi}{4}\right] = \sqrt{2} \sin\left(\frac{\pi}{4} + \frac{A}{2}\right)$$

The right-hand member of this equation is positive if

$\frac{\pi}{4} + \frac{A}{2}$ lie between $2n\pi$ and $2n\pi + \pi$

i.e., if $\frac{A}{2}$ lie between $2n\pi - \frac{\pi}{4}$ and $2n\pi + \frac{3\pi}{4}$

Hence, $\sin\frac{A}{2} + \cos\frac{A}{2}$ is positive if

$\frac{A}{2}$ lie between $2n\pi - \frac{\pi}{4}$ and $2n\pi + \frac{3\pi}{4}$;

it is negative otherwise.

Similarly we can prove that

$$\sin\frac{A}{2} - \cos\frac{A}{2} = \sqrt{2}\sin\left(\frac{A}{2} - \frac{\pi}{4}\right)$$

Therefore, $\sin\frac{A}{2} - \cos\frac{A}{2}$ is positive if

$\left(\frac{A}{2} - \frac{\pi}{4}\right)$ lie between $2n\pi$ and $2n\pi + \pi$

i.e. if $\frac{A}{2}$ lie between $2n\pi + \frac{\pi}{4}$ and $2n\pi + \frac{5\pi}{4}$

It is negative otherwise.

The results of this article are shown graphically in the following figure.

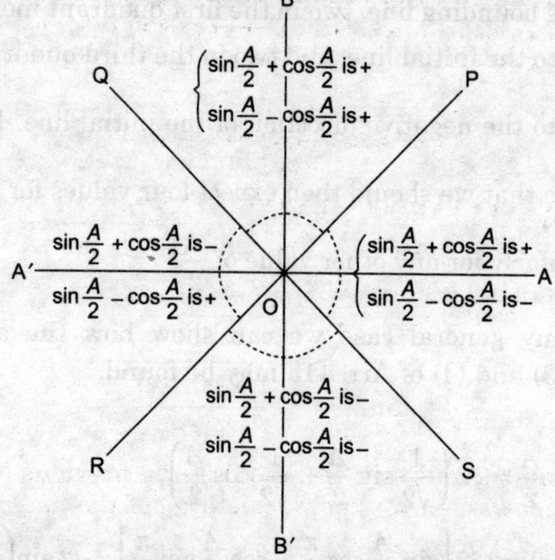

OA is the initial line, and *OP*, *OQ*, *OR* and *OS* bisect the angles in the first, second, third and fourth quadrants respectively.

<u>NUMERICAL EXAMPLE</u> *Within what limits must $\frac{A}{2}$ lie if*

$$2\sin\frac{A}{2} = -\sqrt{1+\sin A} - \sqrt{1-\sin A}\,?$$

In this case the formulae of Art. 113 must clearly be

$$\sin\frac{A}{2} + \cos\frac{A}{2} = -\sqrt{1+\sin A} \qquad \ldots(1)$$

and $\sin\frac{A}{2} - \cos\frac{A}{2} = -\sqrt{1-\sin A}$ ...(2)

For the addition of these two formulae gives the given formula.

From (1) it follows that the revolving line which bounds the angle $\frac{A}{2}$ must lie between OQ and OR or else between OR and OS.

From (2) it follows that the revolving line must lie between OR and OS or else between OS and OP.

Both these conditions are satisfied only when the revolving line lies between OR and OS, and therefore the angle $\frac{A}{2}$ lies between

$$2n\pi - \frac{3\pi}{4} \text{ and } 2n\pi - \frac{\pi}{4}$$

➤ 117. *To express the trigonometrical ratios of* $\frac{A}{2}$ *in terms of* $\tan A$.

From Eq. (3) of Art. 109, we have

$$\tan A = \frac{2\tan\frac{A}{2}}{1-\tan^2\frac{A}{2}}$$

$$\therefore \quad 1-\tan^2\frac{A}{2} = \frac{2}{\tan A}\cdot\tan\frac{A}{2}$$

Hence, $\tan^2\frac{A}{2} + \frac{2}{\tan A}\cdot\tan\frac{A}{2} + \frac{1}{\tan^2 A} = 1 + \frac{1}{\tan^2 A} = \frac{1+\tan^2 A}{\tan^2 A}$

$$\therefore \quad \tan\frac{A}{2} + \frac{1}{\tan A} = \pm\frac{\sqrt{1+\tan^2 A}}{\tan A}$$

$$\therefore \quad \tan\frac{A}{2} = \frac{\pm\sqrt{1+\tan^2 A}-1}{\tan A} \quad \text{...(1)}$$

➤ 118. The ambiguous sign in Eq. (1) of the previous article can only be determined when we know something of the magnitude of A.

<u>EXAMPLE 2</u> *Given* $\tan 15° = 2-\sqrt{3}$, *find* $\tan 7\frac{1}{2}°$.

Putting $A = 15°$ we have, from Eq. (1) of the previous article,

$$\tan 7\frac{1}{2}° = \frac{\pm\sqrt{1+(2-\sqrt{3})^2}-1}{2-\sqrt{3}} = \frac{\pm(\sqrt{8-7\sqrt{3}})-1}{2-\sqrt{3}} \quad \text{...(1)}$$

Now $\tan 7\frac{1}{2}°$ is positive, so that we must take the upper sign.

Hence, $\tan 7\frac{1}{2}° = \frac{+(\sqrt{6}-\sqrt{2})-1}{2-\sqrt{3}}$

$$= (\sqrt{6}-\sqrt{2}-1)(2+\sqrt{3}) = \sqrt{6}-\sqrt{3}+\sqrt{2}-2 = (\sqrt{3}-\sqrt{2})(\sqrt{2}-1)$$

Since, $\tan 15° = \tan 195°$, the equation which gives us $\tan\dfrac{15°}{2}$ in terms of $\tan 15°$ may be expected to give us $\tan\dfrac{195°}{2}$ in terms of $\tan 195°$. In fact the value obtained from Eq. (1) by taking the negative sign before the radical is $\tan\dfrac{195°}{2}$.

Hence, $$\tan\frac{195°}{2} = \frac{-\sqrt{8-4\sqrt{3}}-1}{2-\sqrt{3}} = \frac{-(\sqrt{6}-\sqrt{2})-1}{2-\sqrt{3}}$$
$$= (-\sqrt{6}+\sqrt{2}-1)(2+\sqrt{3}) = -(\sqrt{3}+\sqrt{2})(\sqrt{2}+1),$$

So that $$-\cot 7\frac{1}{2}° = \tan 97\frac{1}{2}° = -(\sqrt{3}+\sqrt{2})(\sqrt{2}+1)$$

➤ ****119.** *To explain why there is ambiguity when* $\tan\dfrac{A}{2}$ *is found from the value of* $\tan A$.

We know, by Art. 84, that, if n be any integer,
$$\tan(n\pi + A) = \tan A = k \text{ (say)}.$$

Hence, any equation which gives us $\tan\dfrac{A}{2}$ in terms of k may be expected to give us $\tan\dfrac{n\pi + A}{2}$ also

First, let n be even and equal to $2m$.

Then, $$\tan\frac{n\pi + A}{2} = \tan\frac{2m\pi + A}{2} = \tan\left(m\pi + \frac{A}{2}\right)$$
$$= \tan\frac{A}{2} \text{ as in Art. 84}$$

Secondly, let n be odd and equal to $2p + 1$

Then, $$\tan\frac{n\pi + 4}{2} = \tan\frac{(2p+1)\pi + 4}{2}$$
$$= \tan\left(p\pi + \frac{\pi + A}{2}\right) = \tan\frac{\pi + A}{2} \quad \text{(Art. 84)}$$
$$= -\cot\frac{A}{2} \quad \text{(Art. 70)}$$

Hence, the formula which gives us the value of $\tan\dfrac{A}{2}$ should be expected to give us also the value of $-\cot\dfrac{A}{2}$.

An illustration of this is seen in the example of the previous article.

EXAMPLES XVIII

1. If $\sin\theta = \frac{1}{2}$ and $\sin\phi = \frac{1}{3}$, find the value of $\sin(\theta + \phi)$ and $\sin(2\theta + 2\phi)$

2. The tangent of an angle is 2.4. Find its cosecant, the cosecant of half the angle, and the cosecant of the supplement of double the angle.

3. If $\cos\alpha = \frac{11}{61}$ and $\sin\beta = \frac{4}{5}$, find the values of $\sin^2\frac{\alpha-\beta}{2}$ and $\cos^2\frac{\alpha+\beta}{2}$, the angles α and β being positive acute angles.

4. If $\cos\alpha = \frac{3}{5}$ and $\cos\beta = \frac{4}{5}$, find the value of $\cos\frac{\alpha-\beta}{2}$, the angles α and β being positive acute angles.

5. Given $\sec\theta = 1\frac{1}{4}$, find $\tan\frac{\theta}{2}$ and $\tan\theta$. Verify by a graph.

6. If $\cos A = 0.28$, find the value of $\tan\frac{A}{2}$, and explain the resulting ambiguity.

7. Find the values of (1) $\sin 7\frac{1}{2}°$, (2) $\cos 7\frac{1}{2}°$ (3) $\tan 22\frac{1}{2}°$, and (4) $\tan 11\frac{1}{4}°$.

8. If $\sin\theta + \sin\phi = a$ and $\cos\theta + \cos\phi = b$, find the value of $\tan\frac{\theta-\phi}{2}$.

Prove that

9. $(\cos\alpha + \cos\beta)^2 + (\sin\alpha - \sin\beta)^2 = 4\cos^2\frac{\alpha+\beta}{2}$

10. $(\cos\alpha + \cos\beta)^2 + (\sin\alpha + \sin\beta)^2 = 4\cos^2\frac{\alpha-\beta}{2}$

11. $(\cos\alpha - \cos\beta)^2 + (\sin\alpha - \sin\beta)^2 = 4\sin^2\frac{\alpha-\beta}{2}$

12. $\sin A = \dfrac{2\tan\frac{A}{2}}{1+\tan^2\frac{A}{2}}$

13. $\cos A = \dfrac{1-\tan^2\frac{A}{2}}{1+\tan^2\frac{A}{2}}$

14. $\sec\left(\frac{\pi}{4}+\theta\right)\sec\left(\frac{\pi}{4}-\theta\right) = 2\sec 2\theta$

15. $\tan\left(45° + \frac{A}{2}\right) = \sqrt{\frac{1+\sin A}{1-\sin A}} = \sec A + \tan A.$

16. $\sin^2\left(\frac{\pi}{8}+\frac{A}{2}\right)-\sin^2\left(\frac{\pi}{8}-\frac{A}{2}\right)=\frac{1}{\sqrt{2}}\sin A$

17. $\cos^2\alpha+\cos^2(\alpha+120°)+\cos^2(\alpha-120°)=\frac{3}{2}$

18. $\cos^4\frac{\pi}{8}+\cos^4\frac{3\pi}{8}+\cos^4\frac{5\pi}{8}+\cos^4\frac{7\pi}{8}=\frac{3}{2}$

19. $\sin^4\frac{\pi}{8}+\sin^4\frac{3\pi}{8}+\sin^4\frac{5\pi}{8}+\sin^4\frac{7\pi}{8}=\frac{3}{2}$

20. $\cos 2\theta\cos 2\phi+\sin^2(\theta-\phi)-\sin^2(\theta+\phi)=\cos(2\theta+2\phi)$

21. $(\tan 4A+\tan 2A)(1-\tan^2 3A\tan^2 A)=2\tan 3A\sec^2 A$

22. $\left(1+\tan\frac{\alpha}{2}-\sec\frac{\alpha}{2}\right)\left(1+\tan\frac{\alpha}{2}+\sec\frac{\alpha}{2}\right)=\sin\alpha\sec^2\frac{\alpha}{2}$

Find the proper signs to be applied to the radicals in the three following formulae.

23. $2\cos\frac{A}{2}=\pm\sqrt{1-\sin A}\pm\sqrt{1+\sin A}$, when $\frac{A}{2}=278°$

24. $2\sin\frac{A}{2}=\pm\sqrt{1-\sin A}\pm\sqrt{1+\sin A}$, when $\frac{A}{2}=\frac{19\pi}{11}$

25. $2\cos\frac{A}{2}=\pm\sqrt{1-\sin A}\pm\sqrt{1+\sin A}$, when $\frac{A}{2}=-140°$

26. If $A=340°$, prove that

$$2\sin\frac{A}{2}=-\sqrt{1+\sin A}+\sqrt{1-\sin A}$$

and
$$2\cos\frac{A}{2}=-\sqrt{1+\sin A}-\sqrt{1-\sin A}$$

27. If $A=460°$, prove that $2\cos\frac{A}{2}=-\sqrt{1+\sin A}+\sqrt{1-\sin A}$

28. If $A=580°$, prove that $2\sin\frac{A}{2}=-\sqrt{1+\sin A}-\sqrt{1-\sin A}$

29. Within what respective limits must $\frac{A}{2}$ lie when

(1) $2\sin\frac{A}{2}=\sqrt{1+\sin A}+\sqrt{1-\sin A}$

(2) $2\sin\frac{A}{2}=-\sqrt{1+\sin A}+\sqrt{1-\sin A}$

(3) $2\sin\frac{A}{2}=+\sqrt{1+\sin A}-\sqrt{1-\sin A}$ and

(4) $2\cos\frac{A}{2}=+\sqrt{1+\sin A}-\sqrt{1-\sin A}$?

30. In the formula

$$2\cos\frac{A}{2} = \pm\sqrt{1+\sin A} \pm \sqrt{1-\sin A}$$

find within what limits $\frac{A}{2}$ must lie when

(1) the two positive signs are taken,

(2) the two negative signs are taken, and

(3) the first sign is negative and the second positive.

31. Prove that the sine is algebraically less than the cosine for any angle between $2n\pi - \frac{3\pi}{4}$ and $2n\pi + \frac{\pi}{4}$, where n is any integer.

32. If $\sin\frac{A}{3}$ be determined from the equation

$$\sin A = 3\sin\frac{A}{3} - 4\sin^3\frac{A}{3},$$

prove that we should expect to obtain also the values of

$$\sin\frac{\pi - A}{3} \text{ and } -\sin\frac{\pi + A}{3}$$

Give also a geometrical illustration.

33. If $\cos\frac{A}{3}$ be found from the equation

$$\cos A = 4\cos^3\frac{A}{3} - 3\cos\frac{A}{3},$$

prove that we should expect to obtain also the values of

$$\cos\frac{2\pi - A}{3} \text{ and } \cos\frac{2\pi + A}{3}$$

Give also a geometrical illustration.

➤ **120.** By the use of the formulae of the present chapter we can now find the trigonometrical ratios of some important angles.

To find the trigonometrical functions of an angle of 18°.

Let θ stand for 18°, so that 2θ is 36° and 3θ is 54°.

Hence, $\quad 2\theta = 90° - 3\theta$

and therefore, $\quad \sin 2\theta = \sin(90° - 3\theta) = \cos 3\theta$

$\therefore \quad 2\sin\theta\cos\theta = 4\cos^3\theta - 3\cos\theta \quad$ (Arts. 105 and 107)

Hence, either $\cos\theta = 0$, which gives $\theta = 90°$, or

$$2\sin\theta = 4\cos^2\theta - 3 = 1 - 4\sin^2\theta$$

$\therefore \quad 4\sin^2\theta + 2\sin\theta = 1$

By solving this quadratic equation, we have

$$\sin\theta = \frac{\pm\sqrt{5} - 1}{4}$$

In our case $\sin\theta$ is necessarily a positive quantity.

Hence, we take the upper sign, and have

$$\sin 18° = \frac{\sqrt{5}-1}{4}$$

Hence, $\cos 18° = \sqrt{1-\sin^2 18°} = \sqrt{1-\frac{6-2\sqrt{5}}{16}} = \sqrt{\frac{10+2\sqrt{5}}{16}}$

$$= \frac{\sqrt{10+2\sqrt{5}}}{4}$$

The remaining trigonometrical ratios of 18° may be now found.

Since 72° is the complement of 18°, the values of the ratios for 72° may be obtained by the use of Art. 69.

➤ **121.** *To find the trigonometrical functions of an angle of* 36°.

Since $\cos 2\theta = 1 - 2\sin^2\theta$, (Art. 105),

$$\therefore \quad \cos 36° = 1 - 2\sin^2 18° = 1 - 2\left(\frac{6-2\sqrt{5}}{16}\right)$$

$$= 1 - \frac{3-\sqrt{5}}{4}$$

So that $\cos 36° = \frac{\sqrt{5}+1}{4}$

Hence, $\sin 36° = \sqrt{1-\cos^2 36°} = \sqrt{1-\frac{6+2\sqrt{5}}{16}} = \frac{\sqrt{10-2\sqrt{5}}}{4}$

The remaining trigonometrical functions of 36° may now be found. Also, since 54° in the complement of 36°, the values of the functions for 54° may be the found by the help of Art. 69.

➤ **122.** The value of $\sin 18°$ and $\cos 36°$ may also be found geometrically as follows.

Let ABC be a triangle constructed so that each of the angles B and C is double of the angle A. Then

$$180° = A + B + C = A + 2A + 2A,$$

so that $A = 36°$

Hence, if AD be drawn perpendicular to BC, we have

$$\angle BAD = 18°$$

By the geometrical construction we know that BC is equal to AX where X is a point on AB, such that

$$AB \cdot BX = AX^2$$

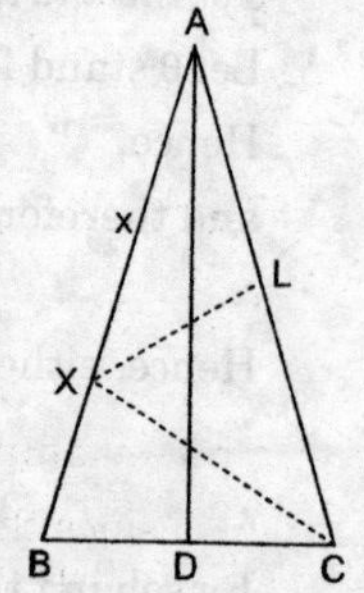

Let $AB = a$, and $AX = x$.

This relation then gives

$$a(a - x) = x^2$$

i.e.
$$x^2 + ax = a^2$$

i.e.
$$x = a\frac{\sqrt{5}+1}{2}$$

Hence,
$$\sin 18° = \sin BAD = \frac{BD}{BA} = \frac{1}{2}\frac{BC}{BA}$$

$$= \frac{1}{2}\frac{x}{a} = \frac{\sqrt{5}-1}{4}$$

Again, by Geometry, we know that AX and XC are equal; hence, if XL be perpendicular to AC, then L bisects AC.

Hence,
$$\cos 36° = \frac{AL}{AX} = \frac{a}{2} \div x = \frac{1}{\sqrt{5}-1}$$

$$= \frac{\sqrt{5}-1}{(\sqrt{5}-1)(\sqrt{5}+1)} = \frac{\sqrt{5}+1}{4}$$

➤ **123.** *To find the trigonometrical functions for an angle of* 9°.

Since sin 9° and cos 9° are both positive, the relation (3) of Art. 113 gives

$$\sin 9° + \cos 9° = \sqrt{1 + \sin 18°} = \sqrt{1 + \frac{\sqrt{5}-1}{4}} = \frac{\sqrt{3+\sqrt{5}}}{2} \quad \text{...(1)}$$

Also, since, cos 9° is greater than sin 9° (Art. 53), the quantity sin 9° – cos 9° is negative. Hence, the relation (4) of Art. 113 gives

$$\sin 9° + \cos 9° = -\sqrt{1 - \sin 18°} = -\sqrt{1 - \frac{\sqrt{5}-1}{4}}$$

$$= -\frac{\sqrt{5-\sqrt{5}}}{2} \quad \text{...(2)}$$

By adding (1) and (2), we have

$$\sin 9° = \frac{\sqrt{3+\sqrt{5}} - \sqrt{5-\sqrt{5}}}{4}$$

and, by subtracting (2) from (1), we have

$$\cos 9° = \frac{\sqrt{3+\sqrt{5}} + \sqrt{5-\sqrt{5}}}{4}$$

The remaining functions for 9° may now be found.

Also since 81° is the complement of 9°, the values of the functions for 81° may be obtained by the use of Art. 69.

EXAMPLES XIX

Prove that

1. $\sin^2 72° - \sin^2 60° = \dfrac{\sqrt{5}-1}{8}$

2. $\cos^2 48° - \sin^2 12° = \dfrac{\sqrt{5}+1}{8}$

3. $\cos 12° + \cos 60° + \cos 84° = \cos 24° + \cos 48°$. Verify by a graph.

4. $\sin\dfrac{\pi}{5}\sin\dfrac{2\pi}{5}\sin\dfrac{3\pi}{5}\sin\dfrac{4\pi}{5} = \dfrac{5}{16}$

5. $\sin\dfrac{\pi}{10} + \sin\dfrac{13\pi}{10} = -\dfrac{1}{2}$

6. $\sin\dfrac{\pi}{10}\sin\dfrac{13\pi}{10} = -\dfrac{1}{4}$

7. $\tan 6° \tan 42° \tan 66° \tan 78° = 1$

8. $\cos\dfrac{\pi}{15}\cos\dfrac{2\pi}{15}\cos\dfrac{3\pi}{15}\cos\dfrac{4\pi}{15}\cos\dfrac{5\pi}{15}\cos\dfrac{6\pi}{15}\cos\dfrac{7\pi}{15} = \dfrac{1}{2^7}$

9. $16\cos\dfrac{2\pi}{15}\cos\dfrac{4\pi}{15}\cos\dfrac{8\pi}{15}\cos\dfrac{14\pi}{15} = 1$

10. Two parallel chords of a circle, which are on the same side of the centre, subtend angles of 72° and 144° respectively at the centre. Prove that the perpendicular distance between the chords is half the radius of the circle.

11. In any circle prove that the chord which subtends 108° at the centre is equal to the sum of the two chords which subtend angles of 36° and 60°.

12. Construct the angle whose cosine is equal to its tangent.

13. Solve the equation

$$\sin 5\theta \cos 3\theta = \sin 9\theta \cos 7\theta.$$

9

IDENTITIES AND TRIGONOMETRICAL EQUATIONS

➤ **124.** The formulae of Arts. 88 and 90 can be used to obtain the trigonometrical ratios of the sum of more than two angles.

For example,

$$\sin(A+B+C) = \sin(A+B)\cos C + \cos(A+B)\sin C$$
$$= [\sin A\cos B + \cos A\sin B]\cos C + [\cos A\cos B - \sin A\sin B]\sin C$$
$$= \sin A\cos B\cos C + \cos A\sin B\cos C + \cos A\cos B\sin C - \sin A\sin B\sin C$$

So, $\cos(A+B+C) = \cos(A+B)\cos C - \sin(A+B)\sin C$
$$= (\cos A\cos B - \sin A\sin B)\cos C - (\sin A\cos B + \cos A\sin B)\sin C$$
$$= \cos A\cos B\cos C - \cos A\sin B\sin C - \sin A\cos B\sin C - \sin A\sin B\cos C.$$

Also, $\tan(A+B+C) = \dfrac{\tan(A+B)+\tan C}{1-\tan(A+B)\tan C}$

$$= \frac{\dfrac{\tan A+\tan B}{1-\tan A\tan B}+\tan C}{1-\dfrac{\tan A+\tan B}{1-\tan A\tan B}\tan C}$$

$$= \frac{\tan A+\tan B+\tan C-\tan A\tan B\tan C}{1-\tan B\tan C-\tan C\tan A-\tan A\tan B}.$$

➤ **125.** The last formula of the previous article is a particular case of a very general theorem which gives the tangent of the sum of any number of angles in terms of the tangents of the angles themselves. The theorem is

$$\tan(A_1+A_2+A_3+\ldots+A_n) = \frac{s_1-s_3+s_5-s_7+\ldots}{1-s_2+s_4-s_6+\ldots} \qquad \ldots(1)$$

where $s_1 = \tan A_1 + \tan A_2 + \ldots + \tan A_n$

$= $ the sum of the tangents of the separate angles,

$s_2 = \tan A_1 \tan A_2 + \tan A_1 \tan A_3 + \ldots$

$= $ the sum of the tangents taken two at a time,

$s_3 = \tan A_1 \tan A_2 \tan A_3 + \tan A_2 \tan A_3 \tan A_4 + \ldots$

$= $ the sum of the tangents taken three at a time, and so on.

Assume the relation (1) to hold for n angles, and add on another angle A_{n+1}.

Then, $\tan(A_1 + A_2 + \ldots + A_{n+1})$

$$= \tan[(A_1 + A_2 + \ldots + A_n) + A_{n+1}]$$

$$= \frac{\tan(A_1 + A_2 + \ldots + A_n) + \tan A_{n+1}}{1 - \tan(A_1 + A_2 + \ldots + A_n) \tan A_{n+1}}$$

$$= \frac{\dfrac{s_1 - s_3 + s_5 - s_7 + \ldots}{1 - s_2 + s_4 - \ldots} + \tan A_{n+1}}{1 - \dfrac{s_1 - s_3 + s_5 - \ldots}{1 - s_2 + s_4 - \ldots} \tan A_{n+1}}$$

Let $\tan A_1, \tan A_2, \ldots \tan A_{n+1}$ be respectively called $t_1, t_2, \ldots, t_{n+1}$.

Then $\tan(A_1 + A_2 + \ldots + A_{n+1})$

$$= \frac{(s_1 - s_3 + s_5 - \ldots) + t_{n+1}(1 - s_2 + s_4 - \ldots)}{(1 - s_2 + s_4 - \ldots) - (s_1 - s_3 + s_5 - \ldots) t_{n+1}}$$

$$= \frac{(s_1 + t_{n+1}) - (s_3 + s_2 t_{n+1}) + (s_5 + s_4 t_{n+1}) - \ldots}{1 - (s_2 + s_1 t_{n+1}) + (s_4 + s_3 t_{n+1}) - (s_6 + s_5 t_{n+1}) + \ldots}$$

But $s_1 + t_{n+1} = (t_1 + t_2 + \ldots + t_n) + t_{n+1}$

$= $ the sum of the $(n + 1)$ tangents,

$s_2 + s_1 t_{n+1} = (t_1 t_2 + t_2 t_3 + \ldots) + (t_1 + t_2 + \ldots + t_n) t_{n+1}$

$= $ the sum, two at a time, of the $(n + 1)$ tangents,

$s_3 + s_2 t_{n+1} = (t_1 t_2 t_3 + t_2 t_3 t_4 + \ldots) + (t_1 t_2 + t_2 t_3 + \ldots) t_{n+1}$

$= $ the sum, three at a time, of the $(n + 1)$ tangents, and so on.

Hence, we see that the same rule holds for $(n + 1)$ angles as for n angles.

Hence, if the theorem be true for n angles, it is true for $(n + 1)$ angles.

But, by Arts. 98 and 124, it is true for two and three angles.

Hence, the theorem is true for four angles; hence for five angles ... Hence, it is true universally.

Cor.: If the angles be all equal, and there be n of them, and each equal to θ, then

$$s_1 = n \tan\theta; \; s_2 = {}^nC_2 \tan^2\theta; \; s_3 = {}^nC_3 \tan^3\theta, \ldots$$

EXAMPLE *Write down the value of* $\tan 4\theta$.

Here, $$\tan 4\theta = \frac{s_1 - s_3}{1 - s_2 + s_4} = \frac{4\tan\theta - {}^4C_3 \tan^3\theta}{1 - {}^4C_2 \tan^2\theta + {}^4C_4 \tan^4\theta}$$
$$= \frac{4\tan\theta - 4\tan^3\theta}{1 - 6\tan^2\theta + \tan^4\theta}.$$

EXAMPLE *Prove that* $\tan 5\theta = \dfrac{5\tan\theta - 10\tan^3\theta + \tan^5\theta}{1 - 10\tan^2\theta + 5\tan^4\theta}$

➤ **126.** By a method similar to that of the previous article it may be shown that

$\sin(A_1 + A_2 + \ldots + A_n) = \cos A_1 \cos A_2 \ldots \cos A_n (s_1 - s_3 + s_5 - \ldots)$ and that $\cos(A_1 + A_2 + \ldots + A_n)$
$$= \cos A_1 \cos A_2 \ldots \cos A_n (1 - s_2 + s_4 - \ldots)$$
where $s_1, s_2, s_3, \ldots$ have the same values as in that article.

➤ 127. Identities holding between the trigonometrical ratios of the angles of a triangle.

When three angles A, B and C, are such that their sum is 180°, many identical relations are found to hold between their trigonometrical ratios.

The method of proof is best seen from the following examples.

EXAMPLE 1 *If* $A + B + C = 180°$,

prove that $\sin 2A + \sin 2B + \sin 2C = 4\sin A \sin B \sin C$.

$\sin 2A + \sin 2B + \sin 2C = 2\sin(A + B)\cos(A - B) + 2\sin C \cos C$

Since, $A + B + C = 180°$

We have $A + B = 180° - C$,

and therefore, $\sin(A + B) = \sin C$

and $\cos(A + B) = -\cos C$ (Art. 72)

Hence, the expression
$$= 2\sin C \cos(A - B) + 2\sin C \cos C$$
$$= 2\sin C[\cos(A - B) + \cos C]$$
$$= 2\sin C\ [\cos(A - B) - \cos(A + B)]$$
$$= 2\sin C \cdot 2\sin A \sin B$$
$$= 4\sin A \sin B \sin C.$$

EXAMPLE 2 *If* $A + B + C = 180°$,

prove that $\cos A + \cos B - \cos C = -1 + 4\cos\dfrac{A}{2}\cos\dfrac{B}{2}\sin\dfrac{C}{2}$.

The expression $= \cos A + (\cos B - \cos C)$
$$= 2\cos^2\frac{A}{2} - 1 + 2\sin\frac{B + C}{2}\sin\frac{C - B}{2}$$

Now, $$B + C = 180° - A,$$

so that $$\frac{B+C}{2} = 90° - \frac{A}{2}$$

and therefore $$\sin\frac{B+C}{2} = \cos\frac{A}{2}$$

and $$\cos\frac{B+C}{2} = \sin\frac{A}{2}$$

Hence, the expression $= 2\cos^2\frac{A}{2} - 1 + 2\cos\frac{A}{2}\sin\frac{C-B}{2}$

$$= 2\cos\frac{A}{2}\left[\cos\frac{A}{2} + \sin\frac{C-B}{2}\right] - 1$$

$$= 2\cos\frac{A}{2}\left[\sin\frac{B+C}{2} + \sin\frac{C-B}{2}\right] - 1$$

$$= 2\cos\frac{A}{2}\cdot 2\sin\frac{C}{2}\cos\frac{B}{2} - 1$$

$$= -1 + 4\cos\frac{A}{2}\cos\frac{B}{2}\sin\frac{C}{2}.$$

EXAMPLE 3 *If* $A + B + C = 180°$,
prove that, $\sin^2 A + \sin^2 B + \sin^2 C = 2 + 2\cos A\cos B\cos C$.

Let $$S = \sin^2 A + \sin^2 B + \sin^2 C,$$

so that $$2S = 2\sin^2 A + 1 - \cos 2B + 1 - \cos 2C$$

$$= 2\sin^2 A + 2 - 2\cos(B+C)\cos(B-C)$$

$$= 2 - 2\cos^2 A + 2 - 2\cos(B+C)\cos(B-C)$$

$\therefore$ $$S = 2 + \cos A[\cos(B-C) + \cos(B+C)]$$

since $$\cos A = \cos\{180° - (B+C)\} = -\cos(B+C)$$

$\therefore$ $$S = 2 + \cos A\cdot 2\cos B\cos C$$

$$= 2 + 2\cos A\cos B\cos C.$$

EXAMPLE 4 If $A + B + C = 180°$
prove that $\tan A + \tan B + \tan C = \tan A\tan B\tan C$.

By the third formula of Art. 124, we have

$$\tan(A+B+C) = \frac{\tan A + \tan B + \tan C - \tan A\tan B\tan C}{1 - (\tan B\tan C + \tan C\tan A + \tan A\tan B)}$$

But $\tan(A+B+C) = \tan 180° = 0.$

Hence, $0 = \tan A + \tan B + \tan C - \tan A\tan B\tan C$

i.e., $\tan A + \tan B + \tan C = \tan A\tan B\tan C$

This may also be proved independently. For

$$\tan(A+B) = \tan(180° - C) = -\tan C$$

$$\therefore \quad \frac{\tan A + \tan B}{1 - \tan A \tan B} = -\tan C$$

$$\therefore \quad \tan A + \tan B = -\tan C + \tan A \tan B \tan C.$$

i.e., $\tan A + \tan B + \tan C = \tan A \tan B \tan C$

EXAMPLE 5 *If* $x + y + z = xyz$,

prove that $\dfrac{2x}{1-x^2} + \dfrac{2y}{1-y^2} + \dfrac{2z}{1-z^2} = \dfrac{2x}{1-x^2} . \dfrac{2y}{1-y^2} . \dfrac{2z}{1-z^2}$

Put $x = \tan A$, $y = \tan B$, and $z = \tan C$, so that we have

$$\tan A + \tan B + \tan C = \tan A \tan B \tan C.$$

$$\therefore \quad \frac{\tan A + \tan B}{1 - \tan A \tan B} = -\tan C,$$

so that $\tan(A+B) = \tan(\pi - C)$ (Art. 72)

Hence $A + B + C = n\pi + \pi$,

$$\therefore \quad \frac{2x}{1-x^2} + \frac{2y}{1-y^2} + \frac{2z}{1-z^2} = \frac{2\tan A}{1-\tan^2 A} + \frac{2\tan B}{1-\tan^2 B} + \frac{2\tan C}{1-\tan^2 C}$$

$$= \tan 2A + \tan 2B + \tan 2C = \tan 2A \tan 2B \tan 2C$$

(by a proof similar to that of the previous example)

$$= \frac{2x}{1-x^2} . \frac{2y}{1-y^2} . \frac{2z}{1-z^2}$$

EXAMPLES XX

If $A + B + C = 180°$, prove that

1. $\sin 2A + \sin 2B - \sin 2C = 4 \cos A \cos B \sin C$
2. $\cos 2A + \cos 2B + \cos 2C = -1 - 4 \cos A \cos B \cos C$
3. $\cos 2A + \cos 2B - \cos 2C = 1 - 4 \sin A \sin B \cos C$
4. $\sin A + \sin B + \sin C = 4 \cos \dfrac{A}{2} \cos \dfrac{B}{2} \cos \dfrac{C}{2}$
5. $\sin A + \sin B - \sin C = 4 \sin \dfrac{A}{2} \sin \dfrac{B}{2} \cos \dfrac{C}{2}$
6. $\cos A + \cos B + \cos C = 1 + 4 \sin \dfrac{A}{2} \sin \dfrac{B}{2} \sin \dfrac{C}{2}$
7. $\sin^2 A + \sin^2 B - \sin^2 C = 2 \sin A \sin B \cos C$
8. $\cos^2 A + \cos^2 B + \cos^2 C = 1 - 2 \cos A \cos B \cos C$
9. $\cos^2 A + \cos^2 B - \cos^2 C = 1 - 2 \sin A \sin B \cos C$
10. $\sin^2 \dfrac{A}{2} + \sin^2 \dfrac{B}{2} + \sin^2 \dfrac{C}{2} = 1 - 2 \sin \dfrac{A}{2} \sin \dfrac{B}{2} \sin \dfrac{C}{2}$
11. $\sin^2 \dfrac{A}{2} + \sin^2 \dfrac{B}{2} - \sin^2 \dfrac{C}{2} = 1 - 2 \cos \dfrac{A}{2} \cos \dfrac{B}{2} \sin \dfrac{C}{2}$

12. $\tan\frac{A}{2}\tan\frac{B}{2}+\tan\frac{B}{2}\tan\frac{C}{2}+\tan\frac{C}{2}\tan\frac{A}{2}=1$

13. $\cot\frac{A}{2}+\cot\frac{B}{2}+\cot\frac{C}{2}=\cot\frac{A}{2}\cot\frac{B}{2}\cot\frac{C}{2}$

14. $\cot B\cot C+\cot C\cot A+\cot A\cot B=1$

15. $\sin(B+2C)+\sin(C+2A)+\sin(A+2B)$
$$=4\sin\frac{B-C}{2}\sin\frac{C-A}{2}\sin\frac{A-B}{2}$$

16. $\sin\frac{A}{2}+\sin\frac{B}{2}+\sin\frac{C}{2}-1=4\sin\frac{\pi-A}{4}\sin\frac{\pi-B}{4}\sin\frac{\pi-C}{4}$

17. $\cos\frac{A}{2}+\cos\frac{B}{2}-\cos\frac{C}{2}=4\cos\frac{\pi+A}{4}\cos\frac{\pi+B}{4}\cos\frac{\pi-C}{4}$

18. $\dfrac{\sin 2A+\sin 2B+\sin 2C}{\sin A+\sin B+\sin C}=8\sin\frac{A}{2}\sin\frac{B}{2}\sin\frac{C}{2}$

19. $\sin(B+C-A)+\sin(C+A-B)+\sin(A+B-C)$
$$=4\sin A\sin B\sin C$$

If $A+B+C=2S$, prove that

20. $\sin(S-A)\sin(S-B)+\sin S\sin(S-C)=\sin A\sin B.$

21. $4\sin S\sin(S-A)\sin(S-B)\sin(S-C)$
$$=1-\cos^2 A-\cos^2 B-\cos^2 C+2\cos A\cos B\cos C$$

22. $\sin(S-A)+\sin(S-B)+\sin(S-C)-\sin S=4\sin\frac{A}{2}\sin\frac{B}{2}\sin\frac{C}{2}$

23. $\cos^2 S+\cos^2(S-A)+\cos^2(S-B)+\cos^2(S-C)$
$$=2+2\cos A\cos B\cos C.$$

24. If $A+B+C=2S$, prove that
$\cos^2 A+\cos^2 B+\cos^2 C+2\cos A\cos B\cos C$
$$=1+4\cos S\cos(S-A)\cos(S-B)\cos(S-C)$$

25. If $\alpha+\beta+\gamma+\delta=2\pi$, prove that

(1) $\cos\alpha+\cos\beta+\cos\gamma+\cos\delta+4\cos\frac{\alpha+\beta}{2}\cos\frac{\alpha+\gamma}{2}\cos\frac{\alpha+\delta}{2}=0$

(2) $\sin\alpha-\sin\beta+\sin\gamma-\sin\delta+4\cos\frac{\alpha+\beta}{2}\sin\frac{\alpha+\gamma}{2}\cos\frac{\alpha+\delta}{2}=0,$

(3) $\tan\alpha+\tan\beta+\tan\gamma+\tan\delta$
$$=\tan\alpha\tan\beta\tan\gamma\tan\delta(\cot\alpha+\cot\beta+\cot\gamma+\cot\delta)$$

26. If the sum of four angles be 180°, prove that the sum of the products of their cosines taken two and two together is equal to the sum of the products of their sines taken similarly.

27. Prove that $\sin 2\alpha+\sin 2\beta+\sin 2\gamma=2(\sin\alpha+\sin\beta+\sin\gamma)$
$$\times(1+\cos\alpha+\cos\beta+\cos\gamma)$$
if $\alpha+\beta+\gamma=0$

28. Verify that

$$\sin^3 a \sin(b-c) + \sin^3 b \sin(c-a) + \sin^3 c \sin(a-b) + \sin(a+b+c)\sin(b-c)\sin(c-a)\sin(a-b) = 0$$

If A, B, C, and D be any angles, prove that

29. $\sin A \sin B \sin(A-B) + \sin B \sin C \sin(B-C) + \sin C \sin A \sin(C-A) + \sin(A-B)\sin(B-C)\sin(C-A) = 0$

30. $\sin(A-B)\cos(A+B) + \sin(B-C)\cos(B+C) + \sin(C-D)\cos(C+D) + \sin(D-A)\cos(D+A) = 0.$

31. $\sin(A+B-2C)\cos B - \sin(A+C-2B)\cos C = \sin(B-C)\cos(B+C-A) + \cos(C+A-B) + \cos(A+B-C)$

32. $\sin(A+B+C+D) + \sin(A+B-C-D) + \sin(A+B-C+D) + \sin(A+B+C-D) = 4\sin(A+B)\cos C \cos D.$

33. If any theorem be true for values of A, B, and C such that

$$A + B + C = 180°$$

prove that the theorem is still true if we substitute for A, B, and C respectively the quantities

(1) $90° - \frac{A}{2}$, $90° - \frac{B}{2}$, and $90° - \frac{C}{2}$,

or (2) $180° - 2A$, $180° - 2B$, and $180° - 2C$.

Hence deduce Ex. 16 from Ex. 6 and Ex. 17 from Ex. 5.

If $x + y + z = xyz$, prove that

34. $\frac{3x-x^3}{1-3x^2} + \frac{3y-y^3}{1-3y^2} + \frac{3z-z^3}{1-3z^2} = \frac{3x-x^3}{1-3x^2} \cdot \frac{3y-y^3}{1-3y^2} \cdot \frac{3z-z^3}{1-3z^2}$

35. $x(1-y^2)(1-z^2) + y(1-z^2)(1-x^2) + z(1-x^2)(1-y^2) = 4xyz$

➤ **128.** The Addition and Subtraction Theorems may be used to solve some kinds of trigonometrical equations.

EXAMPLE *Solve the equation*

$$\sin x + \sin 5x = \sin 3x.$$

By the formulae of Art. 94, the equation is

$$2\sin 3x \cos 2x = \sin 3x$$

$\therefore$ $\sin 3x = 0$, or $2\cos 2x = 1$

If $\sin 3x = 0$, then $3x = n\pi$

If $\cos 2x = \frac{1}{2}$, then $2x = 2n\pi \pm \frac{\pi}{3}$

Hence $x = \frac{n\pi}{3}$ or $n\pi \pm \frac{\pi}{6}$

129. *To solve an equation of the form*

$$a\cos\theta + b\sin\theta = c.$$

Divide both sides of the equation by $\sqrt{a^2+b^2}$, so that it may be written

$$\frac{a}{\sqrt{a^2+b^2}}\cos\theta + \frac{b}{\sqrt{a^2+b^2}}\sin\theta = \frac{c}{\sqrt{a^2+b^2}}$$

Find from the table of tangents the angle whose tangent is $\frac{b}{a}$ and call it α.

Then $\tan\alpha = \frac{b}{a}$, so that

$$\sin\alpha = \frac{b}{\sqrt{a^2+b^2}}, \text{ and } \cos\alpha = \frac{a}{\sqrt{a^2+b^2}}$$

The equation can then be written

$$\cos\alpha\cos\theta + \sin\alpha\sin\theta = \frac{c}{\sqrt{a^2+b^2}}$$

i.e.,
$$\cos(\theta-\alpha) = \frac{c}{\sqrt{a^2+b^2}}$$

Next find from the tables, or otherwise, the angle β whose cosine is

$$\frac{c}{\sqrt{a^2+b^2}}$$

so that
$$\cos\beta = \frac{c}{\sqrt{a^2+b^2}}$$

[N.B. This can only be done when c is $< \sqrt{a^2+b^2}$]

The equation is then $\cos(\theta-\alpha) = \cos\beta$

The solution of this is $\theta - \alpha = 2n\pi \pm \beta$, so that

$$\theta = 2n\pi + \alpha \pm \beta$$

where n is any integer.

Angles, such as α and β, which are introduced into trigonometrical work to facilitate computation are called **Subsidiary Angles.**

130. The above solution may be illustrated graphically as follows:

Measure OM along the initial line equal to a, and MP perpendicular to it, and equal to b. The angle MOP is then the angle whose tangent is $\frac{b}{a}$,

i.e., α

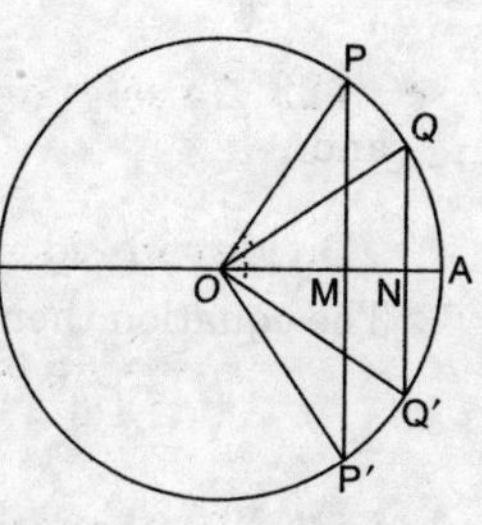

With centre O and radius OP, *i.e.*, $\sqrt{a^2+b^2}$, describe a circle, and measure ON along the initial line equal to c.

Draw QNQ' perpendicular to ON to meet the circle in Q and Q'; the angles NOQ and $Q'ON$ are therefore each equal to β.

The angle QOP is therefore $\alpha - \beta$ and $Q'OP$ is $\alpha + \beta$.

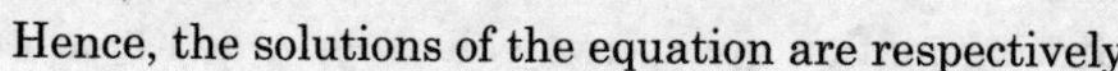

Hence, the solutions of the equation are respectively

$$2n\pi + QOP \text{ and } 2n\pi + Q'OP$$

The construction clearly fails if c be $> \sqrt{a^2+b^2}$, for then the point N would fall outside the circle.

➤ **131.** As a numerical example let us solve the equation

$$5\cos\theta - 2\sin\theta = 2$$

given that $$\tan 21°48' = \frac{2}{5}.$$

Dividing both sides of the equation by

$$\sqrt{5^2+2^2}, \text{ i.e., } \sqrt{29}$$

we have $$\frac{5}{\sqrt{29}}\cos\theta - \frac{2}{\sqrt{29}}\sin\theta = \frac{2}{\sqrt{29}}$$

Hence,

$$\cos\theta\cos 21°48' - \sin\theta\sin 21°48' = \sin 21°48'$$

$$= \sin(90°-68°12') = \cos 68°12'$$

$$\therefore \quad \cos(\theta + 21°48') = \cos 68°12'$$

Hence, $\theta + 21°48' = 2n\times 180° \pm 68°12'$ (Art. 83)

$$\therefore \quad \theta = 2n\times 180° - 21°48' \pm 68°12'$$

$$= 2n\times 180° - 90°, \text{ or } 2n\times 180° + 46°24'$$

where n is any integer.

Aliter: The equation of Art. 129 may be solved in another way.

For let, $$t \equiv \tan\frac{\theta}{2}$$

so that, $$\sin\theta = \frac{2\tan\frac{\theta}{2}}{1+\tan^2\frac{\theta}{2}} = \frac{2t}{1+t^2}$$

and $$\cos\theta = \frac{1-\tan^2\dfrac{\theta}{2}}{1+\tan^2\dfrac{\theta}{2}} = \frac{1-t^2}{1+t^2} \qquad \text{(Art. 109)}$$

The equation then becomes

$$a\frac{1-t^2}{1+t^2} + b\frac{2t}{1+t^2} = c$$

so that, $$t^2(c+a) - 2bt + c - a = 0$$

This is a quadratic equation giving two values for t, and hence two values for $\tan\dfrac{\theta}{2}$.

Thus, the example of this article given

$$7t^2 + 4t - 3 = 0$$

so that $$t = -1 \text{ or } \frac{3}{7}$$

$$= \tan(-45^\circ), \text{ or } \tan 23^\circ 12' \text{ (from the tables)}$$

Hence, $$\frac{\theta}{2} = n\cdot 180^\circ - 45^\circ, \text{ or } n\cdot 180^\circ + 23^\circ 12',$$

i.e., $$\theta = n\cdot 360^\circ - 90^\circ, \text{ or } n\cdot 360^\circ + 46^\circ 24'$$

EXAMPLES XXI

Solve the equations

1. $\sin\theta + \sin 7\theta = \sin 4\theta$
2. $\cos\theta + \cos 7\theta = \cos 4\theta$
3. $\cos\theta + \cos 3\theta = 2\cos 2\theta$
4. $\sin 4\theta - \sin 2\theta = \cos 3\theta$
5. $\cos\theta - \sin 3\theta = \cos 2\theta$
6. $\sin 7\theta = \sin\theta + \sin 3\theta$
7. $\cos\theta + \cos 2\theta + \cos 3\theta = 0$
8. $\sin\theta + \sin 3\theta + \sin 5\theta = 0$
9. $\sin 2\theta - \cos 2\theta - \sin\theta + \cos\theta = 0$
10. $\sin(3\theta + \alpha) + \sin(3\theta - \alpha) + \sin(\alpha - \theta) - \sin(\alpha + \theta) = \cos\alpha$
11. $\cos(3\theta + \alpha)\cos(3\theta - \alpha) + \cos(5\theta + \alpha)\cos(5\theta - \alpha) = \cos 2\alpha$
12. $\cos n\theta = \cos(n-2)\theta + \sin\theta$
13. $\sin\dfrac{n+1}{2}\theta = \sin\dfrac{n-1}{2}\theta + \sin\theta$
14. $\sin m\theta + \sin n\theta = 0$
15. $\cos m\theta + \cos n\theta = 0$
16. $\sin^2 n\theta - \sin^2(n-1)\theta = \sin^2\theta$

17. $\sin 3\theta + \cos 2\theta + 0$

18. $\sqrt{3}\cos\theta + \sin\theta = \sqrt{2}$

19. $\sin\theta + \cos\theta = \sqrt{2}$

20. $\sqrt{3}\sin\theta - \cos\theta = \sqrt{2}$

21. $\sin x + \cos x = \sqrt{2}\cos A$

22. $5\sin\theta + 2\cos\theta = 5$(given $\tan 21°48' = 0.4$)

23. $6\cos x + 8\sin x = 9$ (given $\tan 53°8' = 1\frac{1}{3}$ and $\cos 25°50' = 0.9$)

24. $1 + \sin^2\theta = 3\sin\theta\cos\theta$ (given $\tan 71°34' = 3$)

25. $\operatorname{cosec}\theta = \cot\theta + \sqrt{3}$

26. $\operatorname{cosec} x = 1 + \cot x$

27. $(2 + \sqrt{3})\cos\theta = 1 - \sin\theta$

28. $\tan\theta + \sec\theta = \sqrt{3}$

29. $\cos 2\theta = \cos^2\theta$

30. $4\cos\theta - 3\sec\theta = \tan\theta$

31. $\cos 2\theta + 3\cos\theta = 0$

32. $\cos 3\theta + 2\cos\theta = 0$

33. $\cos 2\theta = (\sqrt{2} + 1)\left(\cos\theta - \frac{1}{\sqrt{2}}\right)$

34. $\cot\theta - \tan\theta = 2$

35. $4\cot 2\theta = \cot^2\theta - \tan^2\theta$

36. $3\tan(\theta - 15°) = \tan(\theta + 15°)$

37. $\tan\theta + \tan 2\theta + \tan 3\theta = 0$

38. $\tan\theta + \tan 2\theta + \sqrt{3}\tan\theta\tan 2\theta = \sqrt{3}$

39. $\sin 3\alpha = 4\sin\alpha\sin(x + \alpha)\sin(x - \alpha)$

40. Prove that the equation $x^3 - 2x + 1 = 0$ is satisfied by putting for x, either of the values

$\sqrt{2}\sin 45°$, $2\sin 18°$ and $2\sin 234°$

41. If $\sin(\pi\cos\theta) = \cos(\pi\sin\theta)$, prove that $\cos\left(\theta \pm \frac{\pi}{4}\right) = \frac{1}{2\sqrt{2}}$

42. If $\sin(\pi\cot\theta) = \cos(\pi\tan\theta)$, prove that either $\operatorname{cosec} 2\theta$ or $\cot 2\theta$ is equal to $n + \frac{1}{4}$, where n is a positive or negative integer.

➤ **132.**

EXAMPLE *To trace the changes in the expression* $\sin x + \cos x$ *as* x *increases from* 0 *to* 2π

We have $\sin x + \cos x = \sqrt{2}\left[\frac{1}{\sqrt{2}}\sin x + \frac{1}{\sqrt{2}}\cos x\right]$

$$= \sqrt{2}\left[\sin x\cos\frac{\pi}{4} + \cos x\sin\frac{\pi}{4}\right] = \sqrt{2}\sin\left(x + \frac{\pi}{4}\right)$$

We thus have the following table to values:

x	0	$\frac{\pi}{4}$	$\frac{3\pi}{4}$	$\frac{5\pi}{4}$	$\frac{7\pi}{4}$	2π
$x+\frac{\pi}{4}$	$\frac{\pi}{4}$	$\frac{\pi}{2}$	π	$\frac{3\pi}{2}$	2π	$\frac{9\pi}{4}$
$\sin\left(x+\frac{\pi}{4}\right)$	$\frac{1}{\sqrt{2}}$	1	0	-1	0	$\frac{1}{\sqrt{2}}$
$\sqrt{2}\sin\left(x+\frac{\pi}{4}\right)$	1	$\sqrt{2}$	0	$-\sqrt{2}$	0	1

As in Art. 62, the graph is as in the following figure.

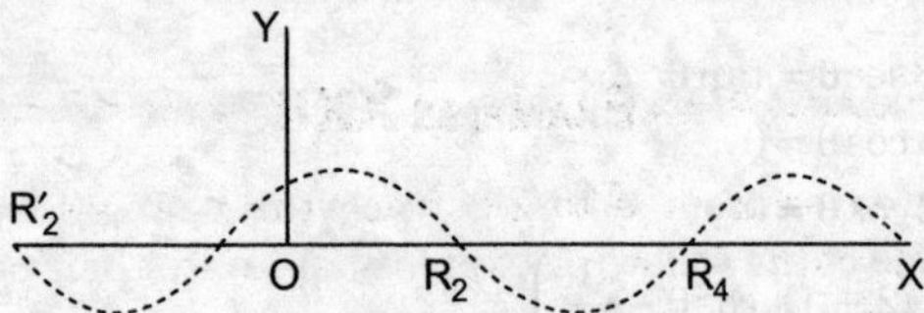

➤ **133.**

EXAMPLE *To trace the changes in the sign and magnitude of* $a\cos\theta + b\sin\theta$*, and to find the greatest value of the expression.*

We have $a\cos\theta + b\sin\theta = \sqrt{a^2+b^2}\left[\frac{a}{\sqrt{a^2+b^2}}\cos\theta + \frac{b}{\sqrt{a^2+b^2}}\sin\theta\right]$

Let α be the smallest positive angle such that

$$\cos\alpha = \frac{a}{\sqrt{a^2+b^2}}, \text{ and } \sin\alpha = \frac{b}{\sqrt{a^2+b^2}}$$

The expression therefore,

$$= \sqrt{a^2+b^2}\,[\cos\theta\cos\alpha + \sin\theta\sin\alpha] = \sqrt{a^2+b^2}\cos(\theta-\alpha)$$

As θ changes from α to $2\pi+\alpha$, the angle $\theta-\alpha$ changes from 0 to 2π, and hence the changes in the sign and magnitude of the expression are easily obtained.

Since, the greatest value of the quantity $\cos(\theta-\alpha)$ is unity, *i.e.*, when θ equals α, the greatest value of the expression is $\sqrt{a^2+b^2}$.

Also the value of θ which gives this greatest value is such that its cosine is $\frac{a}{\sqrt{a^2+b^2}}$.

Similarly, the expression

$$a\sin(\theta+\alpha)+b\sin(\theta+\beta)$$
$$=\sin\theta(a\cos\alpha+b\cos\beta)+\cos\theta(a\sin\alpha+b\sin\beta)$$
$$=R\sin(\theta+\gamma) \qquad \ldots(1)$$

where $R\cos\gamma = a\cos\alpha + b\cos\beta$

and $R\sin\gamma = a\sin\alpha + b\sin\beta$

so that, on squaring and adding

$$R=\sqrt{a^2+b^2+2ab\cos(\alpha-\beta)}$$

and, on division, $\tan\gamma = \dfrac{a\sin\alpha + b\sin\beta}{a\cos\alpha + b\cos\beta}$

The greatest value of (1), *i.e.*, of the given expression, is clearly R corresponding to the value, $\frac{\pi}{2}-\gamma$, of the angle θ.

EXAMPLES XXII

As θ increases from 0 to 2π, trace the changes in the sign and magnitude of the following expressions, state their periods, and plot their graphs.

1. $\sin\theta - \cos\theta$
2. $\sin\theta + \sqrt{3}\cos\theta$

$$\left[\text{N. B. } \sin\theta+\sqrt{3}\cos\theta = 2\left[\frac{1}{2}\sin\theta+\frac{\sqrt{3}}{2}\cos\theta\right]=2\sin\left(\theta+\frac{\pi}{3}\right)\right]$$

3. $\sin\theta - \sqrt{3}\cos\theta$
4. $\cos^2\theta - \sin^2\theta$
5. $\sin\theta\cos\theta$
6. $\sin 3\theta$
7. $\tan 3\theta$
8. $\sec 4\theta$
9. $\dfrac{\sin\theta + \sin 2\theta}{\cos\theta + \cos 2\theta}$
10. $\sin(\pi\sin\theta)$
11. $\cos(\pi\sin\theta)$
12. Trace the changes in the sign and magnitude of $\dfrac{\sin 3\theta}{\cos 2\theta}$ as the angle increases from 0 to 90°.

10

LOGARITHMS

134. Supposing that we know that

$$10^{2.4031205} = 253,\ 10^{2.6095944} = 407$$

and $$10^{5.0127149} = 102971,$$

We can show that $253 \times 407 = 102971$ without performing the operation of multiplication. For

$$253 \times 407 = 10^{2.4031205} \times 10^{2.6095944}$$
$$= 10^{2.4031205 + 2.6095944}$$
$$= 10^{5.0127149} = 102971$$

Here it will be noticed that the process of multiplication has been replaced by the simpler process of addition.

Again, supposing that we know that

$$10^{4.9004055} = 79507$$

and that $$10^{1.6334685} = 43$$

We can easily show that the cube root of 79507 is 43.

For $$\sqrt[3]{79507} = [79507]^{1/3} = (10^{4.9004055})^{1/3}$$
$$= 10^{(1/3) \times 4.9004055} = 10^{1.6334685} = 43$$

Here it will be noticed that the difficult process of extracting the cube root has been replaced by the simpler process of division.

135. Logarithm. Def. *If a be any number, and x and N two other numbers such that $a^x = N$, then x is called the logarithm of N to the base a and is written* $\log_a N$.

The logarithm of a number to a given base is therefore the index of the power to which the base must be raised that it may be equal to the given number.

EXAMPLES Since, $10^2 = 100$, therefore $2 = \log_{10} 100$,

Since, $10^5 = 100000$, therefore, $5 = \log_{10} 100000$

Since, $2^4 = 16$, therefore, $4 = \log_2 16$

Since, $8^{2/3} = [8^{1/3}]^2 = 2^2 = 4$, therefore, $\frac{2}{3} = \log_8 4$.

Since, $9^{-3/2} = \frac{1}{9^{3/2}} = \frac{1}{3^3} = \frac{1}{27}$, therefore $-\frac{3}{2} = \log_9\left(\frac{1}{27}\right)$

N.B. Since $a^0 = 1$ always, the logarithm of unity to any base is always zero.

136. In Algebra, if m and n be any real quantities whatever, the following laws, known as the laws of indices, are found to be true:

(i) $a^m \times a^n = a^{m+n}$

(ii) $a^m \div a^n = a^{m-n}$

(iii) $(a^m)^n = a^{mn}$

Corresponding to these we have three fundamental laws of logarithms, viz.

(i) $\log_a (mn) = \log_a m + \log_a n$

(ii) $\log_a\left(\frac{m}{n}\right) = \log_a m - \log_a n$

(iii) $\log_a m^n = n \log_a m$

The proofs of these laws are given in the following articles.

137. *The logarithm of the product of two quantities is equal to the sum of the logarithms of the quantities to the same base, i.e.,*

$$\log_a (mn) = \log_a m + \log_a n$$

Let $x = \log_a m$, so that $a^x = m$

and $y = \log_a n$, so that $a^y = n$

Then $mn = a^x \times a^y = a^{x+y}$

$\therefore$ $\log_a mn = x + y$ (Art. 135, Def.)

$= \log_a m + \log_a n$.

138. *The logarithm of the quotient of two quantities is equal to the difference of their logarithms, i.e.*

$$\log_a\left(\frac{m}{n}\right) = \log_a m - \log_a n$$

Let $x = \log_a m$, so that $a^x = m$, (Art. 135, Def.)

and $y = \log_a n$, so that $a^y = n$

Then $$\frac{m}{n} = a^x \div a^y = a^{x-y}$$

$\therefore$ $$\log_a\left(\frac{m}{n}\right) = x - y \qquad \text{(Art. 135, Def.)}$$

$$= \log_a m - \log_a n$$

➤ **139.** *The logarithm of a quantity raised to any power is equal to the logarithm of the quantity multiplied by the index of the power, i.e.,*

$$\mathbf{\log_a (m^n) = n \log_a m}$$

Let $$x = \log_a m, \text{ so that } a^x = m$$

Then $$m^n = (a^x)^n = a^{nx}$$

$\therefore$ $$\log_a (m^n) = nx \qquad \text{(Art. 135, Def.)}$$

$$= n \log_a m$$

<u>EXAMPLES</u> $\log 48 = \log(2^4 \times 3) = \log 2^4 + \log 3 = 4 \log 2 + \log 3$

$$\log \frac{63}{484} = \log \frac{7 \times 3^2}{2^2 \times 11^2} = \log 7 + \log 3^2 - \log 2^2 - \log 11^2$$

$$= \log 7 + 2 \log 3 - 2 \log 2 - 2 \log 11$$

$$\log \sqrt[5]{13} = \log 13^{1/5} = \frac{1}{5} \log 13$$

➤ **140. Common system of logarithms.** In the system of logarithms which we practically use the base is always 10, so that, if no base be expressed, the base 10 is always understood. The advantages of using 10 as the base is seen in the three following articles.

➤ **141. Characteristic and Mantissa. Def.** If the logarithm of any number by partly integral and partly fractional, the integral portion of the logarithm is called its characteristic and the decimal portion is called its mantissa.

Thus, supposing that $\log 795 = 2.9003671$, the number 2 is the characteristic and 0.9003671 is the mantissa.

Negative characteristics. Suppose we know that

$$\log 2 = 0.30103$$

Then, by Art. 138,

$$\log \frac{1}{2} = \log 1 - \log 2 = 0 - \log 2 = -0.30103,$$

so that $\log \frac{1}{2}$ is negative.

Now it is found convenient, as will be seen in Art. 143, that the mantissae of all logarithms should be kept positive. We therefore instead of –0.30103 write – (1 – 0.69897), so that

$$\log \frac{1}{2} = -(1 - 0.69897) = -1 + 0.69897$$

For shortness this latter expression is written $\bar{1}.69897$.

The horizontal line over the 1 denotes that the integral part is negative; the decimal part however is positive.

As another example, $\bar{3}.4771213$ stands for

$$-3 + 0.4771213$$

➤ **142.** *The characteristic of the logarithm of any number can always be determined by inspection.*

(i) Let the number be greater than unity.

Since, $10^0 = 1$, therefore, $\log 1 = 0$;

Since, $10^1 = 10$, therefore, $\log 10 = 1$;

Since, $10^2 = 100$, therefore, $\log 100 = 2$;

and so on.

Hence the logarithm of any number lying between 1 and 10 must lie between 0 and 1, that is, it will be a decimal fraction and therefore, have 0 as its characteristic.

So the logarithm of any number between 10 and 100 must lie between 1 and 2, *i.e.* it will have a characteristic equal to 1.

Similarly, the logarithm of any number between 100 and 1000 must lie between 2 and 3, *i.e.* it will have a characteristic equal to 2.

So, if the number lie between 1000 and 10000, the characteristic will be 3.

Generally, *the characteristic of the logarithm of any number will be one less than the number of digits in its integral part.*

EXAMPLES The number 296.3457 has 3 figures in its integral part, and therefore the characteristic of its logarithm is 2.

The characteristic of the logarithm of 29634.57 will be 5 – 1, *i.e.* 4.

(ii) Let the number be less than unity.

Since $10^0 = 1$, therefore $\log 1 = 0$;

Since $10^{-1} = \frac{1}{10} = 0.1$, therefore $\log 0.1 = -1$;

Since $10^{-2} = \frac{1}{10^2} = 0.01$, therefore $\log 0.01 = -2$;

Since $10^{-3} = \frac{1}{10^3} = 0.001$, therefore $\log 0.001 = -3$; and so on.

The logarithm of any number between 1 and 0.1 therefore lies between 0 and −1, and so is equal to −1 + some decimal, *i.e.* its characteristic is 1.

So the logarithm of any number between 0.1 and 0.01 lies between −1 and −2, and hence it is equal to −2 + some decimal, *i.e.* its characteristic is $\bar{2}$.

Similarly, the logarithm of any number between 0.01 and 0.001 lies between −2 and −3, *i.e.* its characteristic is $\bar{3}$.

Generally, *the characteristic of the logarithm of any decimal fraction will be negative and numerically will be greater by unity than the number of cyphers following the decimal point.*

For any fraction between 1 and 0.1 (*e. g.* ,0.5) has no cypher following the decimal point, and we have seen that its characteristic is $\bar{1}$.

Any fraction between 0.1 and 0.01 (*e.g.*, 0.07) has one cypher following the decimal point, and we have seen that its characteristic is $\bar{2}$.

Any fraction between 0.01 and 0.001 (*e.g.*, 0.003) has two cyphers following the decimal point, and we have seen that its characteristic is $\bar{3}$.

Similarly for any fraction.

EXAMPLES The characteristic of the logarithm of the number 0.00835 is $\bar{3}$.

The characteristic of the logarithm of the number 0.0000053 is $\bar{6}$.

The characteristic of the logarithm of the number 0.34567 is $\bar{1}$.

➤ **143.** *The mantissae of the logarithm of all numbers, consisting of the same digits, are the same.*

This will be made clear by an example.

Suppose we are given that

$$\log 66818 = 4.8248935$$

Then

$$\log 668.18 = \log \frac{66818}{100} = \log 66818 - \log 100 \quad \text{(Art. 138)}$$

$$= 4.8248935 - 2 = 2.8248935$$

$$\log 0.66818 = \log \frac{66818}{100000} = \log 66818 - \log 100000 \quad \text{(Art. 138)}$$

$$= 4.8248935 - 5 = \bar{1}.8248935$$

So $$\log 0.00066818 = \log \frac{66818}{10^8} = \log 66818 - \log 10^8$$

$$= 4.8248935 - 8 = \bar{4}.8248935$$

Now the numbers 66818, 668.18, 0.66818, and 0.00066818 consist of the same significant figures, and only differ in the position of the decimal point. We observe that their logarithms have the same decimal portion, *i.e.* the same mantissa, and they only differ in the characteristic.

The value of this characteristic is in each case determined by the rule of the previous article.

It will be noted that the mantissa of a logarithm is always positive.

➤ **144. Tables of logarithms.** The logarithms of all numbers from 1 to 108000 are given in Chambers' Tables of Logarithms. Their values are there given correct to seven places of decimals.

The student should have access to a copy of the above table of logarithms or to some other suitable table. It will be required for many examples in the course of the next few chapters.

On the opposite page is a specimen page selected from Chambers' Tables, it gives the mantissae of the logarithms of all whole numbers from 52500 to 53000.

A table of logarithms, to five places of decimals, is given at the end of this book. It will be found to be sufficiently accurate for most practical purposes.

➤ **145.** To obtain the logarithm of any such number, such as 52687, we proceed as follows. Run the eye down the extreme left-hand column until it arrives at the number 5268. Then look horizontally until the eye sees the figures 7035 which are vertically beneath the number 7 at the top of the page. The number corresponding to 52687 is therefore 7217035. But this last number consists only of the digits of the mantissa, so that the mantissa required is 0.7217035. Also the characteristic for 52687 is 4.

Hence, $\log 52687 = 4.7217035$

So $\log 0.52687 = \bar{1}.7217035$

and $\log 0.00052687 = \bar{4}.7217035$

If, again, the logarithm of 52725 be required, the student will find (on running his eye vertically down the extreme left-hand column as far as 5272 and then horizontally along the row until it comes to the column under the digit 5) the number $\overline{0166}$. The bar which is placed over these digits denotes that to them must be prefixed not 721 but 722. Hence, the mantissa corresponding to the number 52725 is 0.7220166.

No.		0	1	2	3	4	5	6	7	8	9	Diff.
5250	720	1593	1676	1758	1841	1924	2007	2089	2172	2255	2337	
51		2420	2503	2586	2668	2751	2834	2916	2999	3082	3164	
52		3247	3330	3413	3495	3578	3661	3743	3826	3909	3991	
53		4074	4157	4239	4322	4405	4487	4570	4653	4735	4818	
54		4901	4983	5066	5149	5231	5314	5397	5479	5562	5645	
55		5727	5810	5892	5975	6058	6140	6223	6306	6388	6471	
56		6554	6636	6719	6801	6884	6967	7049	7132	7215	7297	
57		7380	7462	7545	7628	7710	7793	7875	7958	8041	8123	
58		8206	8288	8371	8454	8536	8619	8701	8784	8867	8949	
59		9032	9114	9197	9279	9362	9445	9527	9610	9692	9775	
60		9857	9940	0023	0105	0188	0270	0353	0435	0518	0600	
5261	721	0683	0766	0848	0931	1013	1096	1178	1261	1343	1426	
62		1508	1591	1674	1756	1839	1921	2004	2086	2169	2251	
63		2334	2416	2499	2581	2664	2746	2829	2911	2994	3076	
64		3159	3241	3324	3406	3489	3571	3654	3736	3819	3901	
65		3984	4066	4149	4231	4314	4396	4479	4561	4644	4726	
66		4809	4891	4973	5056	5138	5221	5303	5386	5468	5551	
67		5633	5716	5798	5881	5963	6045	6128	6210	6293	6375	
68		6458	6540	6623	6705	6787	6870	6952	7035	7117	7200	
69		7282	7364	7447	7529	7612	7694	7777	7859	7941	8024	
70		8106	8189	8271	8353	8436	8518	8601	8683	8765	8848	
5271		8930	9013	9095	9177	9260	9342	9424	9507	9589	9672	82
72		9754	9836	9919	0001	0084	0166	0248	0331	0413	0495	1 8
73	722	0578	0660	0742	0825	0907	0990	1072	1154	1237	1319	2 16
74		1401	1484	1566	1648	1731	1813	1895	1978	2060	2142	3 25
75		2225	2307	2389	2472	2554	2636	2719	2801	2883	2966	4 33
76		3048	3130	3212	3295	3377	3459	3542	3624	3706	3789	5 41
77		3871	3953	4036	4118	4200	4282	4365	4447	4529	4612	6 49
78		4694	4776	4858	4941	5023	5105	5188	5270	5352	5434	7 57
79		5517	5599	5681	5763	5846	5928	6010	6092	6175	6257	8 66
80		6339	6421	6504	6586	6668	6750	6833	6915	6997	7079	9 74
5281		7162	7244	7326	7408	7491	7573	7655	7737	7820	7902	
82		7984	8066	8148	8231	8313	8395	8477	8559	8642	8724	
83		8806	8888	8971	9053	9135	9217	9299	9382	9464	9546	
84		9628	9710	9792	9875	9957	0039	0121	0203	0286	0368	
85	723	0450	0532	0614	0696	0779	0861	0943	1025	1107	1189	
86		1272	1354	1436	1518	1600	1682	1765	1847	1929	2011	
87		2093	2175	2257	2340	2422	2504	2586	2668	2750	2832	
88		2914	2997	3079	3161	3243	3325	3407	3489	3571	3654	
89		3736	3818	3900	3982	4064	4146	4228	4310	4393	4475	
90		4557	4639	4721	4803	4885	4967	5049	5131	5213	5296	
5291		5378	5460	5512	5624	5706	5788	5870	5952	6034	6116	
92		6198	6280	6362	6445	6527	6609	6691	6773	6855	6937	
93		7019	7101	7183	7265	7347	7429	7511	7593	7675	7757	
94		7839	7921	8003	8085	8167	8250	8332	8414	8496	8578	
95		8660	8742	8824	8906	8988	9070	9152	9234	9316	9398	
96		9480	9562	9644	9726	9808	9890	9972	0054	0136	0218	
97	724	0300	0382	0464	0546	0628	0710	0792	0874	0956	1038	
98		1120	1202	1283	1365	1447	1529	1611	1693	1775	1857	
99		1939	2021	2103	2185	2267	2349	2431	2513	2595	2677	
5300		2759	2841	2923	3005	3086	3168	3250	3332	3414	3496	

Also the characteristic of the logarithm of the number 52725 is 4.

Hence $\log 52725 = 4.7220166$

So $\log 0.052725 = \bar{2}.7220166$

If we use the five-figure tables at the end of this book we proceed thus: Run the eye down the extreme left-hand column of pages xxii and xxiii until it arrives at the number 52; then look horizontally until the eye sees the figures 72099 below the figure 6 at the top of the previous page.

We thus get

No.	log
526	2.72099

The next figure in our number is 8. Look at the extreme right of the page of logarithms for the Mean Differences. Run the eye down the column headed by 8 until it arrives at the horizontal line commencing with 52, and there we find the number 66.

Our last figure is 7 and the corresponding number in the Difference column is 58. We thus, have

	No.	log	
	526	2.72099	
diff. for	0.8	66	
diff. for	0.07	5	8
	526.87	2.72170	8

Hence, as before, $\log 52687 = 4.72171$, correct to five places.

This is as accurate a result as we can get from using a five-figure table with the corresponding table to Mean Differences. It will be noticed that it differs in the fifth place of decimals from the value found above.

We shall now work a few numerical examples to show the efficiency of the application of logarithms for purposes of calculation.

➤ **146. EXAMPLE 1**. *Find the value of* $\sqrt[5]{23.4}$.

Let $x = \sqrt[5]{23.4} = (23.4)^{\frac{1}{5}}$

So that $\log x = \frac{1}{5}\log(23.4)$, by Art. 139.

In a seven-figure table of logarithms we find, opposite the number 234, the logarithm 3692159.

Hence, $\log 23.4 = 1.3692159$

Therefore, $\log x = \frac{1}{5}[1.3692159] = 0.2738432$

Again in the table of logarithms we find, corresponding to the logarithm 2738432, the number 187864, so that

$$\log 1.87864 = 0.2738432$$

$\therefore$ $\boldsymbol{x} = 1.87864.$

EXAMPLE 2 *Using the tables at the end of this book, find the value of*

$$\frac{(6.45)^3 \times \sqrt[3]{0.00034}}{(9.37)^2 \times \sqrt[4]{8.93}}.$$

Let x be the required value so that, by Arts. 138 and 139

$$\log x = \log(6.45)^3 + \log(0.00034)^{\frac{1}{3}} - \log(9.37)^2 - \log(8.93)^{\frac{1}{4}}$$

$$= 3\log(6.45) + \frac{1}{3}\log(0.00034) - 2\log(9.37) - \frac{1}{4}\log 8.93$$

Now in the table of logarithms on pages xxiii to xxv we find

corresponding to the number 645 the logarithm 80956

corresponding to the number 34 the logarithm 53148

corresponding to the number 937 the logarithm 97174

and corresponding to the number 893 the logarithm 95085

Hence,

$$\log x = 3 \times 0.80956 + \frac{1}{3}(\bar{4}.53148) - 2 \times 0.97174 - \frac{1}{4} \times 0.95085$$

But $\frac{1}{3}(\bar{4}.53148) = \frac{1}{3}[\bar{6} + 2.53148]$

$$= \bar{2} + 0.843827$$

$$\therefore \log x = 2.42868 + [\bar{2} + 0.843827] - 1.94348 - 0.237713$$

$$= 3.272507 - 4.181193$$

$$= \bar{1} + 4.272507 - 4.181193$$

$$= \bar{1}.09131, \text{ correct to five places of decimals.}$$

In the table of logarithms on page xxii we find, corresponding to the number 123, the logarithm 0.08991, so that we have

$$\log\ 123 = 2.08991$$

$$\text{diff. for } \underline{0.4 = \quad 140}$$

$$\log 123.4 = 2.09131$$

Hence $\log x = \log 0.12340$

and therefore, $x = 0.12340$

When the logarithm of any number does not quite agree with any logarithm in the tables, but lies between two consecutive logarithms, it will be shown in the next chapter how the number may be accurately found.

EXAMPLE 3 *Having given* $\log 2 = 0.30103$, *find the* number *of digits in* 2^{67} *and the position of the first significant figure in* 2^{-37}.

We have $\log 2^{67} = 67 \times \log 2 = 67 \times 0.30103 = 20.16901$

Since, the characteristic of the logarithm of 2^{67} is 20, it follows, by Art. 142, that in 2^{67} there are 21 digits.

Again, $\log 2^{-37} = -37\log 2 = -37 \times 0.30103$

$$= -11.13811 = \overline{12}.86189$$

Hence, by Art. 142, in 2^{-37} there are 11 cyphers following the decimal point, *i.e.* the first significant figure is in the twelfth place of decimals.

EXAMPLE 4. *Given* $\log 3 = 0.4771213$, $\log 7 = 0.8450980$ *and* $\log 11 = 1.0413927$, *solve the equation*

$$3^x \times 7^{2x+1} = 11^{x+5}$$

Taking logarithms of both sides, we have

$$\log 3^x + \log 7^{2x+1} = \log 11^{x+5}$$

$\therefore \quad x\log 3 + (2x+1)\log 7 = (x+5)\log 11$

$\therefore \quad x[\log 3 + 2\log 7 - \log 11] = 5\log 11 - \log 7$

$\therefore \quad x = \dfrac{5\log 11 - \log 7}{\log 3 + 2\log 7 - 11}$

$$= \frac{5.2069635 - 0.8450980}{0.4771213 + 1.6901960 - 1.0413927}$$

$$= \frac{4.3618655}{1.1259246} = 3.87 \ldots$$

➤ **147.** To prove that

$$\mathbf{\log_a m = \log_b m \times \log_a b}$$

Let $\quad \log_a m = x$, so that $a^x = m$

Also let $\quad \log_a m = y$, so that $b^y = m$

$\therefore \quad a^x = b^y$

Hence $\quad \log_a(a^x) = \log_a(b^y)$

$\therefore \quad x = y\log_a b$ (Art. 139)

Hence $\quad \log_a m = \log_b m \times \log_a b$

By the theorem of the foregoing article we can from the logarithm of any number to a base b find its logarithm to any other base a. It is found convenient, as will appear in Part II, Art. 12, not to calculate the logarithms to base 10 directly, but to calculate them first to another base and then to transform them by this theorem.

EXAMPLES XXIII

1. Given $\log 4 = 0.60206$ and $\log 3 = 0.4771213$, find the logarithms of 0.8, 0.003, 0.0108, and $(0.00018)^{\frac{1}{7}}$.

2. Given $\log 11 = 1.0413927$ and $\log 13 = 1.1139434$, find the values of

(1) $\log 1.43$ (2) $\log 133.1$

(3) $\log \sqrt[4]{143}$, and (4) $\log \sqrt[3]{0.00169}$.

3. What are the characteristics of the logarithms of 243.7, 0.0153, 2.8713, 0.00057, 0.023, $\sqrt[5]{24615}$, and $(24589)^{3/4}$?

4. Find the 5th root of 0.003, having given

$\log 3 = 0.4771213$ and $\log 312936 = 5.4954243$.

5. Find the values of (1) $7^{1/7}$, (2) $(84)^{2/5}$, and (3) $(0.021)^{1/5}$, having given

$$\log 2 = 0.30103, \log 3 = 0.4771213$$
$$\log 7 = 0.8450980, \log 132057 = 5.1207283$$
$$\log 588453 = 5.7697117, \text{ and } \log 461791 = 5.6644438$$

6. Having given $\log 3 = 0.4771213$

find the number of digits in

(1) 3^{43}, (2) 3^{27}, and (3) 3^{62}

and the position of the first significant figure in

(4) 3^{-13}, (5) 3^{-43}, and (6) 3^{-65}

7. Given $\log 2 = 0.30103$, $\log 3 = 0.4771213$, and $\log 7 = 0.8450980$, solve the equations.

(1) $2^x \cdot 3^{x+4} = 7^x$ (2) $2^{2x+1} \cdot 3^{3x+2} = 7^{4x}$

(3) $7^{2x} \div 2^{x-4} = 3^{3x-7}$ and (4) $\left.\begin{array}{r} 7^{x+y} \times 3^{2x+y} = 9 \\ 3^{x-y} \div 2^{x-2y} = 3^x \end{array}\right\}$

8. From the tables find the seventh root of 0.000026751.

Making use of the tables, find the approximate values of

9. $\sqrt[3]{645.3}$

10. $\sqrt[5]{82357}$

11. $\dfrac{\sqrt{5} + \sqrt[3]{7}}{\sqrt[4]{8} \times \sqrt[5]{9}}$

12. $\sqrt[3]{\dfrac{7.2 \times 8.3}{9.4 \div 16.5}}$

13. $\dfrac{\sqrt{8^{1/5} \times 11^{1/3}}}{\sqrt{74} \times \sqrt[5]{62}}$

Draw the graphs of

14. $\log x$

15. $\log \sin x$

16. $\log \cos x$

17. $\log \tan x$

18. $\log \operatorname{cosec} x$

19. $\log \cot x$

11

THE PRINCIPLE OF PROPORTIONAL PARTS

148. We have pointed out that the logarithms of all numbers from 1 to 108000 may be found in Chambers' Mathematical Tables, so that, for example, the logarithms of 74583 and 74584 may be obtained directly therefrom.

Suppose however we wanted the logarithm of a number lying between these two, *e.g.* the number 74583.3.

To obtain the logarithm of this number we use the Principle of Proportional Parts which states that the increase in the logarithm of a number is proportional to the increase in the number itself.

Thus from the tables we find

$$\log 74583 = 4.8726398 \qquad \text{...(1)}$$

and

$$\log 74584 = 4.8726457 \qquad \text{...(2)}$$

The quantity log 74583.3 will clearly lie between log 74583 and log 74584.

Let then

$$\log 74583.3 = \log 74583 + x$$
$$= 4.8726398 + x \qquad \text{...(3)}$$

From (1) and (2), we see that for an increase 1 in the number the increase in the logarithm is 0.0000059.

The Theory of Proportional Parts then states that for an increase of 0.3 in the number the increase in the logarithm is

$$0.3 \times 0.0000059, \text{ i.e., } 0.00000177$$

Hence,

$$\log 74583.3 = 4.8726398 + 0.00000177$$
$$= 4.87264157$$

149. As another example, we shall find the value of log 0.0382757 and shall exhibit the working in a more concise form.

From the table we obtain

$$\log 0.038275 = \bar{2}.5829152$$
$$\log 0.038276 = \bar{2}.5829265$$

Hence the difference for

$$0.000001 = 0.0000113$$

Therefore the difference for

$$0.0000007 = 0.7 \times 0.0000113 = 0.00000791$$

$$\therefore \quad \log 0.0382757 = \bar{2}.5829152 + 0.00000791 = \bar{2}.58292311$$

Since the logarithms we are using the only correct to seven places of decimals, we omit the last digit and the answer is $\bar{2}.5829231$.

150. The converse question is often met with, viz., to find the number whose logarithm is given. If the logarithm be one of the those tabulated, the required number is easily found. The method to be followed when this is not the case is shown in the following example.

EXAMPLE Find the number whose logarithm is 2.6283924.

On reference to the tables we find that the logarithm 6283924 is not tabulated, but that the nearest logarithms are 6283889 and 6283991, between which our logarithm lies.

We have then $\log 425.00 = 2.6283889$ ...(1)

and $\log 425.01 = 2.6283991$ ...(2)

Let $\log (425.00 + x) = 2.6283924$ ...(3)

From (1) and (2), we see that corresponding to a difference of 0.01 in the number there is a difference of 0.0000102 in the logarithm.

From (1) and (3), we see that corresponding to a difference of x in the number there is a difference of 0.0000035 in the logarithm.

Hence $x : 0.01 :: 0.0000035 : 0.0000102$

$$\therefore \quad x = \frac{35}{102} \times 0.01 = \frac{0.35}{102} = 0.00343 \text{ nearly}$$

Hence the required number = 425.00 + 0.00343 = 425.00343.

151. Where logarithms are taken out of the tables the labour of subtracting successive logarithms may be avoided. On reference to page 124 there is found at the extreme right a column headed *Diff.* The number 82 at the head of the figures in this column gives the difference corresponding to a difference of unity in the numbers on that page.

This number 82 means 0.0000082

The rows below the 82 give the differences corresponding to 0.1, 0.2,...Thus the fifth of these rows means that the difference for 0.5 is 0.0000041.

As an example, let us find the logarithm of 52746.74

From page 124, we have

$$\log 52746 = 4.7221895$$

$$\text{diff. for } 0.7 = 0.0000057$$

$$0.04$$

$$\therefore \quad \left(= \frac{1}{10} \times \text{diff. for } 4\right) = 0.0000003$$

$$\therefore \quad \log 52746.74 = 4.7221955$$

We shall solve two more examples, taking all the logarithms from the tables, and only putting down the necessary steps.

EXAMPLE 1 *Find the seventh root of* 0.034574.

If x be the required quantity, we have

$$\log x = \frac{1}{7}\log(0.034574) = \frac{1}{7}(\bar{2}.5387496)$$

$$= \frac{1}{7}(\bar{7} + 5.5387496)$$

$$\therefore \quad \log x = \bar{1}.791299$$

But $\log 0.61837 = \bar{1}.7912484$

$$\text{diff.} = 0.0000015$$

But diff. for $0.00001 = 0.0000071$

$\therefore$ required increase $= 0.0000021$

$$\therefore \quad x = 0.61837211$$

$$\begin{array}{r} 71)150(211 \\ \underline{142} \\ 80 \\ \underline{71} \\ 90 \\ \underline{71} \\ 19 \end{array}$$

EXAMPLE 2 *If* $a = 345.75$ *and* $b = 283.912$, *find the value of the square root of* $a^2 - b^2$, *using the five-figure tables at the end of this book.*

If x be the required quantity, we have

$$2\log x = \log(a^2 - b^2) = \log(a - b) + \log(a + b)$$

$$= \log 61.838 + \log 629.662$$

Now, from page xxiv. $\log 61.8 = 1.79099$

diff. for	0.03 =	21	
" "	0.008 =	5	6
" "	log 629 = 2.79865		
diff. for	0.6 =	42	
" "	0.06 =	4	2
" "	0.002 =		14

Hence, by addition, $2 \log x = 4.59037$, correct to 5 places

$$\therefore \quad \log x = 2.29518 \mid 5$$

But, from page xxii. $\log 197 = 2.29447$

diff. for $0.3 = \quad 67$

" " $0.02 = \quad 4 \mid 5$

$$\therefore \quad \log 197.32 = 2.29518 \mid 5$$

$$\therefore \quad x = 197.32$$

If we used seven-figure logarithms we should obtain a more accurate result, viz. 197.3247.

➤ **152.** The proof of the Principle of Proportional Parts will not be given at this stage. It is not strictly true without certain limitations. If we use seven-figure tables, the numbers to which the principle is applied must contain not less than five significant figures, and then we may rely on the result as correct to seven places of decimals.

For example, we must not apply the principle to obtain the value of log 2.5 from the values of log 2 and log 3.

For, if we did, since these logarithms are 0.30103 and 0.4771213, the logarithm of 2.5 would be 0.389075.

But from the tables the value of log 2.5 is found to be 0.3979400.

Hence the result which we should obtain would be manifestly quite incorrect.

So, if the numbers to which the principle is applied contain not less than four digit, we can rely on the result as correct to five places of decimals.

Similarly, if the numbers contain not less than three digits, the result can be relied upon in general to four places of decimals.

TABLES OF TRIGONOMETRICAL RATIOS

➤ **153.** In Chambers' Tables will be found tables giving the values of the trigonometrical ratios of angles between 0° and 45°, the angles increasing by differences of 1′.

It is unnecessary to separately tabulate the ratios for angles between 45° and 90°, since the ratios of angles between 45° and 90° can be reduced to those of angles between 0° and 45°. (Art 75.)

[For example,

$$\sin 76^\circ 11' = \sin(90^\circ - 13^\circ 49') = \cos 13^\circ 49'$$

and is therefore known.]

Such a table is called a table of natural sines, cosines, etc. to distinguish it from the table of logarithmic sines, cosines, etc.

If we want to find the sine of an angle which contains an integral number of degrees and minutes, we can obtain it from the tables. If, however, the angle contain seconds, we must use the principle of proportional parts.

EXAMPLE 1 Given $\sin 29° \, 14' = 0.4883674,$

and $\sin 29° 15' = 0.4886212,$

find the value of $\sin 29° \, 14' 32''$.

By subtraction we have

difference in the sine for $1' = 0.0002538$

$\therefore$ difference in the sine for $32'' = \dfrac{32}{60} \times 0.0002538 = 0.00013536$

$$\therefore \quad \sin 29° \, 14' 32'' = 0.4883674$$
$$\underline{+\ 0.4883674}$$
$$= 0.488502\underline{76}$$

Since, we want our answer only to seven places of decimals, we omit the last 6, and, since 76 is nearer to 80 than 70, we write

$$\sin 29° \, 14' 32'' = 0.4885028$$

When we omit a figure in the eighth place of decimals we add 1 to the figure in the seventh place, if the omitted figure be 5 or a number greater than 5.

EXAMPLE 2 *Given* $\cos 16° 27' = 0.9590672$

and $\cos 16° 28' = 0.9589848$

find the value of $\cos 16° 27' 47''$.

We note that, as was shown in Art. 55, the cosine decreases as the angle increases.

Hence for an increase of 1′, i.e., 60″, in the angle, there is a decrease of 0.0000824 in the cosine.

Hence for an increase of 47″ in the angle, there is a decreases of $\dfrac{47}{60} \times 0.0000824$ in the cosine.

$$\therefore \quad \cos 16° 27' \, 47'' = 0.9590672 - \frac{47}{60} \times 0.0000824$$
$$= 0.9590672 - 0.000645$$
$$= 0.9590672$$
$$\underline{-\ 0.0000645}$$
$$= 0.9590027$$

$$\begin{array}{r} 824 \\ \underline{47} \\ 5768 \\ \underline{3296} \\ 60)\ \underline{38728} \\ 645 \end{array}$$

In practice this may be abbreviated thus:

$$\cos 16° 28' = 0.9589848$$
$$\underline{\cos 16° 27' = 0.9590672}$$
$$\therefore \quad \text{diff. for} 1' = -0.0000824$$

$\therefore$ diff. for $47'' = -\frac{47}{60} \times 0.0000824$

Ans. $= -0.0000645$

$= 0.9590672$

$\underline{-0.0000645}$

$= 0.9590027$

➤ **154.** An example of the inverse question, to find the angle when one of its trigonometrical ratios is given, will now be given.

<u>EXAMPLE</u> *Find the angle whose cotangent is* 1.4109325, *having given*

$$\cot 35°19' = 1.4114799, \textit{ and } \cot 35°20' = 1.4106098,$$

Let the required angle be $35°19' + x''$

so that $\cot(35°19' + x'') = 1.4109325$

From these three equations we have

For an increase of $60''$ in the angle, a decrease of 0.0008701 in the cotangent,

for an increase of x'' in the angle, a decrease of 0.005474 in the cotangent.

$\therefore$ $x : 60 :: 5474 : 8701$, so that $x = 37.7$

Hence the required angle $= 35°19'37.7''$.

➤ **155.** In working all questions involving the application of the Principle of Proportional Parts, the student must be very careful to note whether the trigonometrical ratios increase or decrease as the angle increases. As a help to his memory, he may observe that in the first quadrant the three trigonometrical ratios whose names begin with co, *i.e.*, the cosine, the cotangent, and the cosecant, all decrease as the angle increases.

TABLES OF LOGARITHMIC SINES, COSINES, ETC.

➤ **156.** In many kinds of trigonometric calculation, as in the solution of triangles, we often require the logarithms of trigonometrical ratios. To avoid the inconvenience of first finding the sine of any angle from the tables and then obtaining the logarithm of this sine by a second application of the tables, it has been found desirable to have separate tables separate tables giving the logarithms of the various trigonometrical functions of angles. As before, it is only necessary to construct the tables for angles between 0° and 45°.

Since the sine of an angle is always less than unity, the logarithm of its sine is always negative (Art. 142).

Again, since the tangent of an angle between 0° and 45° is less than unity its logarithm is negative, whilst the logarithm of the tangent of an angle between 45° and 90° is the logarithm of a number greater than unity and is therefore positive.

➤ **157.** To avoid the trouble and inconvenience of printing the proper sign to the logarithms of the trigonometric functions, the logarithms as tabulated are not the true logarithms, but the true logarithms *increased by* 10.

For example, $\sin 30° = \frac{1}{2}$

Hence, $\log \sin 30° = \log \frac{1}{2} = -\log 2$

$= -0.30103 = \bar{1}.69897$

The logarithm tabulated is therefore

$10 + \log \sin 30°$, *i.e.*, 9.69897.

Again, $\tan 60° = \sqrt{3}$

Hence, $\log \tan 60° = \frac{1}{2} \log 3 = \frac{1}{2}(0.4771213)$

$= 0.2385606$

The logarithm tabulated is therefore

$10 + 0.2385606$, *i.e.*, 10.2385606

The symbol L is used to denote these "tabular logarithms,", *i.e.*, the logarithms as found in the English books of tables.

Thus $L \sin 15°25' = 10 + \log \sin 15°25'$

and $L \sec 48°23' = 10 + \log \sec 48°23'$

➤ **158.** If we want to find the tabular logarithm of any function of an angle, which contains an integral number of degrees and minutes, we can obtain it directly from the tables. If, however, the angle contain seconds we must use the principle of proportional parts. The method of procedure is similar to that of Art. 153. We give an example and also one of the inverse question.

EXAMPLE 1 *Given* $L\text{cosec } 32°21' = 10.2715733$

and $L\text{cosec } 32°22' = 10.2713740$

find $L \text{ cosec } 32°21'51''$

For an increase of 60″ in the angle, there is a *decreases* of 0.0001993 in the logarithm.

Hence, for an increases of 51″ in the angle, the corresponding *decreases* is $\frac{51}{60} \times 0.0001993$, *i.e.*, 0.0001694.

Hence, L cosec $32°21'51'' = 10.2715733$

$$\underline{-\,0.0001694}$$

$$= 10.2714039$$

EXAMPLE 2 *Find the angle such that the tabular logarithm of its tangent is* 9.4417250.

Let x be the required angle.

From the tables, we have

$$L\tan x = 9.4417250 \qquad L\tan 15°28' = 9.4420062$$

$$\underline{L\tan 15°27' = 9.4415145} \qquad \underline{L\tan 15°27' = 9.4415145}$$

$$\text{diff.} \qquad = 2105 \qquad \text{diff. for} \qquad 1' = 4917$$

Corresponding increase $= \dfrac{2105}{4917} \times 60''$

$$= 25.7''$$

$$\therefore \qquad x = 15°27'26''$$

$$\begin{array}{r} 2105 \\ \underline{60} \\ 4917)126300(25.7 \\ \underline{9837} \\ 27690 \\ \underline{24585} \\ 33750 \end{array}$$

EXAMPLE 3 *Given* $L\sin 14°6' = 9.3867040$, *find* $L\text{cosec}14°6'$.

Here, $\log\sin 14°6' = L\sin 14°6' - 10$

$$= -1 + 0.3867040$$

Now $\log\text{cosec}14°6' = \log\dfrac{1}{\sin 14°6'}$

$$= -\log\sin 14°6' = 10 - L\sin 14°6'$$

$$= 10 - 9.3867040 = 0.6132960$$

Hence $L\text{cosec}\ 14°6' = 10.6132960$

More generally, we have $\sin\theta \times \text{cosec}\ \theta = 1$

$$\therefore \qquad \log\sin\theta + \log\text{cosec}\ \theta = 0$$

$$\therefore \qquad L\sin\theta + L\text{cosec}\ \theta = 20$$

The error to be avoided is this; the student sometimes assumes that, because

$$\log\text{cosec}\ 14°6' = -\log\sin 14°6'.$$

he may therefore assume that

$$L\text{cosec}\ 14°6' = -L\sin 14°6'.$$

This is obviously untrue.

EXAMPLES XXIV

1. Given $\log 35705 = 4.5527290$

and $\log 35706 = 4.5527412$

find the values of $\log 35705.7$ and $\log 35.70585$

2. Given $\log 5.8742 = 0.7689487$
and $\log 587.43 = 2.7689561$
find the values of log 58742.57 and log 0.00587422.

3. Given $\log 47847 = 4.6798547$
and $\log 47848 = 4.6798638,$
find the numbers whose logarithms are respectively

$$2.6798593 \text{ and } \bar{3}.6798617$$

4. Given $\log 258.36 = 2.4122253$
and $\log 2.5837 = 0.4122421,$
find the numbers whose logarithms are

$$0.4122378 \text{ and } \bar{2}.4122287.$$

5. From the table on page 124 find the logarithms of
(1) 52538.97, (2) 527.286, (3) 0.000529673
and the numbers whose logarithms are
(4) 3.7221098, (5) $\bar{2}.7240075$, and (6) 0.7210386

6. Given $\sin 43°23' = 0.6868761$
and $\sin 43°24' = 0.6870875,$
find the value of $\sin 43°23'47''$.

7. Find also the angle whose sine is 0.6870349.

8. Given $\cos 32°16' = 0.8455726$
and $\cos 32°17' = 0.8454172,$
find the values of $\cos 32°16'24''$ and of $\cos 32°16'47''$

9. Find also the anlges whose cosines are

$$0.8454832 \text{ and } 0.8455176$$

10. Given $\tan 76°21' = 4.1177784$
and $\tan 76°22' = 4.1230079$
find the values of $\tan 76°21'29''$ and $\tan 76°21'47''$.

11. Given $\text{cosec} 13°8' = 4.4010616$
and $\text{cosec} 13°9' = 4.3955817,$
find the values of $\text{cosec} 13°8'19''$ and $\text{cosec } 13°8'37''$.

12. Find also the angle whose cosecant is 4.396789.

13. Given $L \cos 34°44' = 9.9147729$
and $L \cos 34°45' = 9.9146852,$
find the value of $L \cos 34°44'27''$

14. Find also the angle θ, where

$$L \cos \theta = 9.9147328$$

15. Given $L \cot 71°27' = 9.5257779$
and $L \cot 71°28' = 9.5253589$
find the value of $L \cot 71°27'47''$
and solve the equation $L \cot \theta = 9.5254782$

16. Given $L\sec 18°27' = 10.0229168$

and $L\sec 18°28' = 10.0229590$,

find the value of $L\sec 18°27'35''$.

17. Find also the angle whose $L\sec$ is 10.0229285.

18. Find in degrees, minutes, and seconds the angle whose sine is 0.6, given that

$$\log 6 = 0.7781513,\ L\sin 36°52' = 9.7781186$$

and $L\sin 36°53' = 9.7782870$.

➤ **159.** On the next page is printed a specimen page taken from Chambers' Tables. It gives the tabular logarithms of the trigonometrical ratios of angle between 32° and 33° and also between 57° and 58°.

The first column gives the L sine for each minute between 32° and 33°.

In the second column under the word Diff. is found the number 2021. This means that 0.0002021 is the difference between $L\sin 32°0'$ and $L\sin 32°1'$; this may be verified by subtracting 9.7242097 from 9.7244118. It will also be noted that the figures 2021 are printed halfway between the numbers 9.7242097 and 9.7244118. thus clearly showing between the numbers it is the difference.

This same column of Differences also applies to the column on its right-hand side which is headed Cosec.

Similarly the fifth column, which is also headed Diff. may be used with the two columns on the right and left on it.

➤ **160.** There is one point to be noticed in using the columns headed Diff. It has been pointed out that 2021 (at the top of the second column) means 0.0002021. Now the 790 (at the top of the eighth column) means *not* 0.000790, but 0.0000790. The rule is this; the right-hand figure of the Diff. must be placed in the seventh place of decimals and the requisite number of cyphers prefixed.

Thus,

Diff = 9 means that the difference is 0.0000009

Diff = 74 means that the difference is 0.000007

Diff = 735 means that the difference is 0.0000735

Diff = 2021 means that the difference is 0.0002021

whilst Diff = 12348 means that the difference is 0.0012348.

➤ **161.** Page 139 also gives the tabular logs. of ratios between 57° and 58°. Suppose we wanted $L\tan 57°20'$. We now start with the line at the *bottom* of the page and run our *eye up* the column which has Tang. at its *foot*. We go up this column until we arrive at the number which is on the same level as the number 20 in the extreme *right-hand* column. This number we find to be 10.1930286, which is therefore the value of $L\tan 57°20'$

LOGARITHMIC SINES, TANGENTS, SECANTS, ETC.

32° Deg

	Sine	Diff.	Cosec.	Tang.	Diff.	Cotang.	Secant	Diff.	Cosine	
0	9.7242097	2021	10.2757903	9.7957892	2811	10.20421 08	10.0715795	790	9.9284205	60
1	9.7244118	2020	10.2755882	9.7960703	2810	10.20392 7	10.0716585	790	9.9283415	59
2	9.7246138	2018	10.2751863	9.7963513	2809	10.203648 7	10.0717375	791	9.9282625	58
3	9.7248156	2018	10.2751844	9.7966322	2808	10.2033678	10.0718166	791	9.9281834	57
4	9.7250174	2015	10.2749826	9.7969130	2808	10.2030870	10.0718957	792	9.9281043	56
5	9.7252189	2015	10.2747811	9.7971938	2807	10.2028062	10.0719749	792	9.9280251	55
6	9.7254204	2013	10.2745796	9.7974745	2806	10 2025255	10.0720541	793	9 9279459	54
7	9.7256217	2012	10.2743783	9.7977551	2805	10.2022449	10.0721334	793	9.9278666	53
8	9.7258229	2011	10.2741771	9 7980356	2804	10.2019644	10.0722127	794	9.9277873	52
9	9.7260240	2009	10.2739760	9.7983160	2804	10.201h840	10.0722921	794	9.9277079	51
10	9.7262249	2008	10.2737751	9.79H5964	2803	10.2014036	10.0723715	795	9.9276285	50
11	9.7264257	2007	10.2735743	9.7988767	2802	10.20 0112233	10.0724510	795	9.9275490	49
12	9.7266264	2005	10.2733736	9.7991569	2801	10.2008431	10,0725305	796	9.9274695	48
13	9.7268269	2004	10.2731731	9.7994370	2800	10.2005630	10.0726101	796	9.9273899	47
14	9.7270273	2003	10,2729727	9.7997170	2800	10.2002830	10,0726897	797	9.9273103	46
15	9.7272276	2002	10.2727724	9.7999970	2799	10.2000030	10.0727694	797	9.9272306	45
16	9.7274278	2000	10.2725722	9.8002769	2798	10. 1997231	10.0728491	798	9,9271509	44
17	9.7276278	1999	10.2723722	9.8005567	2798	10.1994433	10.0729289	798	9.9270711	43
18	9,7278277	1998	10.2721723	9.8008365	27%	10.1991635	10.0730087	799	9.9269913	42
19	9.7280275	1996	10.2719725	9.8011161	2796	10.1988839	10.0730886	800	9.9269114	41
20.	9.7282271	1996	10.2717729	9.8013957	2795	10.1986043	10.0731686	800	9.9268314	40
21	9.7284267	1993	10.2715733	9.8016752	2794	10.1983248	10.0732486	800	9.9267514	39
22	9.7286260	1993	10.2713740	9.8019546	2794	10.1980454	10.0733286	801	9.9266714	38
23	9.7388253	1991	10.2711747	9.8022340	2793	10. 977660	10.0734087	801	9.9265913	37
24	9 7290244	1990	10.2709756	9.8025133	2792	10.1974867	10.0734888	802	9.9265112	36
25	9.7292234	1989	10.2707766	9.8027925	2791	10.1972075	10.0735690	803	9.9264310	35
26	9.7294223	1988	10.2705777	9.8030716	2790	10.1969284	10.0736493	803	9.9263507	34
27	9.7296211	1986	10.2703789	9.8033506	3790	10.1966494	10.0737296	803	9.9262704	33
28	9.7298197	1985	10.270 1803	9.8036296	2789	10.1963704	10.0738099	805	9.9261901	32
29	9.7300182	1983	10.2699818	9.8039085	2788	10.1960915	10.0738904	804	9.9261096	31
30	9.7302165	1983	10.2697S35	9.804 1873	2788	10.1958127	10.0739708	R05	9.9260292	30
31	9.7304148	1981	10.2695852	9.8044661	2788	10.1955339	10.0740513	806	9,9259487	29
32	9.7306129	1970	10.2693871	9.8047447	2786	10.1952553	10.0741319	806	9.9258681	28
.13	9.7308109	1976	10.2691891	9.8050233	2786	10.1949767	10.0742125	806	9.9257075	27
34	9.7310087	1977	10.2689913	9.8053019	2784	10.1946981	10.0742931	808	9.9257069	26
35	9.7313064	1976	10.2687936	9.8055803	2784	10.1944197	10.0743739	807	9.92556261	25
36	9.7314040	1975	10.26859611	9.8058587	2783	10.1941413	10.0744546	808	9.9255454	24
37	9.7316015	1974	10.2683985	9.8061370	.2782	10.1938630	10.0745354	809	9.9254646	23
38	9.7317989	1972	10.2682011	9.8064152	2781	10.1935848	10.0746166	809	9.9253837	22
39	9.731 9961	1971	10.2680039	9.8066933	2781	10.1933067	10.0746972	810	9.9253028	21
40	9.7321932	1970	10.2678068	9.8069714	2780	10.1930286	10.0747782	810	9.92522.18	20
41	9.7323902	1968	10.2676098	9.8072404	2779	10.1927506	10.0748392	811	9.9251408	19
42	9.732S870	1967	10.2674130	9.8075273	2779	10.1924727	10.0749403	811	9.9250597	18
43	9.7327837	1966	10.2672163	9.8078052	2777	10.1921948	10.0750214	812	9.9249786	17
44	9.7329803	1965	10.2670197	9.8080829	2777	10.1919171	10.0751026	813	9.9248974	16
45	9.7331768	1963	10.2668232	9.80083606	2777	10.1916394	10.0751839	812	9.924816	15
46	9.7333731	1962	10.2666269	9.8086383	2775	10.1913617	10.0752651	814	9.9247349	14
47	9.7335693	1961	10.2664317	9.8089158	2775	10.1910842	10.0753465	814	9.9246535	13
48	9.7337654	I960	10.2662346	9.8091913	2774	10.1908067	10.0754279	814	9.9245721	12
49	9.7339614	1958	10.2660386	9.8094707	2773	10.1905293	10.0755093	815	9.9244907	11
50	9.7341572	1957	10.2658428	9.8097480	2773	10.1902520	10.0755908	815	9.9244092	10
51	9.7343529	1956	10.2656471	9.8100253	2772	10.1899747	10.0756723	816	9.9243277	9
52	9. 7345485	1955	10.2654515	9.8103025	2771	10.189675	10.0757539	817	9.92 42461	8
53	9.7347440	1953	10.2652560	9.8105796	2770	10.1894204	10.0758356	817	9.9241644	7
54	9.7349393	1952	10.2650607	9,8108566	2770	10.1891434	10.0759173	817	9.9240827	6
55	9.7351345	1951	10.2648655	9.8111336	2769	10.1888664	10.0759990	819	9.9240010	5
56	9.7353298	1950	10.2646704	9.8114105	2768	10.1885895	10. 0760809	818	9.9239191	4
57	9.7355246	1949	10.2644754	98116873	2768	10.1883127	10.0761627	819	9.9238373	3
58	9.7357195	1947	10.2642805	9.8119641	2767	10.18R0359	10.0762446	820	9.9237554	2
59	9.7359142	1946	10.2640858	9.8122408	2766	10.1877592	10.0763266	820	9.923673-1	1
60	9.7361088		10.2638912	9.8125I74		10.1874826	10.0764086		9.9235914	0
	Cosine	Diff.	Secant	Cotang.	Diff.	Tang.	Cosec.	Diff.	Sine	

57° Deg.

EXAMPLES XXV

1. Find θ, given that $\cos\theta = 0.9725382$

$\cos 13°27' = 0.9725733$, diff. for $1' = 677$.

2. Find the angle whose sine is $\frac{3}{8}$, given

$\sin 22°1' = 0.3748763$, diff. for $1' = 2696$.

3. Given $\text{cosec}\ 65°24' = 1.0998243$,

diff. for $1' = 1464$,

find the value of $\text{cosec} 65°24'37''$,

and the angle whose cosec is 1.0997938.

4. Given $L \tan 22°37' = 9.6197205$,

diff. for $1' = 3557$,

find the value of $L \tan 22°37'22''$,

and the angle whose $L \tan$ is 9.6195283.

5. Find the angle whose $L \cos$ is 9.993, given

$L \cos 10°15' = 9.9930131$, diff. for $1' = 229$.

6. Find the angle whose $L \sec$ is 10.15 given

$L \sec 44°55' = 10.1498843$, diff. for $1' = 1260$.

7. From the table on page 139 find the values of

1. $L \sin 32°18'23''$ 2. $L \cos 32°16'49''$
3. $L \cot 32°29'43''$ 4. $L \sec 32°52'27''$
5. $L \tan 57°45'28''$ 6. $L \text{cosec}\ 57°48'21''$
7. $L \cos 57°58'29''$

8. With the help of the same page solve the equations

1. $L \tan\theta = 10.1959261$
2. $L\ \text{cosec}\ \theta = 10.0738125$
3. $L \cos\theta = 9.9259283$
4. $L \sin\theta = 9.924135$

9. Take out of the tables $L \tan 16°6'23''$ and calculate the value of the square root of the tangent.

10. Change into a form more convenient for logarithmic computation (*i.e.*, express in the form of products of quantities) the quantities

1. $1 + \tan x \tan y$ 2. $1 - \tan x \tan y$
3. $\cot x + \tan y$ 4. $\cot x - \tan y$
5. $\dfrac{1 - \cos 2x}{1 + \cos 2x}$ 6. $\dfrac{\tan x + \tan y}{\cot x + \cot y}$

12

RELATIONS BETWEEN THE SIDES AND THE TRIGONOMETRICAL RATIOS OF THE ANGLES OF A TRIANGLE

➤ **162.** In any triangle ABC, the side BC, opposite to the angle A, is denoted by a ; the sides CA and AB opposite to the angles B and C respectively, are denoted by b and c.

➤ **163. Theorem :** *In any triangle ABC,*

$$\frac{\sin A}{a} = \frac{\sin B}{b} = \frac{\sin C}{c}$$

i.e., the sines of the angles are proportional to the opposite sides.

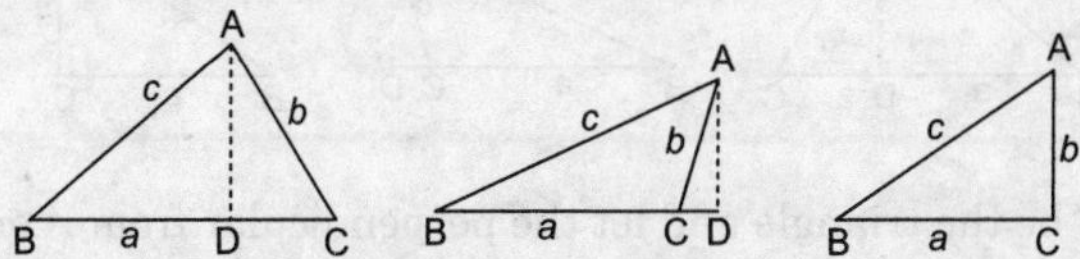

Draw AD perpendicular to the opposite side meeting it, produced if necessary, in the point D.

In the triangle ABD, we have

$$\frac{AD}{AB} = \sin B, \text{ so that } AD = c \sin B.$$

In the triangle ACD, we have

$$\frac{AD}{AC} = \sin C, \text{ so that } AD = b \sin C$$

[If the angle C be obtuse, as in the second figure, we have

$$\frac{AD}{b} = \sin ACD = \sin(180° - C) = \sin C \qquad \text{(Art. 72)}$$

so that $$AD = b \sin C]$$

Equating these two values of AD, we have

$$c\sin B = b\sin C$$

i.e.,
$$\frac{\sin B}{b} = \frac{\sin C}{c}$$

In a similar manner, by drawing a perpendicular from B upon CA, we have

$$\frac{\sin C}{c} = \frac{\sin A}{a}$$

If one of the angles, C, be a right angle, as in the third figure, we have

$$\sin C = 1, \sin A = \frac{a}{c}, \text{ and } \sin B = \frac{b}{c}$$

Hence,
$$\frac{\sin A}{a} = \frac{\sin B}{b} = \frac{1}{c} = \frac{\sin C}{c}$$

We therefore, have in all cases,

$$\boldsymbol{\frac{\sin A}{a} = \frac{\sin B}{b} = \frac{\sin C}{c}}$$

➤ **164.** *In any triangle, to find the cosine of an angle in terms of the sides.*

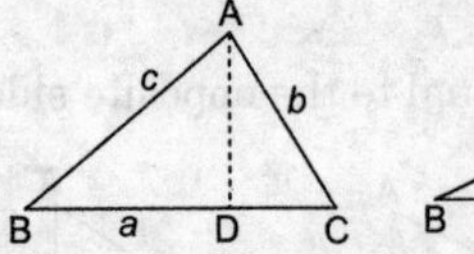

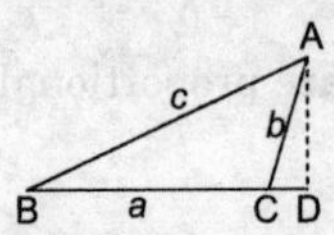

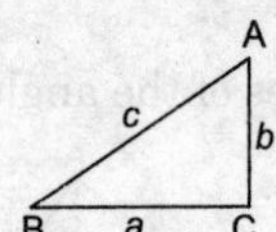

Let ABC be the triangle and let the perpendicular from A on BC meet it, produced if necessary, in the point D.

First., let the angle C be **acute**, as in the first figure.

By Geometry, we have

$$AB^2 = BC^2 + CA^2 - 2BC \cdot CD \qquad \text{...(1)}$$

But
$$\frac{CD}{CA} = \cos C, \text{ so that } CD = b\cos C$$

Hence, (i) becomes

$$c^2 = a^2 + b^2 - 2ab\cos C$$

i.e.,
$$2ab\cos C = a^2 + b^2 - c^2$$

i.e.,
$$\cos C = \frac{a^2 + b^2 - c^2}{2ab}$$

Secondly, let the angle C be **obtuse**, as in the second figure.

By Geometry, we have

$$AB^2 = BC^2 + CA^2 + 2BC \cdot CD \quad \text{...(ii)}$$

But $$\frac{CD}{CA} = \cos ACD = \cos(180° - C) = -\cos C \quad \text{(Art. 72)}$$

so that $$CD = -b\cos C$$

Hence, (ii) becomes

$$c^2 = a^2 + b^2 + 2a(-b\cos C) = a^2 + b^2 - 2ab\cos C$$

so that, as in the first case, we have

$$\cos C = \frac{a^2 + b^2 - c^2}{2ab}$$

In a similar manner it may be shown that

$$\boldsymbol{\cos A = \frac{b^2 + c^2 - a^2}{2bc}}$$

and $$\cos B = \frac{c^2 + a^2 - b^2}{2ca}$$

If one of the angles, C, be a right angle, the above formula would give $c^2 = a^2 + b^2$ so that $\cos C = 0$. This is correct, since C is a right angle.

The above formula is therefore true for all values of C.

EXAMPLE $a = 15$, $b = 36$, and $c = 39$

then $$\cos A = \frac{36^2 + 39^2 - 15^2}{2 \times 36 \times 39} = \frac{3^2(12^2 + 13^2 - 5^2)}{2 \times 3^2 \times 12 \times 13} = \frac{288}{24 \times 13} = \frac{12}{13}.$$

➤ **165.** *To find the sines of half the angles in terms of the sides.*

In any triangle we have, by Art. 164,

$$\cos A = \frac{b^2 + c^2 - a^2}{2bc}$$

By Art. 109, we have

$$\cos A = 1 - 2\sin^2\frac{A}{2}$$

Hence, $$2\sin^2\frac{A}{2} = 1 - \cos A = 1 - \frac{b^2 + c^2 - a^2}{2bc}$$

$$= \frac{2bc - b^2 - c^2 + a^2}{2bc} = \frac{a^2 - (b^2 + c^2 - 2bc)}{2bc} = \frac{a^2 - (b - c)^2}{2bc}$$

$$= \frac{[a + (b - c)][a - (b - c)]}{2bc} = \frac{(a + b - c)(a - b + c)}{2bc} \quad \text{...(1)}$$

Let $2s$ stand for $a + b + c$, so that s is equal to half the sum of the sides of the triangle, *i.e.*, s is equal to the semi-perimeter of the triangle.

We then have

$$a + b - c = a + b + c - 2c = 2s - 2c = 2(s - c)$$

and $$a - b + c = a + b + c - 2b = 2s - 2b = 2(s - b)$$

The relation (1) therefore, becomes

$$2\sin^2\frac{A}{2} = \frac{2(s-c)\times 2(s-b)}{2bc}$$

$$= 2\frac{(s-b)(s-c)}{bc}$$

$$\therefore \quad \sin\frac{A}{2} = \sqrt{\frac{(s-b)(s-c)}{bc}} \quad \text{...(2)}$$

Similarly,

$$\sin\frac{B}{2} = \sqrt{\frac{(s-c)(s-a)}{ca}}, \text{ and } \sin\frac{C}{2} = \sqrt{\frac{(s-a)(s-b)}{ab}}$$

➤ 166. *To find the cosines of half the angles in terms of the sides.*

By Art. 109, we have

$$\cos A = 2\cos^2\frac{A}{2} - 1$$

Hence, $$2\cos^2\frac{A}{2} = 1 + \cos A = 1 + \frac{b^2 + c^2 - a^2}{2bc}$$

$$= \frac{2bc + b^2 + c^2 - a^2}{2bc} = \frac{(b+c)^2 - a^2}{2bc}$$

$$= \frac{[(b+c)+a][(b+c)-a]}{2bc} = \frac{(a+b+c)(b+c-a)}{2bc} \quad \text{...(1)}$$

Now, $b + c - a = a + b + c - 2a = 2s - 2a = 2(s - a)$

so that (1) becomes

$$2\cos^2\frac{A}{2} = \frac{2s\times 2(s-a)}{2bc} = 2\frac{s(s-a)}{bc}$$

$$\therefore \quad \cos\frac{A}{2} = \sqrt{\frac{s(s-a)}{bc}} \quad \text{...(2)}$$

Similarly, $\cos\frac{B}{2} = \sqrt{\frac{s(s-b)}{ca}}$, and $\cos\frac{C}{2} = \sqrt{\frac{s(s-c)}{ab}}$

➤ 167. *To find the tangents of half the angles in term of the sides.*

Since, $$\tan\frac{A}{2} = \frac{\sin\frac{A}{2}}{\cos\frac{A}{2}}$$

we have, by (2) of Arts. 165 and 166.

$$\tan\frac{A}{2}=\sqrt{\frac{(s-b)(s-c)}{bc}}\div\sqrt{\frac{s(s-a)}{bc}}$$

$$=\sqrt{\frac{(s-b)(s-c)}{s(s-a)}}$$

Similarly, $\tan\frac{B}{2}=\sqrt{\frac{(s-c)(s-a)}{s(s-b)}}$

and $\tan\frac{C}{2}=\sqrt{\frac{(s-a)(s-b)}{s(s-c)}}$

Since, in a triangle, A is always $< 180°$, $\frac{A}{2}$ is always $< 90°$.

The sine, cosine, and tangent of $\frac{A}{2}$ are therefore always positive (Art. 52).

The positive sign must therefore always be prefixed to the radical sign in the formulae of this and the previous two articles.

168.

EXAMPLE *If* $a=13$, $b=14$ *and* $c=15$

then $s=\frac{13+14+15}{2}=21$, $s-a=8$, $s-b=7$ and $s-c=6$

Hence,
$$\sin\frac{A}{2}=\sqrt{\frac{7\times 6}{14\times 15}}=\frac{1}{\sqrt{5}}=\frac{1}{5}\sqrt{5}$$

$$\sin\frac{B}{2}=\sqrt{\frac{6\times 8}{15\times 13}}=\frac{4}{\sqrt{65}}=\frac{4}{65}\sqrt{65}$$

$$\cos\frac{C}{2}=\sqrt{\frac{21\times 6}{13\times 14}}=\frac{3}{\sqrt{13}}=\frac{3}{13}\sqrt{13}$$

and
$$\tan\frac{B}{2}=\sqrt{\frac{6\times 8}{21\times 7}}=\frac{4}{7}$$

169. *To express the sine of any angle of a triangle in terms of the sides.*

We have, by Art. 109,

$$\sin A=2\sin\frac{A}{2}\cos\frac{A}{2}$$

But, by the previous articles,

$$\sin\frac{A}{2}=\sqrt{\frac{(s-b)(s-c)}{bc}}\text{ and }\cos\frac{A}{2}=\sqrt{\frac{s(s-a)}{bc}}$$

Hence, $$\sin A = 2\sqrt{\frac{(s-b)(s-c)}{bc}} \cdot \sqrt{\frac{s(s-a)}{bc}}$$

$\therefore$ $$\mathbf{\sin A = \frac{2}{bc}\sqrt{s(s-a)(s-b)(s-c)}}$$

EXAMPLES XXVI

In a triangle

1. Given $a = 25$, $b = 52$ and $c = 63$
find $\tan\frac{A}{2}$, $\tan\frac{B}{2}$, and $\tan\frac{C}{2}$.

2. Given $a = 125$, $b = 123$, and $c = 62$
find the sines of half the angles and the sines of the angles.

3. Given $a = 18$, $b = 24$, and $c = 30$
find $\sin A$, $\sin B$, and $\sin C$.

4. Given $a = 35$, $b = 84$ and $c = 91$
find $\tan A$, $\tan B$, and $\tan C$.

5. Given $a = 13$, $b = 14$, and $c = 15$
find the sines of the angles. Verify by a graph.

6. Given $a = 287$, $b = 816$, and $c = 865$
find the values of $\tan\frac{A}{2}$ and $\tan A$.

7. Given $a = \sqrt{3}$, $b = \sqrt{2}$, and $c = \frac{\sqrt{6}+\sqrt{2}}{2}$
find the angles.

➤ **170.** *In any triangle, to prove that*

$$a = b\cos C + c\cos B$$

Take the figures of Art. 164.

In the first case, we have

$$\frac{BD}{BA} = \cos B, \text{ so that } BD = c\cos B$$

and $$\frac{CD}{CA} = \cos C, \text{ so that } CD = b\cos C$$

Hence, $$a = BC = BD + DC = c\cos B + b\cos C$$

In the second case, we have

$$\frac{BD}{BA} = \cos B, \text{ so that } BD = c\cos B$$

and $$\frac{CD}{CA} = \cos ACD = \cos(180° - C) = -\cos C \qquad \text{(Art. 72)}$$

so that $CD = -b\cos C$

Hence, in this case,

$$a = BC = BD - CD = c\cos B - (-b\cos C)$$

so that in each case

$$\boldsymbol{a = b\cos C + c\cos B}$$

Similarly, $\quad b = c\cos A + a\cos C$

and $\quad c = a\cos B + b\cos A$

➤ **171.** *In any triangle, to prove that*

$$\tan\frac{B-C}{2} = \frac{b-c}{b+c}\cot\frac{A}{2}.$$

In any triangle, we have

$$\frac{b}{c} = \frac{\sin B}{\sin C}$$

$$\therefore \quad \frac{b-c}{b+c} = \frac{\sin B - \sin C}{\sin B + \sin C} = \frac{2\cos\frac{B+C}{2}\sin\frac{B-C}{2}}{2\sin\frac{B+C}{2}\cos\frac{B-C}{2}}$$

$$= \frac{\tan\frac{B-C}{2}}{\tan\frac{B+C}{2}} = \frac{\tan\frac{B-C}{2}}{\tan\left(90^\circ - \frac{A}{2}\right)}$$

$$= \frac{\tan\frac{B-C}{2}}{\cot\frac{A}{2}} \qquad \text{(Art. 69)}$$

Hence, $\quad \boldsymbol{\tan\frac{B-C}{2} = \frac{b-c}{b+c}\cot\frac{A}{2}}$

➤ **172.**

EXAMPLE From the formulae of Art. 164 deduce those of Art. 170 and vice versa.

The first and third formulae of Art. 164 *give*.

$$b\cos C + c\cos B = \frac{a^2+b^2-c^2}{2a} + \frac{c^2+a^2-b^2}{2a} = \frac{2a^2}{2a} = a$$

so that $\quad a = b\cos C + c\cos B$

Similarly, the other formulae of Art. 170 may be obtained

Again, the three formulae of Art.170 give

$$a = b\cos C + c\cos B$$

$$b = c\cos A + a\cos C$$

and $\quad c = a\cos B + b\cos A$

Multiplying these in succession by a, b and $-c$ we have, by addition,

$$a^2+b^2-c^2 = a\,(b\cos C + c\cos B) + b\,(c\cos A + a\cos C) - c\,(a\cos B + b\cos A)$$
$$= 2ab\cos C$$

$$\therefore \qquad \cos C = \frac{a^2+b^2-c^2}{2ab}$$

Similarly, the other formulae of Art. 162 may be found.

➤ **173.** The student will often meet with identities, which he is required to prove, which involve both the sides and the angles of a triangle.

It is, in general, desirable in the identity to substitute for the sides in terms of the angles, or to substitute for the ratios of the angles in terms of the sides.

EXAMPLE 1 *Prove that* $a\cos\frac{B-C}{2} = (b+c)\sin\frac{A}{2}$.

By Art. 163, we have

$$\frac{b+c}{a} = \frac{\sin B + \sin C}{\sin A} = \frac{2\sin\frac{B+C}{2}\cos\frac{B-C}{2}}{2\sin\frac{A}{2}\cos\frac{A}{2}}$$

$$= \frac{\cos\frac{A}{2}\cos\frac{B-C}{2}}{\sin\frac{A}{2}\cos\frac{A}{2}} = \frac{\cos\frac{B-C}{2}}{\sin\frac{A}{2}}$$

$$\therefore \qquad (b+c)\sin\frac{A}{2} = a\cos\frac{B-C}{2}$$

EXAMPLE 2 *In any triangle prove that*

$$(b^2-c^2)\cot A + (c^2-a^2)\cot B + (a^2-b^2)\cot C = 0$$

By Art. 163, we have

$$\frac{\sin A}{a} = \frac{\sin B}{b} = \frac{\sin C}{c} = k \text{ (say)}$$

Hence, the given expression

$$= (b^2-c^2)\frac{\cos A}{ak} + (c^2-a^2)\frac{\cos B}{bk} + (a^2-b^2)\frac{\cos C}{ck}$$

$$= \frac{1}{k}\left[(b^2-c^2)\frac{b^2+c^2-a^2}{2abc} + (c^2-a^2)\frac{c^2+a^2-b^2}{2abc} + (a^2-b^2)\frac{a^2+b^2-c^2}{2abc}\right]$$

$$= \frac{1}{2abck}\,[b^4-c^4-a^2(b^2-c^2)+c^4-a^4-b^2(c^2-a^2)$$
$$+ a^4-b^4-c^2(a^2-b^2)]$$

$$= 0$$

EXAMPLE 3 *In any triangle prove that*

$$(a+b+c)\left(\tan\frac{A}{2}+\tan\frac{B}{2}\right)=2c\cot\frac{C}{2}$$

The left hand member

$$=2s\left[\sqrt{\frac{(s-b)(s-c)}{s(s-a)}}+\sqrt{\frac{(s-c)(s-a)}{s(s-b)}}\right]\text{by} \qquad \text{Art. } 167$$

$$=2s\sqrt{\frac{s-c}{s}}\left[\sqrt{\frac{s-b}{s-a}}+\sqrt{\frac{s-a}{s-b}}\right]=2\sqrt{s(s-c)}\left[\frac{s-b+s-a}{\sqrt{(s-a)(s-b)}}\right]$$

$$=\frac{2\sqrt{s(s-c)}\cdot c}{\sqrt{(s-a)(s-b)}} \text{ since } 2s=a+b+c$$

$$=2c\cot\frac{C}{2}$$

This identity may also be proved by substituting for the sides. We have, by Art. 163,

$$\frac{a+b+c}{c}=\frac{\sin A+\sin B+\sin C}{\sin C}$$

$$=\frac{4\cos\frac{A}{2}\cos\frac{B}{2}\cos\frac{C}{2}}{2\sin\frac{C}{2}\cos\frac{C}{2}}, \text{ as in Art. 127, } =\frac{2\cos\frac{A}{2}\cos\frac{B}{2}}{\sin\frac{C}{2}}$$

Also,

$$\frac{2\cot\frac{C}{2}}{\tan\frac{A}{2}+\tan\frac{B}{2}}=\frac{2\cos\frac{C}{2}\cos\frac{A}{2}\cos\frac{B}{2}}{\sin\frac{C}{2}\left[\sin\frac{A}{2}\cos\frac{B}{2}+\cos\frac{A}{2}\sin\frac{B}{2}\right]}$$

$$=\frac{2\cos\frac{A}{2}\cos\frac{B}{2}\cos\frac{C}{2}}{\sin\frac{C}{2}\sin\frac{A+B}{2}}=\frac{2\cos\frac{A}{2}\cos\frac{B}{2}}{\sin\frac{C}{2}} \qquad \text{(Art. 69)}$$

We have therefore,

$$\frac{a+b+c}{c}=\frac{2\cot\frac{C}{2}}{\tan\frac{A}{2}+\tan\frac{B}{2}}$$

so that $$(a+b+c)\left(\tan\frac{A}{2}+\tan\frac{B}{2}\right)=2c\cot\frac{C}{2}.$$

EXAMPLE 4 *If the sides of a triangle be in Arithmetical Progression, prove that so also are the cotangents of half the angles.*

We have given that $a+c=2b$ ...(1)

and we have to prove that

$$\cot\frac{A}{2}+\cot\frac{C}{2}=2\cot\frac{B}{2} \qquad ...(2)$$

Now, (2) is true if

$$\sqrt{\frac{s(s-a)}{(s-b)(s-c)}}+\sqrt{\frac{s(s-c)}{(s-a)(s-b)}}=2\sqrt{\frac{s(s-b)}{(s-c)(s-a)}}$$

or, by multiplying both sides by

$$\sqrt{\frac{(s-a)(s-b)(s-c)}{s}}$$

If $\quad (s-a)+(s-c)=2(s-b)$

i.e., $\quad 2s-(a+c)=2s-2b$

i.e., if $a+c=2b$, which is relation (1).

Hence, if relation (1) be true, so also is relation Eq. (2).

EXAMPLES XXVII

In any triangle ABC, prove that

1. $\sin\frac{B-C}{2}=\frac{b-c}{a}\cos\frac{A}{2}$

2. $b^2\sin 2C+c^2\sin 2B=2\,bc\sin A$

3. $a\,(b\cos C-c\cos B)=b^2-c^2$

4. $(b+c)\cos A+(c+a)\cos B+(a+b)\cos C=a+b+c$

5. $a\,(\cos B+\cos C)=2\,(b+c)\sin^2\frac{A}{2}$

6. $a(\cos C-\cos B)=2\,(b-c)\cos^2\frac{A}{2}$

7. $\frac{\sin(B-C)}{\sin(B+C)}=\frac{b^2-c^2}{a^2}$

8. $\frac{a+b}{a-b}=\tan\frac{A+B}{2}\cot\frac{A-B}{2}$

9. $a\sin\left(\frac{A}{2}+B\right)=(b+c)\sin\frac{A}{2}$

In any triangle ABC, prove that

10. $\frac{a^2\sin(B-C)}{\sin B+\sin C}+\frac{b^2\sin(C-A)}{\sin C+\sin A}+\frac{c^2\sin(A-B)}{\sin A+\sin B}=0$

11. $(b+c-a)\left(\cot\frac{B}{2}+\cot\frac{C}{2}\right)=2a\cot\frac{A}{2}$

12. $a^2+b^2+c^2=2\,(bc\cos A+ca\cos B+ab\cos C)$

13. $(a^2-b^2+c^2)\tan B=(a^2+b^2-c^2)\tan C$

14. $c^2 = (a-b)^2 \cos^2 \frac{C}{2} + (a+b)^2 \sin^2 \frac{C}{2}$

15. $a \sin(B-C) + b \sin(C-A) + c \sin(A-B) = 0$

16. $\frac{a \sin(B-C)}{b^2 - c^2} = \frac{b \sin(C-A)}{c^2 - a^2} = \frac{c \sin(A-B)}{a^2 - b^2}$

17. $a \sin \frac{A}{2} \sin \frac{B-C}{2} + b \sin \frac{B}{2} \sin \frac{C-A}{2} + c \sin \frac{C}{2} \sin \frac{A-B}{2} = 0$

18. $a^2(\cos^2 B - \cos^2 C) + b^2(\cos^2 C - \cos^2 A) + c^2(\cos^2 A - \cos^2 B) = 0$

19. $\frac{b^2 - c^2}{a^2} \sin 2A + \frac{c^2 - a^2}{b^2} \sin 2B + \frac{a^2 - b^2}{c^2} \sin 2C = 0$

20. $\frac{(a+b+c)^2}{a^2 + b^2 + c^2} = \frac{\cot \frac{A}{2} + \cot \frac{B}{2} + \cot \frac{C}{2}}{\cot A + \cot B + \cot C}$

21. $a^3 \cos(B-C) + b^3 \cos(C-A) + c^3 \cos(A-B) = 3abc$

22. In a triangle whose sides are 3, 4 and $\sqrt{38}$ metres respectively, prove that the largest angle is greater than 120°.

23. The sides of a right-angled triangle are 21 and 28 cm; find the length of the perpendiculars drawn to the hypotenuse from the right angle.

24. If in any triangle the angles be to one another as 1 : 2 : 3, prove that the corresponding sides are as $1 : \sqrt{3} : 2$.

25. In any triangle, if

$$\tan \frac{A}{2} = \frac{5}{6} \text{ and } \tan \frac{B}{2} = \frac{20}{37}$$

find $\tan \frac{C}{2}$, and prove that in this triangle $a + c = 2b$.

26. In an isosceles right-angled triangle a straight line is drawn from the middle point of one of the equal sides to the opposite angle. Show that it divides the angle into parts whose cotangents are 2 and 3.

27. The perpendicular *AD* to the base of a triangle *ABC* divides it into segments such that *BD*, *CD* and *AD* are in the ratio of 2, 3 and 6; prove that the vertical angle of the triangle is 45°.

28. A ring, 10 cm in diameter, is suspended from a point 12 cm above its centre by 6 equal strings attached to its circumference at equal intervals. Find the cosine of the angle between consecutive strings.

29. If a^2, b^2 and c^2 be in A.P. prove that $\cot A$, $\cot B$ and $\cot C$ are in A.P. also.

30. If a, b and c be in A.P. prove that $\cos A \cot \frac{A}{2}$, $\cos B \cot \frac{B}{2}$, and $\cos C \cot \frac{C}{2}$ are in A.P.

31. If a, b and c are in H.P. prove that $\sin^2\frac{A}{2}$, $\sin^2\frac{B}{2}$ and $\sin^2\frac{C}{2}$ are also in H.P.

32. The sides of a triangle are in A.P. and the greatest and least angles are θ and ϕ; prove that

$$4(1-\cos\theta)(1-\cos\phi)=\cos\theta+\cos\phi$$

33. The sides of a triangle are in A.P. and the greatest angle exceeds the least by 90°; prove that the sides are proportional to $\sqrt{7}+1$, $\sqrt{7}$ and $\sqrt{7}-1$.

34. If $C=60°$, then prove that

$$\frac{1}{a+c}+\frac{1}{b+c}=\frac{3}{a+b+c}$$

35. In any triangle ABC if D be any point of the base BC, such that $BD:DC::m:n$ and if $\angle BAD=\alpha$, $\angle DAC=\beta$, $\angle CDA=\theta$, and $AD=x$, prove that

$$(m+n)\cot\theta=m\cot\alpha-n\cot\beta$$
$$=n\cot B-m\cot C$$

and $$(m+n)^2:x^2=(m+n)(mb^2+nc^2)-mna^2$$

36. If in a triangle the bisector of the side c be perpendicular to the side d, prove that

$$2\tan A+\tan C=0$$

37. In any triangle prove that, if θ be any angle, then

$$b\cos\theta=c\cos(A-\theta)+a\cos(C+\theta)$$

38. If p and q be the perpendiculars from the angular points A and B on any line passing through the vertex C of the triangle ABC, then prove that

$$a^2p^2+b^2q^2-2abpq\cos C=a^2b^2\sin^2 C$$

39. In the triangle ABC, lines OA, OB and OC are drawn so that the angles OAB, OBC and OCA are each equal to ω; prove that

$$\cot\omega=\cot A+\cot B+\cot C$$

and $$\operatorname{cosec}^2\omega=\operatorname{cosec}^2 A+\operatorname{cosec}^2 B+\operatorname{cosec}^2 C.$$

13

SOLUTION OF TRIANGLES

➤ **174.** In any triangle the three sides and the three angles are often called the elements of the triangle. When any three elements of the triangle are given, provided they be not the three angles, the triangle is in general completely known, *i.e.,* its other angles and sides can be calculated. When the three angles are given, only the ratios of the lengths of the sides can be found, so that the traingle is given in *shape* only and not in *size.* When three elements of a triangle are given, the process of calculating its other three elements is called the **Solution of the Triangle.**

We shall first discuss the solution of right-angled triangles, *i.e.* triangles which have one angle given equal to a right angle.

The next four articles refer to such triangles, and C denotes the right angle.

➤ **175.** *Case I. Given the hypothenuse and one side, to solve the triangle.*

Let b the given side and c the given hypothenuse.

The angle B is given by the relation.

$$\sin B = \frac{b}{c}$$

$\therefore$ $$L \sin B = 10 + \log b - \log c$$

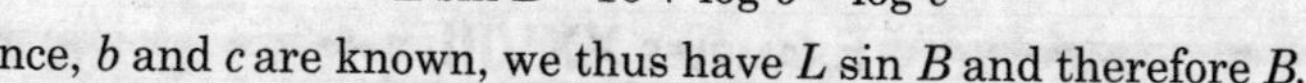

Since, b and c are known, we thus have $L \sin B$ and therefore B.

The angle A $(= 90° - B)$ is then known.

The side a is obtained from either of the relations

$$\cos B = \frac{a}{c}, \tan B = \frac{b}{a}, \text{or } a = \sqrt{(c-b)(c+b)}$$

➤ **176.** *Case II. Given the two sides a and b, to solve the triangle.*

Here B is given by

$$\tan B = \frac{b}{a}$$

so that $$L \tan B = 10 + \log b - \log a$$

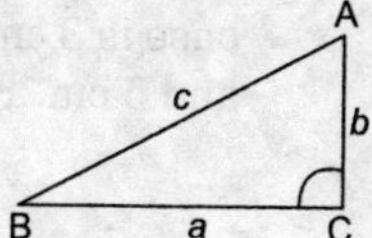

Hence, $L \tan B$, and therefore B, is known.

The angle A $(= 90° - B)$ is then known.

The hypothenuse c is given by the relation $c = \sqrt{a^2 + b^2}$

This relation is not however very suitable for logarithmic calculation, and c is best given by

$$\sin B = \frac{b}{c} \quad i.e., \quad c = \frac{b}{\sin B}$$

$$\therefore \qquad \log c = \log b - \log \sin B = 10 + \log b - L \sin B$$

Hence, c is obtained.

➤ **177.** *Case III. Given an angle B and one of the sides a, to solve the triangle.*

Here A $(= 90° - B)$ is known

The side b is found from the relation

$$\frac{b}{a} = \tan B$$

and c from the relation

$$\frac{a}{c} = \cos B$$

➤ **178.** *Case IV. Given an angle B and the hypothenuse c, to solve the triangle.*

Here A is known, and a and b are obtained from the relations

$$\frac{a}{c} = \cos B, \text{ and } \frac{b}{c} = \sin B$$

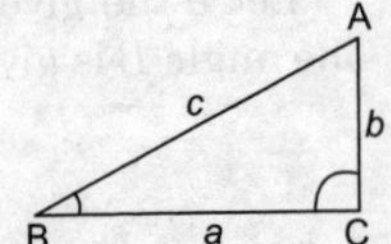

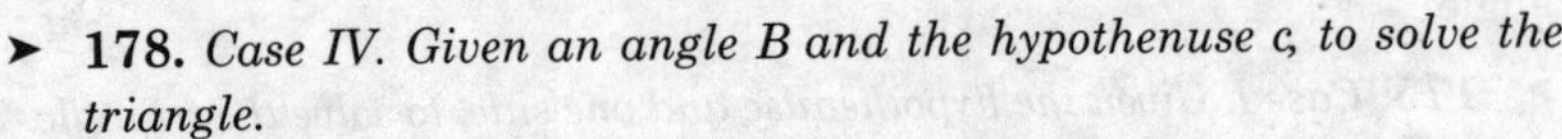

EXAMPLES XXVIII

1. In a right-angled triangle ABC, where C is the right angle, if $a = 50$ and $B = 75°$, find the sides. $(\tan 75° = 2 + \sqrt{3})$.
2. Solve the triangle of which two sides are equal to 10 and 20 cm and of which the included angle is 90°; given that $\log 20 = 1.30103$, and

$$L \tan 26° \, 33' = 9.6986847, \text{ duff, for } 1' = 3160$$

3. The length of the perpendicular from one angle of a triangle upon the base is 3 cm and the lengths of the sides containing this angle are 4 and 5 cm. Find the angles, having given

$$\log 2 = 0.30103, \log 3 = 0.4771213$$
$$L \sin 36° \, 52' = 9.7781186 \text{ diff. for } 1' = 1684$$

and $L \sin 48° 35' = 9.8750142$, diff. for $1' = 1115$

4. Find the acute angles of a right-angled triangle whose hypothenuse is four times as long as the perpendicular drawn to it from the opposite angle.

➤ **179.** We now proceed to the case of the triangle which is not given to be right-angled.

The different cases to be considered are :

Case I. The three sides given;

Case II. Two sides and the included angle given;

Case III. Two sides and the angle opposite one of them given;

Case IV. One side and two angles given;

Case V. The three angles given.

➤ **180.** *Case I. The three sides a, b and c given.*

Since the sides are known, the semi-perimeter s is known and hence also the quantities $s-a$, $s-b$, and $s-c$.

The half-angles $\frac{A}{2}$, $\frac{B}{2}$ and $\frac{C}{2}$ are then found from the formulae

$$\tan\frac{A}{2} = \sqrt{\frac{(s-b)(s-c)}{s(s-a)}}, \quad \tan\frac{B}{2} = \sqrt{\frac{(s-c)(s-a)}{s(s-b)}}$$

and
$$\tan\frac{C}{2} = \sqrt{\frac{(s-a)(s-b)}{s(s-c)}}$$

Only two of the angles need be found, the third being known since the sum of the three angles is always 180°.

The angles may also be found by using the formulae for the sine or cosine of the semi-angles.

(Arts. 165 and 166.)

The above formulae are all suited for logarithmic computation.

The angle A may also be obtained from the formula

$$\cos A = \frac{b^2 + c^2 - a^2}{2bc} \qquad \text{(Art.164)}$$

This formula is not, in general, suitable for logarithmic calculation. It may be conveniently used however when the sides a, b, and c are small numbers.

EXAMPLE *The sides of a triangle are* 32,40, *and* 66 *cm.; find the angle opposite the greatest side, by using the five-figure tables at the end of this book.*

Here $a = 32$, $b = 40$ and $c = 66$

so that $s = \dfrac{32 + 40 + 66}{2} = 69$, $s - a = 37$, $s - b = 29$, and $s - c = 3$

Hence, $$\cot \frac{C}{2} = \sqrt{\frac{s(s-c)}{(s-a)(s-b)}} = \sqrt{\frac{69 \times 3}{37 \times 9}}$$

$$\therefore \quad L \cot \frac{C}{2} = 10 + \frac{1}{2} [\log 3 + \log 69 - \log 37 - \log 29]$$

$$= 10 + \frac{1}{2} [0.47712 + 1.83885 - 1.56820 - 1.46240]$$

$$= 10 + 1.157985 - 1.51530$$

$$= 9.642685 \qquad \dots (1)$$

From page xxix of the tables, we have

$$L \cot 66° \, 10' = 9.64517 \qquad \dots (2)$$

and $$L \cot 66° \, 20' = 9.64175 \qquad \dots (3)$$

and hence we see that $\dfrac{C}{2}$ lies between 66°10′ and 66°20′.

Let then $$\frac{C}{2} = 66°10' + x'$$

For an *increase* of x' in the angle we see, from (1) and (2), that the *decrease* in the logarithm = 0.002485.

For an *increase* of 10′ of the angle we see, from (2) and (3), that the *decrease* in the logarithm = 0.00342.

Hence, $$\frac{x}{10} = \frac{0.002485}{0.00342} = \frac{2485}{3420}$$

$$\therefore \quad x' = 7\frac{91'}{342} = 7' \, 16'' \qquad \text{(nearly)}$$

$$\therefore \quad \frac{C}{2} = 66° \, 17' \, 16'', \text{ and hence } C = 132° \, 34' \, 32''$$

EXAMPLES XXIX

[The student should verify the results of some of the following examples (*e.g., Nos.* 1, 7, 8, 10, 11, 12) by an accurate graph.]

1. If the sides of a triangle be 56, 56, and 33 cm., find the greatest angle.
2. The sides of a triangle are 7, $4\sqrt{3}$, and $\sqrt{13}$ metres respectively. Find the number of degrees in its smallest angle.
3. The sides of a traingle are $x^2 + x + 1$, $2x + 1$, and $x^2 - 1$; prove that the greatest angle is 120°.
4. The sides of triangle are a, b, and $\sqrt{a^2 + ab + b^2}$ cm; find the greatest angle.
5. If $a = 2$, $b = \sqrt{6}$, and $c = \sqrt{3} - 1$, solve the triangle.

6. If $a = 2, b = \sqrt{6}$, and $c = \sqrt{3} + 1$, solve the triangle.

7. If $a = 9, b = 10$, and $c = 11$, find B, given

$$\log 2 = 0.30103, L \tan 29°29' = 9.7523472$$

and $\tan 29° 30' = 9.7526420$

8. The sides of a triangle are 130, 123, and 77 cm. Find the greatest angle, having given

$$\log 2 = 0.30103, L \tan 38°39' = 9.9029376$$

and $L \tan 38° 40' = 9.9031966$

9. Find the greatest angle of a triangle whose sides are 242, 188, and 270 cm, having given

$$\log 2 = 0.30103, \log 3 = 0.4771213, \log 7 = 0.8450980$$

$$L \tan 38° 20' = 9.8980104 \text{ and } L \tan 38° 19' = 9.8977507.$$

10. The sides of a triangle are 2, 3, and 4; find the greatest angle, having given

$$\log 2 = 0.30103, \log 3 = 0.4771213$$

$$L \tan 52° 14' = 10.1108395$$

and $L \tan 52° 15' = 10.1111004$

Making use of the tables, find all the angles when

11. $a = 25, b = 26$, and $c = 27$

12. $a = 17, b = 20$, and $c = 27$

13. $a = 2000, b = 1050$, and $c = 1150$

➤ **181.** *Case II. Given* two sides b and c and the included angle A. Taking b to be the greater of the two given sides , we have

$$\tan \frac{B - C}{2} = \frac{b - c}{b - c} \cot \frac{A}{2} \qquad \text{(Art. 171)} \quad ...(1)$$

and $$\frac{B + C}{2} = 90° - \frac{A}{2} \qquad ...(2)$$

These two relations give us

$$\frac{B - C}{2} \text{ and } \frac{B + C}{2}$$

and therefore, by addition and subtraction, B and C.

The third side a is then known from the relation

$$\frac{a}{\sin A} = \frac{b}{\sin B}$$

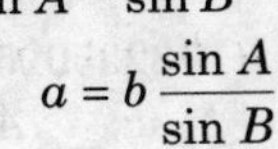

which gives, $$a = b\frac{\sin A}{\sin B}$$

and thus determines a.

The side a may also be found from the formula

$$a^2 = b^2 + c^2 - 2bc \cos A$$

This is not adapted to logarithmic calculation but is sometimes useful, especially when the sides a and b are small numbers.

➤ 182.

EXAMPLE 1 If $b = \sqrt{3}$ $c = 1$ and $A = 30°$, *solve the triangle.*

We have $\tan \dfrac{B-C}{2} = \dfrac{b-c}{b+c} \cot \dfrac{A}{2} = \dfrac{\sqrt{3}-1}{\sqrt{3}+1} \cot 15°$

Now, $\tan 15° = \dfrac{\sqrt{3}-1}{\sqrt{3}+1}$ (Art. 101)

so that, $\cot 15° = \dfrac{\sqrt{3}+1}{\sqrt{3}-1}$

Hence, $\tan \dfrac{B-C}{2} = 1$

$\therefore \quad \dfrac{B-C}{2} = 45°$ ...(1)

Also, $\dfrac{B+C}{2} = 90° - \dfrac{A}{2} = 90° - 15° = 75°$ ...(2)

By addition, $B = 120°$

By subtraction, $C = 30°$

Since, $A = C$, we have $a = c = 1$

Otherwise. We have

$$a^2 = b^2 + c^2 - 2bc \cos A = 3 + 1 - 2\sqrt{3} \cdot \frac{\sqrt{3}}{2} = 1$$

so that $a = 1 = c$

$\therefore \quad C = A = 30°$

and $B = 180° - A - C = 120°$

EXAMPLE 2 *If* $b = 215$, $c = 105$, *and* $A = 74° 27'$, *find the remaining angles and also the third side a, having given*

$$\log 2 = 0.3010300, \log 11 = 1.0413927$$

$$\log 105 = 2.0211893, \log 212.476 = 2.3273103$$

$$L \cot 37° 13' = 10.1194723, \text{ diff. for } 1' = 2622$$

$$L \tan 24° 20' = 9.6553477, \text{ diff. for } 1' = 3364$$

$$L \sin 74° - 27' = 9.9838052$$

and $L \operatorname{cosec} 28° 25' = 10.3225025$, diff. for $1' = 2334$

Here, $\tan \dfrac{B-C}{2} = \dfrac{b-c}{b+c} \cot \dfrac{A}{2} = \dfrac{11}{32} \cot 37° 13' 30''$

Now, $L \cot 37°13' = 10.1194723$

diff. for $30'' = -0.1311$

$\therefore$ $L \cot 37° 13' 30'' = 10.1193412$

$\log 11 = 1.0413927$

11.1607339

$\log 32 = 1.50515$

$\therefore$ $L \tan \frac{1}{2}(B - C) = 9.6555839$

But $L \tan 24° 20' = 9.6553477$

diff. $= 2362$

$= \text{diff. for } \frac{2362}{3364} \text{ of } 60''$

$= \text{diff. for } 42.1''$

$\therefore$ $\frac{B - C}{2} = 24° 20' 42''$

But $\frac{B + C}{2} = 90° - \frac{A}{2} = 52° 46' 30''$

$\therefore$ by addition, $B = 77° 7' 12''$

and by subtraction $C = 28° 25' 48''$

Again, $\frac{a}{\sin A} = \frac{c}{\sin C} = c \operatorname{cosec} C$

$\therefore$ $a = 105 \sin 74° 27' \operatorname{cosec} 28° 25' 48'$

But $L \operatorname{cosec} 28° 25' = 10.3225025$

diff. for $48'' = -0.1867$

$L \operatorname{cosec} 28° 25' 48'' = 10.3223158$

$L \sin 74° 27' = 9.9838052$

$\log 105 = 2.0211893$

22.3273103

20

$\therefore$ $\log a = 2.3273103$

$\mathbf{a = 212.476}$

$$\begin{array}{r} .30103 \\ 5 \\ \hline 1.50515 \end{array}$$

$$\begin{array}{r} 2362 \\ 60 \\ \hline 3364)141720(42.1 \\ 13456 \\ \hline 7160 \\ 6728 \\ \hline 4320 \end{array}$$

$\frac{48}{60} \times 2334$

$= \frac{4}{5} \times 2334$

$= 1867.$

➤ **183.** There are ways of finding the third side a of the triangle in the previous case without first finding the angles B and C.

Two methods are as follows:

(1) Since, $a^2 = b^2 + c^2 - 2bc \cos A$

$$= b^2 + c^2 - 2bc\left(2 \cos^2 \frac{A}{2} - 1\right)$$

$$= (b + c)^2 - 4bc\cos^2\frac{A}{2}$$

$$\therefore \qquad a^2 = (b + c)^2\left[1 - \frac{4bc}{(b + c)^2}\cos^2\frac{A}{2}\right]$$

Hence, if $\qquad \sin^2\theta = \dfrac{4bc}{(b + c)^2}\cos^2\dfrac{A}{2}$

We have $\qquad a^2 = (b + c)^2\,[1 - \sin^2\theta] = (b + c)^2\cos^2\theta$

If then $\sin\theta$ be calculated from the relation

$$\sin\theta = \frac{2\sqrt{bc}}{b + c}\cos\frac{A}{2}$$

we have $\qquad a = (b + c)\cos\theta$

(2) We have

$$a^2 = b^2 + c^2 - 2bc\cos A = b^2 + c^2 - 2bc\left(1 - 2\sin^2\frac{A}{2}\right)$$

$$= (b - c)^2 + 4bc\sin^2\frac{A}{2}$$

$$= (b - c)^2\left[1 + \frac{4bc}{(b - c)^2}\sin^2\frac{A}{2}\right]$$

Let $\qquad \dfrac{4bc}{(b - c)^2}\sin^2\dfrac{A}{2} = \tan^2\phi$

so that $\qquad \tan\phi = \dfrac{2\sqrt{bc}}{b - c}\sin\dfrac{A}{2}$

and hence ϕ is known

Then, $\qquad a^2 = (b - c)^2\,[1 + \tan^2\phi] = \dfrac{(b - c)^2}{\cos^2\phi}$

so that $\qquad a = (b - c)\sec\phi$

and is therefore easily found

An angle, such as θ or ϕ above, introduced for the purpose of facilitating calculation is called a subsidiary angle (Art. 129).

EXAMPLES XXX

[*The student should verify the results of some of the following examples (e.g.* Nos. 4, 5, 6, 11*) by an accurate graph.*]

1. If $b = 90$, $c = 70$, and $A = 72°\,48'\,30''$, find B and C, given

$$\log 2 = 0.30103,\ L\cot 36°\,24'15'' = 10.1323111$$

$$L\tan 9°\,37' = 9.2290071$$

and $\qquad L\tan 9°\,38' = 9.2297735$

2. If $a = 21$, $b = 11$, and $C = 34°42'\ 30''$, find A and B give

$$\log 2 = 0.30103$$

and $\quad L \tan 72°38'45'' = 10.50515$

3. If the angles of a triangle be in A.P. and the lengths of the greatest and least sides be 24 and 16 cm respectively, find the length of the third side and the angles, given

$$\log 2 = 0.30103, \log 3 = 0.4771213$$

and $\quad L \tan 19°\ 6' = 9.5394287$, diff. for $1' = 4084$

4. If $a = 13$, $b = 7$, and $C = 60°$, find A and B given that

$$\log 3 = 0.4771213$$

and $L \tan 27°27' = 9.7155508$, diff. for $1' = 3087$

5. If $a = 2b$, and $C = 120°$, find the values of A, B, and the ratio of c to a, given that

$$\log 3 = 0.4771213$$

and $L \tan 10°53' = 9.2837070$, diff. for $1' = 6808$

6. If $b = 14$, $c = 11$, and $A = 60°$ find B and C given that

$$\log 2 = 0.30103, \log 3 = 0.4771213$$

$$L \tan 11°\ 44' = 9.3174299$$

and $\quad L \tan 11°\ 45' = 9.3180640$

7. The two sides of a triangle are 540 and 420 metres long respectively and include an angle of $52°\ 6'$. Find the remaining angles, given that

$$\log 2 = 0.30103, L \tan 26°3' = 9.6891430$$

$$L \tan 14°20' = 9.4074189$$

and $\quad L \tan 14°\ 21' = 9.4079453$

8. If $b = 2\frac{1}{2}$ cm, $c = 2$ cm, and $A = 22°\ 20'$, find the other angles, and show that the third side is nearly one cm., given

$$\log 2 = 0.30103, \log 3 = 0.47712$$

$$L \cot 11°\ 10' = 10.70465, L \sin 22°20' = 9.57977$$

$$L \tan 29°\ 22'\ 20'' = 9.75038, L \tan 29°\ 22'\ 30'' = 9.75043$$

and $L \sin 49°\ 27'\ 34' = 9.88079$

9. If $a = 2$, $b = 1 + \sqrt{3}$, and $C = 60°$, solve the triangle.

10. Two sides of a triangle are $\sqrt{3} + 1$ and $\sqrt{3} - 1$, and the included angle is 60°; find the other side and angles.

11. If $b = 1$, $c = \sqrt{3} - 1$, and $A = 60°$, find the length of the side a.

12. If $b = 91$, $c = 125$, and $\tan \dfrac{A}{2} = \dfrac{17}{6}$, prove that $a = 204$.

13. If $a = 5$, $b = 4$, and $\cos (A - B) = \dfrac{31}{32}$, prove that the third side c will be 6.

14. One angle of a triangle is 30° and the lengths of the sides adjacent to it are 40 and $40\sqrt{3}$ metres. Find the length of the third side and the number of degrees in the other angles.

15. The sides of triangle are 9 and 3, and the difference of the angles opposite to them is 90°. Find the base and the angles, having given.

$$\log 2 = 0.30103,\ \log 3 = 0.4771213$$

$$\log 75894 = 4.8802074,\ \log 75895 = 4.8802132,$$

$$L\tan 26°33' = 9.6986847 \text{ and } L\tan 26°\,34' = 9.6990006$$

16. If $\tan\phi = \dfrac{a-b}{a+A}\cot\dfrac{C}{2}$ prove that, $c = (a+b)\dfrac{\sin\dfrac{C}{2}}{\cos\phi}$

If $a = 3$, $b = 1$ and $C = 53°7'48''$, find c without getting A and B, given

$$\log 2 = 0.30103,\ \log 25298 = 4.4030862$$

$$\log 25299 = 4.4031034,\ L\cos 26°\,33'\,54'' = 9.9515452$$

and $$L\tan 26°\,33'\,54'' = 9.6989700$$

17. Two sides of a triangle are 237 and 158 cm. and the contained angle is 66° 40′; find the base and the other angles, having given

$$\log 2 = 0.30103,\ \log 79 = 1.89763$$

$$\log 22687 = 4.35578,\ L\cot 33°\,20' = 10.18197$$

$$L\sin 33°\,20' = 9.73998,\ L\tan 16°\,54' = 9.48262$$

$$L\tan 16°\,55' = 9.48308,\ L\sec 16°\,54' = 10.01917$$

and $$L\sec 16°\,55' = 10.01921$$

[Use the formula $\cos\dfrac{B-C}{2} = \dfrac{b+c}{a}\sin\dfrac{A}{2}$]

In the following four examples, the required logarithms must be taken from the tables.

18. If $a = 242.5$, $b = 164.3$, and $C = 54°36'$, solve the triangle.

19. If $b = 130$, $c = 63$, and $A = 42°\,15'30''$, solve the triangle.

20. Two sides of a triangle being 2265.4 and 1779 cm., and the including angle 58°17′, find the remaining angles.

21. Two sides of a triangle being 237.09 and 130.96 cm., and the included angle 57°59′, find the remaining angles.

➤ **184.** *Case III. Given* two sides b and c and the angle B opposite to *one of them.*

The angle C is given by the relation

$$\frac{\sin C}{c} = \frac{\sin B}{b}$$

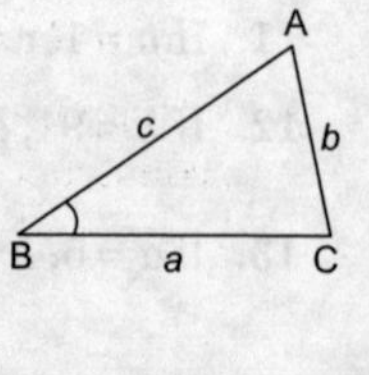

i.e. $$\sin C = \frac{c}{b}\sin B \qquad \ldots(1)$$

Taking logarithms, we determine C, and then A $(=180° - B - C)$ is found.

The remaining side a is then found from the relation

$$\frac{a}{\sin A} = \frac{b}{\sin B}$$

i.e., $$a = b\frac{\sin A}{\sin B} \qquad ...(2)$$

➤ **185.** The Eq. (1) of the previous article gives in some cases no value, in some cases one, and sometimes two values for C.

First, let B be an acute angle.

(α) If $b < c \sin B$, the right-hand member of (1) is greater than unity, and hence there is no corresponding values for C.

(β) If $b = c \sin B$, the right-hand member of (1) is equal to unity and the corresponding value of C is 90°.

(γ) If $b > c \sin B$, there are two values of C having $\frac{c \sin B}{b}$ as its sine, one value lying between 0° and 90° and the other between 90° and 180°.

Both of these values are not however always admissible.

For if $b > c$, then $B > C$. The obtuse-angled value of C is now not admissible; for, in this case, C cannot be obtuse unless B is obtuse also and it is manifestly impossible to have two obtuse angles in a triangle.

If $b < c$ and B is an acute angle, both values of C are admissible. Hence there are two values found for A, and hence the relation (2) gives two values for a. In this case there are therefore two triangles satisfying the given conditions.

Secondly, let B be an obtuse angle.

If b is < or = c, then B would be less than, or equal to, C, so that C, would be an obtuse angle. The triangle would then be impossible.

If b is > c, the acute value of C, as deterinimed from (1) would be admissible, but not the obtuse value. We should therefore only have one admissible solution.

Since, for some values of b, c and B, there is a doubt or ambiguity in the determination of the triangle, this case is called the **Ambiguous Case** of the solution of triangles.

➤ **186.** The Ambiguous Case may also be discussed in a geometrical manner.

Suppose we were given the elements b, c, and B, and that we proceeded to construct, or attempted to construct, the triangle.

We first measure an angle ABD equal to the given angle B.

We then measure along BA a distance BA equal to the given distance c, and thus determine the angular point A.

We have now to find a third point C, which must lie on BD and must also be such that its distance from A shall be equal to b.

To obtain it, we describe with centre A a circle whose radius is b.

The point or points, if any, in which this circle meets BD will determine the position of C.

Draw AD perpendicular to BD, so that

$$AD = AB \sin B = c \sin B$$

One of the following events will happen.

The circle may not reach BD (Fig. 1) or it may touch BD (Fig. 2), or it may meet BD in two points C_1 and C_2 (Figs. 3 and 4)

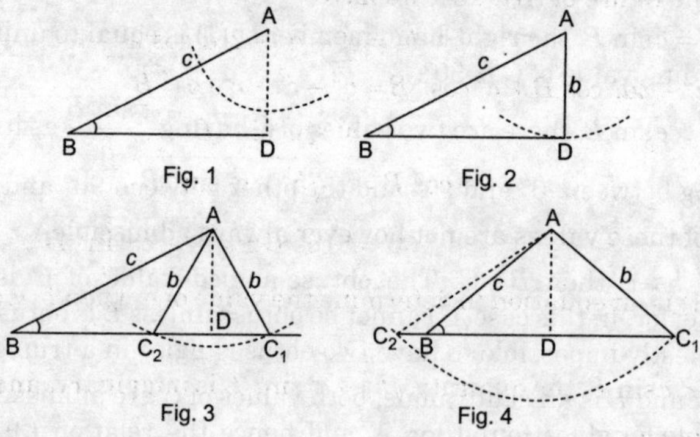

Fig. 1 Fig. 2 Fig. 3 Fig. 4

In the case of Fig. 1, it is clear that there is no triangle satisfying the given condition.

Here, $b < AD$ *i.e.*; $< c \sin B$

In the case of fig. 2 there is one triangle ABD which is right angled at D

Here, $b = AD = c \sin B$

In the case of Fig. 3, there are two triangles ABC_1 and ABC_2. Here b lies in magnitude between AD and c, *i.e.*, b is $> c \sin B$ and $< c$.

In the case of Fig. 4, there is only one triangle ABC_1 satisfying the given conditions [the triangle ABC_2 is inadmissible, for its angle at B is not equal to B but is equal to $180° - B$].

Here b is greater than both $c \sin B$ and c.

In the case when B is obtuse, the proper figures should be drawn. It will then be seen that when $b < c$ there is no triangle (for in the corresponding triangles ABC_1 and ABC_2 the angle at B will be $180° - B$ and not B). If $b > c$, it will be seen that there is one triangle, and only one, satisfying the given conditions.

To sum up : Given the elements b, c, and B of a triangle.

(α) If b is $< c \sin B$, there is no triangle.

(β) If $b = c \sin B$ and B is acute, there is one triangle right-angled.

(γ) If b is $> c \sin B$ and $< c$ and B is acute, there are two triangles satisfying the given conditions.

(δ) If b is $< c$, there is only one triangle.

Clearly, if $b = c$, the points B and C_2 in Fig. 3 coincide and there is only one triangle.

(ε) If B is obtuse, there is no triangle except when $b > c$.

➤ **187.** The ambiguous case may also be considered algebraically as follows.

From the figure of Art. 184, we have

$$b^2 = c^2 + a^2 - 2ca \cos B$$

$$\therefore \quad a^2 - 2ac \cos B + c^2 \cos^2 B = b^2 - c^2 + c^2 \cos^2 B$$

$$= b^2 - c^2 \sin^2 B$$

$$\therefore \quad a - c \cos B = \pm \sqrt{b^2 - c^2 \sin^2 B}$$

i.e.
$$a = c \cos B \pm \sqrt{b^2 - c^2 \sin^2 B} \qquad ...(1)$$

Now, (1) is an equation to determine the value of a when b, c, and B are given.

(α) If $b < c \sin B$, the quantity $\sqrt{b^2 - c^2 \sin^2 B}$ is imaginary, and (1) gives no real value for a.

(β) If $b = c \sin B$, there is only one value, $c \cos B$, for a; there is thus only one triangle which is right angled.

(γ) If $b > c \sin B$, there are two values for a. But, since a must be positive, the value obtained by taking the lower sign affixed to the radical is inadmissible unless.

$$c \cos B - \sqrt{b^2 - c^2 \sin^2 B} \text{ is positive,}$$

i.e., unless
$$\sqrt{b^2 - c^2 \sin^2 B} < c \cos B$$

i.e., unless
$$b^2 - c^2 \sin^2 B < c^2 \cos^2 B$$

i.e., unless
$$b^2 < c^2$$

There are therefore two triangles only when b is $> c \sin B$ and at the same time $< c$.

(δ) If B is an obtuse angle, then $c \cos B$ is negative, and one value of a is always negative and the corresponding triangle impossible.

The other value will be positive only when

$$c \cos B + \sqrt{b^2 - c^2 \sin^2 B} \text{ is positive}$$

i.e. only when $\sqrt{b^2 - c^2 \sin^2 B} > -c \cos B$

i.e. only when $b^2 > c^2 \sin^2 B + c^2 \cos^2 B$

i.e. only when $b > c$

Hence B, being obtuse, there is not triangle if $b < c$, and only one triangle when $b > c$.

➤ **188.**

EXAMPLE Given $b = 16, c = 25$, and $B = 33°15'$, *prove that the triangle is ambiguous and find the other angles, using the five-figure tables at the end of this book.*

We have

$$\sin C = \frac{c}{b} \sin B = \frac{25}{6} \sin B = \frac{100}{64} \sin B = \frac{10^2}{2^6} \sin 33°15'$$

Hence $\quad L \sin C = 2 + L \sin 33°15' - 6 \log 2$

$$= 2 + 9.73901 - 1.80618$$

$$= 9.93283$$

From the tables on page xxxvi we see that this lies between $L \sin 58° 50'$ and $L \sin 59°$. We thus have

$$\begin{array}{ll} L \sin C = 9.93283 & L \sin 59° = 9.93307 \\ \underline{L \sin 58° 50' = 9.93230} & \underline{L \sin 58°50' = 9.93230} \\ \text{Diff.} = 0.00053 & \text{Diff. for } 10' = 0.00077 \end{array}$$

$\therefore \quad$ angular diff. $= \frac{53}{77} \times 10'$

$$= 6'53'' \text{ nearly}$$

$\therefore \quad C = 58° 56' 53''$ or $180° - 58° 56' 53''$

Hence (Fig. 3, Art. 186) we have

$$C_1 = 58° 56' 53''$$

and $\quad C_2 = 121° 3'7''$

$\therefore \quad \angle BAC_1 = 180° - 33°15' - 58°56'53'' = 87° 48'7''$

and $\quad \angle BAX_2 = 180° - 33°15' - 121° 3'7'' = 25° 41' 53''$

If we had used seven-figure tables we should have obtained the more accurate results, $C_1 = 58° 56' 5''$ and $C_2 = 121° 3' 4''$.

EXAMPLES XXXI

[*The student should verify the results of some of the following examples (e.g., Nos.* 3, 5, 6, 8, 9, 10, 12, 13) by an accurate graph.]

1. If $a = 5$, $b = 7$ and $\sin A = \frac{3}{4}$, is three any ambiguity?

2. If $a = 2$, $c = \sqrt{3} + 1$, and $A = 45°$, solve the triangle.

3. If $a = 100$, $c = 100\sqrt{2}$ and $A = 30°$, solve the triangle.

4. If $2b = 3a$, and $\tan^2 A = \frac{3}{5}$, prove that there are two values to the third side, one of which is double the other.

5. If $A = 30°$, $b = 8$, and $a = 6$, find c.

6. Give $B = 30°$, $c = 150$, and $b = 50\sqrt{3}$, prove that of the two triangles which satisfy the data one will be isosceles and the other right angled. Find the greater value of the third side.

Would the solution have been ambiguous had

$$B = 30°, c = 150, \text{and } b = 75?$$

7. In the ambiguous case, given a, b, and A, prove that the difference between the two values of c is $2\sqrt{a^2 - b^2 \sin^2 A}$.

8. If $a = 5$, $b = 4$, and $A = 45°$, find the other angles, having given

$$\log 2 = 0.30103, L \sin 34° 26' = 9.7523919$$

and $$L \sin 34°27' = 9.7525761.$$

9. If $a = 9$, $b = 12$, and $A = 30°$, find c, having given

$$\log 2 = 0.30103, \quad \log 3 = 0.47712$$

$$\log 171 = 2.23301, \quad \log 368 = 2.56635$$

$$L \sin 11° 48'39'' = 9.31108, L \sin 41° 48' 39'' = 9.82391$$

and $$L \sin 108° 11' 21'' = 9.97774$$

10. Point out whether or no the solutions of the following triangles are ambiguous.

Find the smaller value of the third side in the ambiguous case and the other angles in both cases.

(1) $A = 30°$, $c = 250$ metres, and $a = 125$ metres;

(2) $A = 30°$, $c = 250$ metres, and $a = 200$ metres.

Given $\log 2 = 0.30103$, $\log 6.03893 = 0.7809601$

$$L \sin 38°41' = 9.7958800 \quad \text{and} \quad L \sin 8° 41' = 9.1789001$$

11. Given $a = 250$, $b = 240$, and $A = 72°4',48''$, find the angles B and C, and state whether they can have more than one value, given

$$\log 2.5 = 0.3979400, \log 2.4 = 0.3802112$$

$$L \sin 72° 4' = 9.9783702, L \sin 72°5' = 9.9784111$$

and $$L \sin 65° 59' = 9.9606739.$$

12. Two straight roads intersect at an angle of 30°; from the point of junction two pedestrians A and B start at the same time, A walking along one road at the rate of 5 km per hour and B walking uniformly along the other road. At the end of 3 hours they are 9 km. apart. Show that there are two rates at which B may walk to fulfil this condition and find them.

In the following three examples the required logarithms must be taken from the tables.

13. Two sides of a triangle are 1015 cm. and 732 cm., and the angle opposite the latter side is 40°; find the angle opposite the former and prove that more than one value is admissible.

14. Two sides of a triangle being 5374.5 and 18586.6 metres, and the angle opposite the latter being 15°11′, calculate the other angles of the triangle or triangles.

15. Given $A = 10°$, $a = 2308.7$, and $b = 7903.2$, find the smaller value of c.

➤ 189. *Case IV. Given one side and two angles, viz. a, B, and C.*

Since, the three angles of a triangle are together equal to two right angles, the third angles is given also.

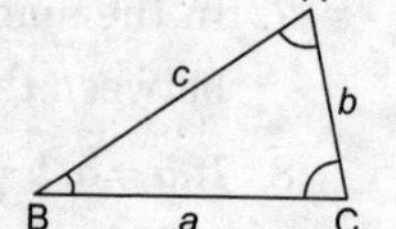

The sides b and c are now obtained from the relations

$$\frac{b}{\sin B} = \frac{c}{\sin C} = \frac{a}{\sin A}$$

giving, $$b = a\frac{\sin B}{\sin A}$$

and $$c = a\frac{\sin C}{\sin A}$$

➤ 190. *Case V.* The three angles A, B and C given.

Here the ratios only of the sides can be determined by the formula

$$\frac{a}{\sin A} = \frac{b}{\sin B} = \frac{c}{\sin C}$$

Their absolute magnitudes cannot be found.

EXAMPLES XXXII

1. If $\cos A = \frac{17}{22}$ and $\cos C = \frac{1}{14}$, find the ratio of $a : b : c$.

2. The angles of a triangle are as 1 : 2: 7; prove that the ratio of the greatest side to the least side is $\sqrt{5} + 1 : \sqrt{5} - 1$.

3. If $A = 45°$, $B = 75°$, and $C = 60°$, prove that $a + c\sqrt{2} = 2b$.

4. Two angles of a triangles are 41°13′22″ and 71°19′5″ and the side opposite the first angles is 55; find the side opposite the latter angle, given

$$\log 55 = 1.7403627, \log 79063 = 4.8979775$$

$$L \sin 41°13'22'' = 9.8188779$$

and $$L \sin 71°\,19'\,5'' = 9.9764927$$

5. From each of two ships, one km. apart, the angle is observed which is subtended by the other ship and a beacon on shore; these angles are found to be 52° 25′15″ and 75° 9′ 30″ respectively. Given

$$L \sin 75°\,9'\,30'' = 9.9852635$$

$$L \sin 52°25'15'' = 9.8990055, \log 1.2197 = 0.0862530$$

and $$\log 1.2198 = 0.0862886,$$

find the distance of the beacon from each of the ships.

6. The base angles of a triangle are $22\frac{1}{2}°$ and $112\frac{1}{2}°$; prove that the base is equal to twice the height.

For the following five examples the required logarithms must be *taken from the tables.*

7. The base of a triangle being 7 cm. and the base angles 129° 23′ and 38° 36′, find the length of its shorter side.

8. If the angles of a triangle be as 5:10:21, and the side opposite the smaller angle be 3 cm., find the other sides.

9. The angles of a triangle being 150°, 18° 20′, and 11° 40′, and the longest side being 10 metres, find the length of the shortest side.

10. To get the distance of a point *A* from a point *B*, a line *BC* and the angles *ABC* and *BCA* are measured, and are found to be 287 metres and 55°32′10″ and 51°8′20″ respectively. Find the distance *AB*.

11. To find the distance from *A* to *P* a distance, *AB*, of 1 km is measured in a convenient direction. At *A* the angle *PAB* is found to be 41°18′ and at *B* the angle *PBA* is found to be 114°38′. What is the required distance to the nearest metre?

14

HEIGHTS AND DISTANCES

➤ **191.** In the present chapter we shall consider some questions of the kind which occur in land-surveying. Simple questions of this kind have already been considered in Chapter 3.

➤ **192.** *To find the height of an inaccessible tower by means of observations made at distant points.*

Suppose PQ to be the tower and that the ground passing through the foot Q of the tower is horizontal. At a point A on this ground measure the angle of elevation α of the top of the tower.

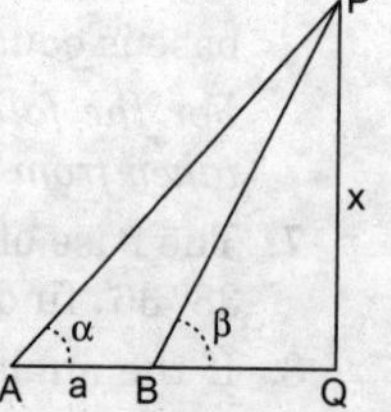

Measure off a distance $AB\ (= a)$ from A directly toward the foot of the tower, and at B measure the angle of elevation β.

To find the unknown height x of the tower, we have to connect it with the measured length a. This is best done as follows :

From the triangle PBQ, we have

$$\frac{x}{BP} = \sin\beta \qquad \text{...(1)}$$

and, from the triangle PAB, we have

$$\frac{PB}{a} = \frac{\sin PAB}{\sin BPA} = \frac{\sin\alpha}{\sin(\beta-\alpha)} \qquad \text{...(2)}$$

since, $\qquad \angle BPA = \angle QBP - \angle QAP = \beta - \alpha$

From (1) and (2), by multiplication, we have

$$\frac{x}{a} = \frac{\sin\alpha\sin\beta}{\sin(\beta-\alpha)}$$

i.e., $$x = a\,\frac{\sin\alpha\sin\beta}{\sin(\beta-\alpha)}$$

The height x is therefore given in a form suitable for logarithmic calculation.

Numerical Example. If $a = 100$ metres, $\alpha = 30°$, and $\beta = 60°$, then

$$x = 100\,\frac{\sin 30°\,\sin 60°}{\sin 30°} = 100 \times \frac{\sqrt{3}}{2} = 86.6 \text{ metres}$$

➤ **193.** It is often not convenient to measure AB directly towards Q.

Measure therefore AB in any other suitable direction on the horizontal ground, and at A measure the angle of elevation α of P, and also the angle PAB $(=\beta)$

At B measure the angle PBA $(=\gamma)$

In the triangle PAB, we have then

$$\angle APB = 180° - \angle PAB - \angle PBA = 180° - (\beta + \gamma)$$

Hence, $$\frac{AP}{a} = \frac{\sin PBA}{\sin BPA} = \frac{\sin \gamma}{\sin (\beta + \gamma)}$$

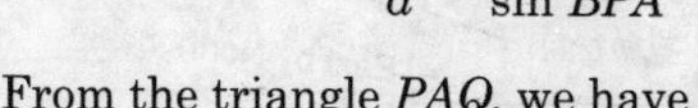

From the triangle PAQ, we have

$$x = AP \sin \alpha = a\,\frac{\sin \alpha \sin \gamma}{\sin (\beta + \gamma)}$$

Hence, x is found by an expression suitable for logarithmic calculation.

➤ **194.** *To find the distance between two inaccessible points by means of observations made at two points the distance between which is known, all four points being supposed to be in one plane.*

Let P and Q be two points whose distance apart, PQ is required.

Let A and B be the two known points whose distance apart, AB, is given to be equal to a.

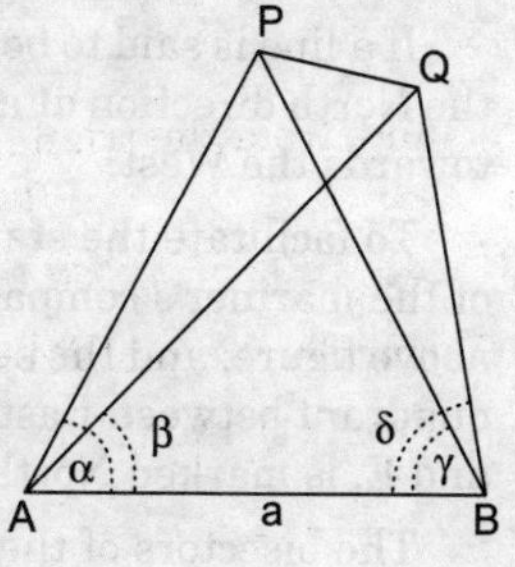

At A measure the angles PAB and QAB, and let them be α and β respectively.

At B measure the angle PBA and QBA, and let them be γ and δ respectively.

Then in the triangle PAB we have one side a and the two adjacent angles α and γ given, so that, as in Art. 163, we have AP given by the relation

$$\frac{AP}{a} = \frac{\sin \gamma}{\sin APB} = \frac{\sin \gamma}{\sin (\alpha + \gamma)} \quad \text{...(1)}$$

In the triangle QAB we have, similarly

$$\frac{AQ}{a} = \frac{\sin \delta}{\sin (\beta + \delta)} \quad \text{...(2)}$$

In the triangle APQ we have now determined the sides AP and AQ; also the included angle PAQ $(=\alpha - \beta)$ is known. We can therefore find the side PQ by the method of Art. 181.

If the four points A, B, P and Q be not in the same plane, we must, in addition, measure the angle PAQ; for in this case PAQ is not equal to $\alpha - \beta$. In other respects the solution will be the same as above.

➤ **195. Bearings and Points of the Compass :** The bearing of given point B as seen from a given point O is the direction in which B is seen from O. Thus, if the direction of OB bisect the angle between East and North, the bearing of B is said to be North-East.

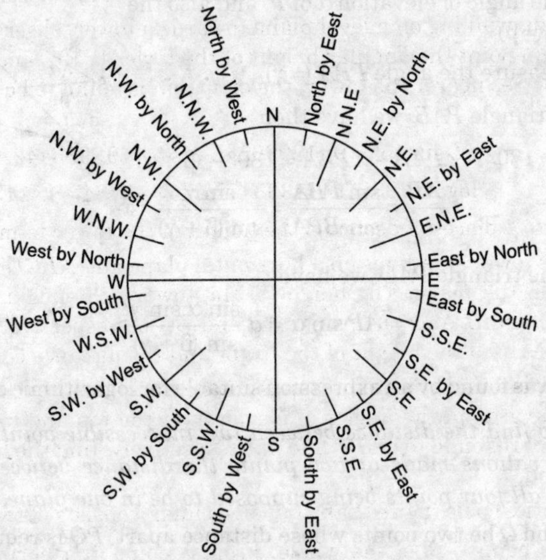

If a line is said to bear 20° West of North, we mean that it is inclined to the North direction at an angle of 20°, this angle measured from the North towards the West.

To facilitate the statement of the bearing of a point the circumference of the mariner's compass-card is divided into 32 equal portions, as in the above figure, and the subdivisions marked as indicated. Consider only the quadrant between East and North. The middle point of the arc between N. and E. is marked North-East (N.E.).

The bisectors of the arcs between N.E. and N. and E. are respectively called North-North-East and East-North-East (N.N.E. and E.N.E.). The other four subdivisions, reckoning from N., are called North by East, N.E. by North, N.E. by East, and East by North. Similarly the other three quadrants are subdivided.

It is clear that the arc between two subdivisions of the card subtends an angle of $\frac{360°}{32}$, *i.e.*, $11\frac{1}{4}°$, at the centre O.

EXAMPLES XXXIII

1. A flagstaff stands on the middle of a square tower. A man on the ground, opposite the middle of one face and distant from it 100 metres, just sees the flag; on his receding another 100 metres, the tangents of elevation of the top of the tower and the top of the flagstaff are found to be $\frac{1}{2}$ and $\frac{5}{9}$. Find the dimensions of the tower and the height of the flagstaff, the ground being horizontal.
2. A man, walking on a level plane towards a tower, observes that at a certain point the angular height of the tower is 10°, and after going 50 metres nearer the tower, the elevation is found to be 15°, Having given

$$L \sin 15° = 9.4129962, L \cos 5° = 9.9983442$$
$$\log 25.783 = 1.4113334 \text{ and } \log 25.784 = 1.4113503$$

find to 4 places of decimals the height of the tower in metres.
3. DE is tower standings on a horizontal plane and $ABCD$ is a straight line in the plane. The height of the tower subtends an angle θ at $A, 2\theta$ and B, and 3θ at C. If AB and BC be respectively 50 and 20 metres, find the height of the tower and the distance CD.
4. A tower, 50 metres high, stands on the top of a mound; from a point on the ground the angles of elevation of the top and bottom of the tower are found to be 75° and 45° respectively; find the height of the mound.
5. A vertical pole (more than 10 metres high) consists of two parts, the lower being $\frac{1}{3}$ rd of the whole. From a point in a horizontal plane through the foot of the pole and 4 metres from it, the upper part subtends an angle whose tangent is $\frac{1}{2}$. Find the height of the pole.
6. A tower subtends an angle α at a point on the same level as the foot of the tower, and at a second point, h metres above the first, the depression of the foot of the tower is β. Find the height of the tower.
7. A person in a balloon, which has ascended vertically from flat land at the sea-level, observes the angle of depression of a ship at anchor to be 30°; after descending vertically for 600 metres, he finds the angle of depression to be 15°; find the horizontal distance of the ship from the point of ascent.
8. PQ is a tower standing on a horizontal plane. Q being its foot; A and B are two points on the plane such that the $\angle QAB$ is 90°, and AB is 4 metres. It is found that

$$\cot PAQ = \frac{3}{10} \text{ and } \cot PBQ = \frac{1}{2}$$

Find the height of the tower.

9. A column is E.S.E. of an observer, and at noon the end of the shadow is North-East of him. The shadow is 80 metres long and the elevation of the column at the observer's station is 45°. Find the height of the column.

10. A tower is observed from two stations *A* and *B*. It is found to be due north of *A* and north-west of *B*. *B* is due east of *A* and distant from it 10 metres. The elevation of the tower as seen from *A* is the complement of the elevation as seen from *B*. Find the height of the tower.

11. The elevation of a steeple at a place due south of it is 45° and at another place due west of the former place the elevation is 15°. If the distance between the two places be *a*, prove that the height of the steeple is

$$\frac{a(\sqrt{3}-1)}{2\sqrt[4]{3}}$$

12. A person stands in the diagonal produced of the square base of a church tower, at a distance $2a$ from it, and observes the angles of elevation of each of the two outer corners of the top of the tower to be 30°, whilst that of the nearest corner is 45°. Prove that the breadth of the tower is $a(\sqrt{10}-\sqrt{2})$.

13. A person standing at a point *A* due south of a tower built on a horizontal plane observes the altitude of the tower to be 60°. He then walks to *B* due west of *A* and observes the altitude to be 45°, and again at *C* in *AB* produced he observes it to be 30°. Prove that *B* is midway between *A* and *C*.

14. At each end of a horizontal base of length $2a$ it is found that the angular height of a certain peak is θ and that at the middle point it is ϕ. Prove that the vertical height of the peak is

$$\frac{a\sin\theta\sin\phi}{\sqrt{\sin(\phi+\theta)\sin(\phi-\theta)}}$$

15. *A* and *B* are two stations 1000m apart'; *P* and *Q* are two stations in the same plane as *AB* and on the same side of it; the angles *PAB*, *PBA*, *QAB* and *QBA* are respectively 75°, 30°, 45° and 90°; find how far *P* is from *Q* and how far each is from *A* and *B*

For the following seven examples the required logarithms must be taken from the tables.

16. At a point on a horizontal plane the elevation of the summit of a mountain is found to be 22°15′, and at another point on the plane, 1 km. father away in a direct line, its elevation is 10°12′; find the height of the mountain.

17. From the top of a hill the angles of depression of two successive points, 1 km. apart, on level ground and in the same vertical plane with the observer, are found to be 5° and 10° respectively. Find the height of the hill and the horizontal distance to the nearest point.

18. A cliff and a tower stand on the same horizontal plane. The height of the cliff is 140 metres, and the angles of depression of the top and bottom of the tower as seen from the top of the cliff are 40° and 80° respectively. Find the height of the tower.

19. A tower PN stands on level ground. A base AB is measured at right angles to AN, the points A, B and N being in the same horizontal plane, and the angles PAN and PBN are found to be α and β respectively. Prove that the height of the tower is

$$AB = \frac{\sin\alpha\sin\beta}{\sqrt{\sin(\alpha-\beta)\sin(\alpha+\beta)}}$$

If $AB = 100$m, $\alpha = 70°$, and $\beta = 50°$, calculate the height.

20. A man, standing due south of a tower on a horizontal plane through its foot, finds the elevation of the top of the tower to be 54°16′; he goes east 100 metres and finds the elevation to be then 50°8′. Find the height of the tower.

21. A man in a balloon observes that the angle of depression of an object on the ground bearing due north is 33°; the balloon drifts 3 km due west and the angle of depression is how found to be 21°. Find the height of the balloon.

22. From the extremities of a horizontal base-line AB, whose length is 1km, the bearings of the foot C of a tower are observed and it is found that $\angle CAB = 56°23'$, $\angle CBA = 47°15'$, and the elevation of the tower from A is 9°25′; find the height of the tower.

➤ **196.**

<u>EXAMPLE 1</u> *A flagstaff is on the top of a tower which stands on a horizontal plane. A person observes the angles, α and β, subtended at a point on the horizontal plane by the flagstaff and the tower; he then walks a known distance a toward the tower and finds that the flagstaff subtends the same angle as before; prove that the height of the tower and the length of the flagstaff are respectively.*

$$\frac{a\sin\beta\cos(\alpha+\beta)}{\cos(\alpha+2\beta)} \text{ and } \frac{a\sin\alpha}{\cos(\alpha+2\beta)}$$

Let P and Q be the top and foot of the tower, and let PR be the flagstaff. Let A and B be the points at which the measurements are taken, so that $\angle PAQ = \beta$ and $\angle PAR = \angle PBR = \alpha$. Since the two latter angles are equal, a circle will go through the four points A, B, P and R.

To find the height of the flagstaff we have to connect the unknown length PR with the known length AB.

This may be done by connecting each with the length AR.

To do this, we must first determine the angles of the triangles ARP and ARB.

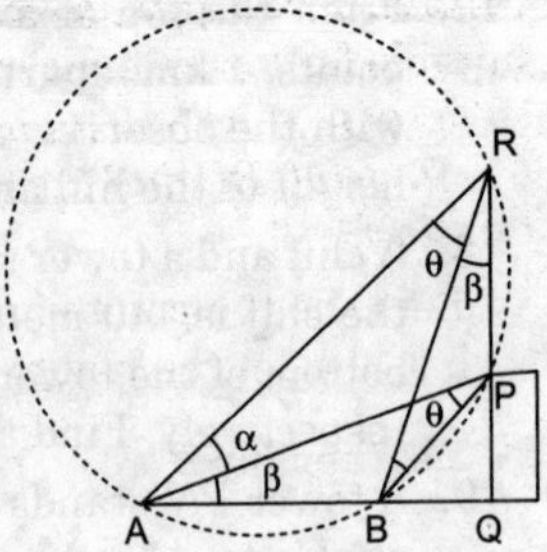

Since, A, B, P and R lie on a circle, we have

$$\angle BRP = \angle BAP = \beta$$

and $\angle APB = \angle ARB = \theta$ (say)

Also, $\angle APR = 90° + \angle PAQ = 90° + \beta$

Hence, since the angles of the triangle APR are together equal to two right angles, we have

$$180° = \alpha + (90° + \beta) + (\theta + \beta)$$

so that $$\theta = 90° - (\alpha + 2\beta) \quad \ldots(1)$$

From the triangles APR and ABR we then have

$$\frac{PR}{\sin\alpha} = \frac{AR}{\sin RPA} = \frac{AR}{\sin RBA} = \frac{a}{\sin\theta} \quad \text{(Art. 163)}$$

[It will be found in Chap. 15 that each of these quantities is equal to the diameter of the circle.]

Hence, the height of the flagstaff

$$= PR = \frac{a\sin\alpha}{\sin\theta} = \frac{a\sin\alpha}{\cos(\alpha + 2\beta)} \quad \text{[by (1)]}$$

Again, $$\frac{PQ}{PB} = \cos BPQ = \cos(\alpha + \beta) \quad \ldots(2)$$

and $$\frac{PB}{a} = \frac{\sin PAB}{\sin APB} = \frac{\sin\beta}{\sin\theta} \quad \ldots(3)$$

Hence, from (2) and (3), by multiplication,

$$\frac{PQ}{a} = \frac{\sin\beta\cos(\alpha + \beta)}{\sin\theta} = \frac{\sin\beta\cos(\alpha + \beta)}{\cos(\alpha + 2\beta)} \quad \text{[by (1)]}$$

Also, $$BQ = PQ\tan BPQ = PQ\tan(\alpha + \beta)$$

$$= a\,\frac{\sin\beta\sin(\alpha + \beta)}{\cos(\alpha + 2\beta)}$$

and $$AQ = a + BQ = a\,\frac{\cos(\alpha + 2\beta) + \sin\beta\sin(\alpha + \beta)}{\cos(\alpha + 2\beta)}$$

$$= a\,\frac{\cos\beta\cos(\alpha + \beta)}{\cos(\alpha + 2\beta)}$$

If a, α and β be given numerically, these results are all in a form suitable for logarithmic computation.

EXAMPLE 2 *At a distance a from the foot of a tower AB, of known height b, a flagstaff BC and the tower subtend equal angles. Find the height of the flagstaff.*

Let O be the point of observation and let the angles AOB and BOC be each θ; also let the height BC be y.

We then have $$\tan\theta = \frac{b}{a}, \text{ and } \tan 2\theta = \frac{b+y}{a}$$

Hence, $$\frac{b+y}{a} = \tan 2\theta = \frac{2\tan\theta}{1-\tan^2\theta} = \frac{2\frac{b}{a}}{1-\frac{b^2}{a^2}}$$

so, that $$\frac{b+y}{a} = \frac{2ab}{a^2-b^2}$$

Then, $$y = \frac{2a^2b}{a^2-b^2} - b = b\frac{a^2+b^2}{a^2-b^2}$$

If a and b be given numerically, we thus easily obtain y.

➤ 197.

EXAMPLE *A man walks along a straight road and observes that the greatest angle subtended by two objects α; from the point where this greatest angle is subtended he walks a distance c along the road, and finds that the two objects are now in a straight line which makes an angle β with* the road; *prove that the distance between the objects is*

$$c\sin\alpha\sin\beta\sec\frac{\alpha+\beta}{2}\sec\frac{\alpha-\beta}{2}$$

Let P and Q be the two points, and let PQ meet the road in B.

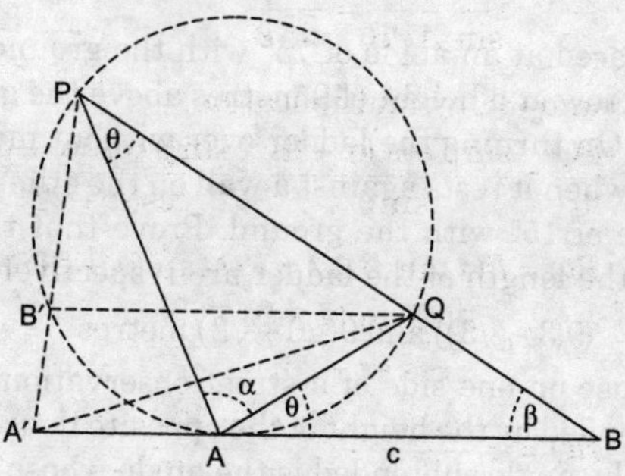

If A be the point at which the greatest angle is subtended, then A must be the point where a circle drawn through P and Q touches the road.

[For, take *any* other point A' on AB, and join it to P cutting the circle in B', and join $A'Q$ and $B'Q$]

Then, $\angle PA'Q < \angle PB'Q$

and therefore, $< \angle PAQ$]

Let the angle QAB be called θ. Then the angle APQ is θ also.

Hence, $180° =$ sum of the angles of the triangle PAB

$$= \theta + (\alpha + \theta) + \beta$$

so that $$\theta = 90° - \frac{\alpha + \beta}{2}$$

From the triangles PAQ and QAB we have

$$\frac{PQ}{AQ} = \frac{\sin\alpha}{\sin\theta}, \text{ and } \frac{AQ}{c} = \frac{\sin\beta}{\sin AQB} = \frac{\sin\beta}{\sin(\theta + \alpha)}$$

Hence, by multiplication, we have

$$\frac{PQ}{c} = \frac{\sin\alpha \sin\beta}{\sin\theta \sin(\theta + \alpha)}$$

$$= \frac{\sin\alpha \sin\beta}{\cos\frac{\alpha+\beta}{2} \cos\frac{\alpha-\beta}{2}}$$

$$\therefore PQ = c \sin\alpha \sin\beta \sec\frac{\alpha+\beta}{2} \sec\frac{\alpha-\beta}{2}$$

EXAMPLES XXXIV

1. A bridge has 5 equal spans, each of 10 m measured from the centre of the piers, and a boat is moored in a line with one of the middle piers. The whole length of the bridge subtends a right angle as seen from the boat. Prove that the distance of the boat from the bridge is $10\sqrt{6}$ m.
2. A ladder placed at an angle of 75° with the ground just reaches the sill of a window at a height of 9 metres above the ground on one side of a street. On turning the ladder over without moving its foot, it is found that when it rests against a wall on the other side of street it is at an angle of 15° with the ground. Prove that the breadth of the street and the length of the ladder are respectively.

   $$(9(3 - \sqrt{3})) \text{ and } 9(\sqrt{6} - \sqrt{2}) \text{ metres}$$
3. From a house on one side of a street observations are made of the angle subtended by the height of the opposite house; from the level of the street the angle subtended is the angle whose tangent is 3; from the windows one above the other the angle subtended is found to be the angle whose tangent is –3; the height of the opposite house being 30 metres, find the height above the street of each of the two windows.

4. A rod of given length can turn in a vertical plane passing through the sun, one end being fixed on the ground; find the longest shadow it can cast on the ground.

   Calculate the altitude of the sun when the longest shadow it can cast is $3^{1/2}$ times the length of the rod.

5. A person on a ship *A* observes another ship *B* leaving a harbour, whose bearing is then N.W.. After 10 minutes *A*, having sailed one km. N.E., sees *B* due west and the harbour then bears 60° west of north. After another 10 minutes *B* is observed to bear S.W.. Find the distances between *A* and *B* at the first observation and also the direction and rate *B*.

6. A person on a ship sailing north sees two lighthouses, which are 6 km. apart, in a line due west; after an hour's sailing one of them bears S.W. and the other S.S.W.. Find the ship's rate.

7. A person on a ship sees a lighthouse N.W. of himself. After sailing for 12 km. in a direction 15° south of W. the lighthouse is seen due N. Find the distance of the lighthouse from the ship in each position.

8. A man travelling west along a straight road, observes that when he is due south of a certain windmill the straight line drawn to a distant tower makes an angle of 30° with the road. One km farther on the bearings of the windmill and tower are respectively N.E. and N.W.. Find the distances of the tower from the windmill and from the nearest point of the road.

9. An observer on a headland sees a ship due north of him; after a quarter of an hour he sees it due east and after another half-hour he sees it due south-east; find the angle that the ship's course makes with the meridian and the time after the ship is first seen until it is nearest the observer, supposing that it sails uniformly in a straight line.

10. A man walking along a straight road, which runs in a direction 30° east of north, notes when he is due south of a certain house; when he has walked 1 km. farther, he observes that the house lies due west and that a windmill on he opposite side of the road is N.E. of him; three km. farther on he finds that he is due north of the windmill, prove that the line joining the house and the windmill makes with the road the angle whose tangent is

$$\frac{48-25\sqrt{3}}{11}$$

11. *A*, *B* and *C* are three consecutive stones 1 km. apart on a straight road from each of which a distant spire is visible. The spire is observed to bear north-east at *A*, east of *B*, and 60° east of south at *C*. Prove that the shortest distance of the spire from the road is $\frac{7+5\sqrt{3}}{13}$ km.

12. Two stations due south of a tower, which leans towards the north, are at distances a and b from its foot; if α and β are the elevations of the top of the tower from these stations, prove that its inclination to the horizontal is

$$\cot^{-1}\frac{b\cot\alpha - a\cot\beta}{b-a}$$

13. From a point A on a level plane the angle of elevation of a balloon is α, the balloon being south of A; from a point B, which is at a distance c south of A, the balloon is seen northwards at and elevation of β; find the distance of the balloon from A and its height above the ground.

14. A statue on the top of a pillar subtends the same angle α at distances of 9 and 11 m. from the pillar; if $\tan\alpha = \frac{1}{10}$, find the height of the pillar and of the statue.

15. A flagstaff on the top of a tower is observed to subtend the same angle α at two points on a horizontal plane, which lie on a line passing through the centre of the base of the tower and whose distance from one another is $2a$, and an angle β at a point halfway between them. Prove that the height of the flagstaff is

$$a\sin\alpha\sqrt{\frac{2\sin\beta}{\cos\alpha\sin(\beta-\alpha)}}$$

16. An observer in the first place stations himself at a distance a metres from a column standing upon a mound. He finds that the column subtends an angle, whose tangent is $\frac{1}{2}$, at his eye which may be supposed to be on the horizontal plane through the base of the mound. On moving $\frac{2}{3}a$ m nearer the column, he finds that the angle subtended is unchanged. Find the height of the mound and of the column.

17. A church tower stands on the bank of a river, which is 50 m. wide and on the top of the tower is a spire 10 m high. To an observer on the opposite bank of the river the spire subtends the same angle that a pole 2 m high subtends when placed upright on the ground at the foot of the tower. Prove that the height of the tower is nearly 95 m.

18. A person, wishing to ascertain the height of a tower, stations himself on a horizontal plane through its foot at a point at which the elevation of the top is 30°. On walking a distance a in a certain direction he finds that the elevation of the top is the same as before, and on then walking a distance $\frac{5}{3}a$ at right angles to his former

direction he finds the elevation of the top to be 60°. Prove that the height of the tower is either $\sqrt{\frac{5}{6}}\,a$ or $\sqrt{\frac{85}{48}}\,a$.

19. The angles of elevation of the top of a tower, standing on a horizontal plane, from two points distant a m. from the base and in the same straight line with it are complementary. Prove that the height of the tower is $\sqrt{ab}$ m and θ be the angle subtended at the top of the tower by the line joining the two point, then $\sin\theta = \dfrac{a \sim b}{a+b}$.

20. A tower 150 m. high stands on the top of a cliff 80 m. high. To an observer on a ship, the tower and cliff subtend equal angles. How far from the cliff is the observer if he is 5 m. above the plane passing through the foot of the cliff?

21. A statue on the top of a pillar, standing on level ground, is found to subtend the greatest angle α at the eye of an observer when his distance from the pillar is cm; prove that the height of the statue is $2c \tan\alpha$ m; and find the height of the pillar.

22. A tower stood at the foot of an inclined plane whose inclination to the horizon was 9°. A line 100 m in length was measured straight up the incline from the foot of the tower, and at the end of this line the tower subtend an angle of 54°. Find the height of the tower, having

given $\log 2 = 0.30103, \log 114.4123 = 2.0584726$

and $$L\sin 54° = 9.9079576$$

23. A vertical tower stands on a declivity which is inclined at 15° to the horizon. From the foot of the tower a man ascends the declivity for 80 metres, and then finds that the tower subtends an angle of 30°. Prove that the height of the tower is $40(\sqrt{6}-\sqrt{2})$ metres.

24. The altitude of a certain rock is 47° and after walking towards it 1 km up a slope inclined at 30° to the horizon an observer finds its altitude to be 77°. Find the vertical height of the rock above the first point of observation, given that

$$\sin 47° = 0.73135.$$

25. A man observes that, when he has walked c metres up an inclined plane, the angular depression of an object in a horizontal plane through the foot of the slope is α, and that, when he was walked a further distance of c feet, the depression is β. Prove that the inclination of the slope to the horizon is the angle whose cotangent is

$$(2\cot\beta + \cot\alpha)$$

26. A regular pyramid on a square base has an edge 150 m. long and the length of the side of its base is 200 m. Find the inclination of its face to the base.

27. A pyramid has for base a square of side a ; its vertex lies on a line through the middle point of the base and perpendicular to it, and at a distance h from it; prove that the angle α between the two lateral faces is given by the equation

$$\sin\alpha = \frac{2h\sqrt{2a^2+4h^2}}{a^2+4h^2}$$

28. A flagstaff, 10 metres high, stands in the centre of an equilateral triangle which is horizontal. From the top of the flagstaff each side subtends an angle 60°; prove that the length of the side of the triangle is $5\sqrt{6}$ metres.

29. The extremity of the shadow of a flagstaff, which is 6 m. high and stands on the top of a pyramid on a square base, just reaches the side of the base and is distant 56 and 8 m. respectively from the extermities of that side. Find the sun's altitude if the height of the pyramid be 34 metres.

30. The extremity of the shadow of a flagstaff, which is 6 metres high and stands on the top of a pyramid on a square base, just reaches the side of the base and is distant x feet and y feet respectively from the ends of that side; prove that the height of the pyramid is

$$\frac{\sqrt{x^2+y^2}}{2}\tan\alpha - 6$$

where α is the elevation of the sun.

31. The angle of elevation of a cloud from a point h metres above a lake is α, and the angle of depression of its reflexion in the lake is β; prove that its height is $h\dfrac{\sin(\beta+\alpha)}{\sin(\beta-\alpha)}$.

32. The shadow of a tower is observed to be half the known height of the tower and sometime afterwards it is equal to the known height how much will the sun have gone down in the interval, given

$$\log 2 = 0.30103,\ L\tan 63°26' = 10.3009994$$

and diff. for $1' = 3159$?

33. An isosceles triangle of wood is placed in a vertical plane, vertex upwards, and faces the sun. If $2a$ be the base of the triangle, h its height and 30° the altitude of the sun, prove that the tangent of the angle at the apex of the shadow is $\dfrac{2ah\sqrt{3}}{3h^2-a^2}$.

34. A rectangular target faces due south, being vertical and standing on a horizontal plane. Compare the area of the target with that of its shadow on the ground when the sun is $\beta°$ from the south at an altitude of $\alpha°$.

35. A spherical ball, of diameter δ, subtends an angle α at a man's eye when the elevation of its centre is β; prove that the height of the centre of the ball is $\frac{1}{2}\delta \sin\beta \operatorname{cosec}\frac{\alpha}{2}$.

36. A man standing on a plane observes a row of equal and equidistant pillars, the 10th and 17th of which subtend the same angle that they would do if they were in the position of the first and were respectively $\frac{1}{2}$ and $\frac{1}{3}$ of their height. Prove that, neglecting the height of the man's eye, the line of pillars is inclined to the line drawn from his eye to the first at an angle whose secant is nearly 2.6.

For the following nine examples the required lagarithms must be taken from the tables.

37. A and B are two points, which are on the banks of a river and opposite to one another and between them is the mast, PN of a ship the breadth of the river is 100 metres and the angular elevation of P at A is 14°20′ and at B 8°10′. What is the height of P above AB?

38. AB is a line 1000 metres long; B is due north of A and from B a distant point P bears 70° east of north; at A it bears 41°22′ east of north; find the distance from A to P.

39. A is a station exactly 10 km west of B. The bearing of a particular rock from A is 74°19′ east of north, and its bearing from B is 26°51′ west of north. How far is it north the line AB?

40. The summit of a spire is vertically over the middle point of a horizontal square enclosure whose side is of length a metre; the height of the spire is h metres above the level of the square. If the shadow of the spire just reaches a corner of the square when the sun has an altitude θ, prove that

$$h\sqrt{2} = a \tan\theta$$

Calculate h, having given $a = 100$ metres and $\theta = 25°15'$.

41. Walking along a straight level road in a direction N.W. I notice two spires, P and Q in a straight line with me on a bearing N. 20° F, P being the nearer spire. After walking 4 km. farther along the road, P bears E. 22°S. and Q bears E. 26°N. Find the distance between the spires.

42. AB is a road running uphill in a direction due east at an inclination of 10°, B being above A and at a distance of 500 metres from A. The bearing of an object C from A is E. 50° N. at an elevation of 43°, and the bearing of C from B is W. 65° N. Calculate the horizontal and vertical distance of C from A.

43. A wireless signal from an aeroplane is intercepted at two direction finding stations, A and B, which are five km apart in a north and south line. From A the direction of the aeroplane is found to be 66° west of north and from B it is found to be 20° west of south. At the same time the altitude of the aeroplane is observed from A to be 40°. Find the height of the aeroplane above A.

44. An observer sees an aeroplane due N at an elevation of 8°. Two minutes later he sees it N.E. at the same elevation. It is known to be going due E, the horizontal component of its velocity being 80 km an hour. Show that it is rising at the rate of nearly 77.615 metres per minute.

45. A small balloon is released from a point on a level plain, and ascends with a constant vertical velocity of 100 metres per minute. After it has risen for 10 minutes it is at P and one minute late is at Q. At a station O on the plain the bearing of P is due east, and OP makes an angle of 63° with the plain. At O the bearing of Q is 29° north of east, and OQ makes an angle of 70° with the plain . Assuming the wind to blow with constant horizontal velocity, find this velocity, and show that its direction is about 50°37′ north of west.

15

PROPERTIES OF TRIANGLE

➤ **198. Area of a given triangle.** Let ABC be any triangle, and AD the perpendicular drawn from A upon the opposite side.

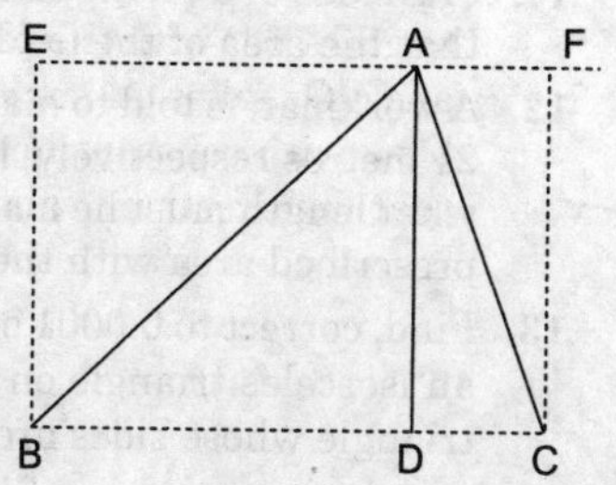

Through A draw EAF parallel to BC, and draw BE and CF perpendicular to it.

By Geometry, the area of the trianlge ABC

$$= \frac{1}{2} \text{ rectangle } BF = \frac{1}{2} BC \cdot CF = \frac{1}{2} a \cdot AD$$

But $$AD = AB \sin B = c \sin B$$

The area of the triangle ABC therefore $= \frac{1}{2} ca \sin B$.

This area is denoted by Δ.

Hence, $$\Delta = \frac{1}{2} ca \sin B = \frac{1}{2} ab \sin C = \frac{1}{2} bc \sin A \qquad \text{...(1)}$$

By Art. 169, we have $\sin A = \frac{2}{bc}\sqrt{s(s-a)(s-b)(s-c)}$

so that $$\Delta = \frac{1}{2} bc \sin A = \sqrt{s(s-a)(s-b)(s-c)} \qquad \text{...(2)}$$

This latter quantity is often called S.

EXAMPLES XXXV

Find the area of the triangle ABC when

1. $a = 13$, $b = 14$, and $c = 15$

2. $a = 18$, $b = 24$, and $c = 30$

3. $a = 25$, $b = 52$, and $c = 63$

4. $a = 125$, $b = 123$, and $c = 62$
5. $a = 15$, $b = 36$, and $c = 39$
6. $a = 287$, $b = 816$, and $c = 865$
7. $a = 35$, $b = 84$, and $c = 91$
8. $a = \sqrt{3}$, $b = \sqrt{2}$ and $c = \dfrac{\sqrt{6} + \sqrt{2}}{2}$
9. If $B = 45°$, $C = 60°$ and $a = 2(\sqrt{3} + 1)$ cm, prove that area of the triangle is $(6 + 2\sqrt{3})$ sq.cm.
10. The sides of a triangle are 119, 111, and 92 metres; prove that its area is 4830 sq.m.
11. The sides of a triangular field are 242, 1212 and 1450 metres, prove that the area of the field is 29,040 sq.m.
12. A workman is told to make a triangular enclosure of sides 50, 41 and 21 metres respectively; having made the first side one yard too long, what length must he make the other two sides in order to enclose the prescribed area with the perscribed length of fencing?
13. Find, correct to 0.0001 of a cm. the length of one of the equal sides of an isosceles triangle on a base of 14 cm. having the same area as a triangle whose sides are 13.6, 15 and 15.4 cm.
14. If one angle of a triangle be 60°, the area $10\sqrt{3}$ sq.cm, and the perimeter 20 cm., find the lengths of the sides.
15. The sides of a triangle are in A.P. and its area is $\frac{3}{5}$ths of an equilateral triangle of the same perimeter; prove that its sides are in the ratio 3:5:7, and find the greatest angle of the triangle.
16. In a triangle the least angle is 45° and the tangents of the angles are in A.P. If its are be 27 sq.cm. prove that the lengths of the sides are $3\sqrt{5}$, 6, $\sqrt{2}$ and 9 cm., and that the tangents of the other angles are respectively 2 and 3.
17. The lengths of two sides of a triangle are 12 cm. and $12\sqrt{2}$ cm respectively and the angle opposite the shorter side is 30°; prove that there are two triangles satisfying these conditions, find their angles, and show that their areas are in the ratio
$$\sqrt{3} + 1 : \sqrt{3} - 1$$
18. Find by the aid of the tables the area of the larger of the two triangles given by the data
$$A = 31°15', \ a = 5 \text{ cm, and } b = 7 \text{ cm}$$

➤ **199. On the circles connected with a given triangle**: The circle which passes through the angular points of a triangle *ABC* is called its circumscribing circle or, more beifly, its **circumcircle**. The centre of this circle is found by the construction of Art. 200. Its radius is always called *R*.

The circle which can be inscribed within the triangle so as to touch each of the sides is called its inscribed circle or, more briefly, its **incircle**.

The centre of this circle is found by the construction of Art. 202. Its radius will be denoted by r.

The circle which touches the side BC and the two sides AB and AC produced is called the **escribed** circle opposite the angle A. Its radius will be denoted by r_1.

Similarly r_2 denotes the radius of the circle which touches the side CA and the two sides BC and BA produced. Also r_3 denotes the radius of the circle touching AB and the two sides CA and CB produced.

➤ **200.** *To find the magnitude of R, the radius of the circumcircle of any triangle ABC.*

Bisect the two sides BC and CA in D and E respectively, and draw DO and EO perpendicular to BC and CA.

By Geometry, O is the centre of the circumcircle. Join OB and OC.

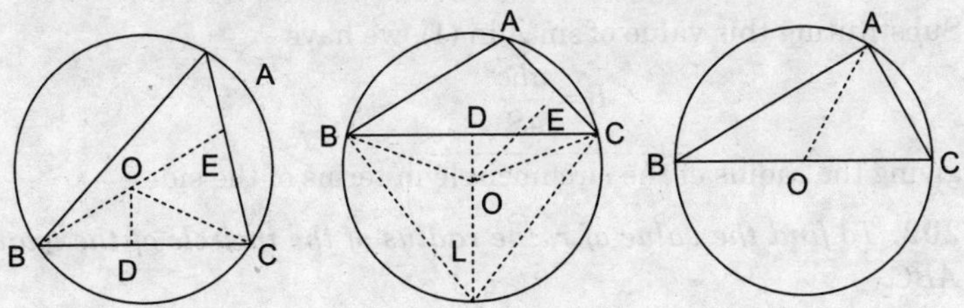

The point O may either lie within the triangle as in Fig. 1, or without it as in Fig. 2, or upon one of the sides as in Fig. 3.

Taking the first figure, the two triangles BOD and COD are equal in all respects, so that

$$\angle BOD = \angle COD$$

$$\therefore \quad \angle BOD = \frac{1}{2}\angle BOC = \angle BAC$$

$$= A$$

Also $$BD = BO \sin BOD$$

$$\therefore \quad \frac{a}{2} = R \sin A$$

If A be obtuse, as in Fig. 2, we have

$$\angle BOD = \frac{1}{2}\angle BOC = \angle BLC = 180° - A,$$

so that, as before $\quad \sin BOD = \sin A$

and $$R = \frac{a}{2 \sin A}$$

If A be a right angle, as in Fig. 3 we have

$$R = OA = OC = \frac{a}{2}$$

$$= \frac{a}{2\sin A}, \text{ since in this case } \sin A = 1.$$

This relation found above is therefore true for all triangles.

Hence, in all three cases, we have

$$R = \frac{a}{2\sin A} = \frac{b}{2\sin B} = \frac{c}{2\sin C} \qquad ...(1)$$

➤ **201.** In Art. 169 we have shown that

$$\sin A = \frac{2}{bc}\sqrt{s(s-a)(s-b)(s-c)} = \frac{2S}{bc}$$

where S is that area of the triangle.

Substituting this value of $\sin A$ in (1), we have

$$R = \frac{abc}{4S}$$

giving the radius of the circumcircle in terms of the sides.

➤ **202.** *To find the value of r, the radius of the incircle of the triangle ABC.*

Bisect the two angles B and C by the two lines BI and CI meeting in I.

By Geometry, I is the centre of the incircle, join IA, and draw ID, IE and IF perpendicular to the three sides.

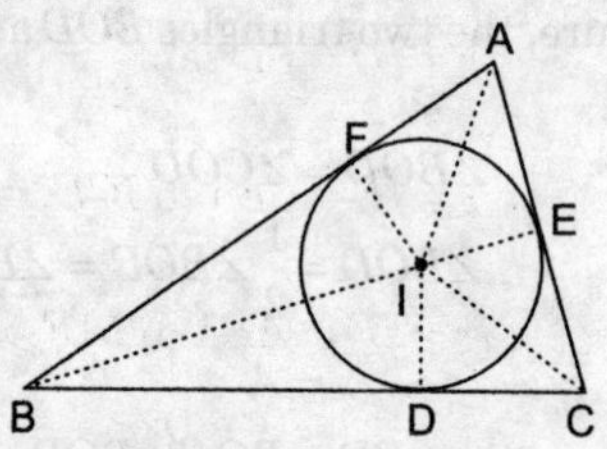

Then, $\qquad ID = IE = IF = r$

We have $\qquad$ area of $\Delta IBC = \frac{1}{2} ID \cdot BC = \frac{1}{2} r \cdot a$

area of $\Delta ICA = \frac{1}{2} IE \cdot CA = \frac{1}{2} r \cdot b$

and $\qquad$ area of $\Delta IAB = \frac{1}{2} IF \cdot AB = \frac{1}{2} r \cdot c$

Hence, by addition, we have

$\frac{1}{2} r \cdot a + \frac{1}{2} r \cdot b + \frac{1}{2}\frac{1}{r} \cdot c =$ sum of the areas of the triangles IBC, ICA and IAB

$$= \text{area of the } \Delta ABC$$

i.e., $$r\frac{a+b+c}{2} = S$$

so that $$r \cdot s = S$$

$\therefore$ $$r = \frac{S}{s}$$

➤ **203.** Since, the angles *IBD* and *IDB* are respectively equal to the angles *IBF* and *IFB*, the two triangles *IDB* and *IFB* are equal in all respects.

Hence, $BD = BF$, so that $2\,BD = BD + BF$

So also $AE = AF$, so that $2\,AE = AE + AF$

and $CE = CD$, so that $2\,CE = CE + CD$

Hence, by addition, we have

$$2\,BD + 2\,AE + 2\,CE = (BD + CD) + (CE + AE) + (AF + BF)$$

i.e., $$2BD + 2AC = BC + CA + AB$$

$\therefore$ $$2\,BD + 2\,b = a + b + c = 2\,s$$

Hence, $$BD = s - b = BF;$$

so $$CE = s - c = CD$$

and $$AF = s - a = AE$$

Now, $$\frac{ID}{BD} = \tan IBD = \tan\frac{B}{2}$$

$\therefore$ $$r = ID = BD\tan\frac{B}{2} = (s-b)\tan\frac{B}{2}$$

So, $$r = IE = CE\tan ICE = (s-c)\tan\frac{C}{2}$$

and also $$r = IF = AF\tan IAF = (s-a)\tan\frac{A}{2}$$

Hence, $\boldsymbol{r = (s-a)\tan\frac{A}{2} = (s-b)\tan\frac{B}{2} = (s-c)\tan\frac{C}{2}}$

➤ **204.** A third value for *r* may be found as follows we have

$$a = BD + CD = ID\cot IBD + ID\cot ICD$$

$$= r\cot\frac{B}{2} + r\cot\frac{C}{2}$$

$$= r\left[\frac{\cos\frac{B}{2}}{\sin\frac{B}{2}} + \frac{\cos\frac{C}{2}}{\sin\frac{C}{2}}\right]$$

$$\therefore \quad a \sin\frac{B}{2}\sin\frac{C}{2} = r\left[\sin\frac{C}{2}\cos\frac{B}{2} + \cos\frac{C}{2}\sin\frac{B}{2}\right]$$

$$= r\sin\left(\frac{B}{2}+\frac{C}{2}\right) = r\sin\left[90° - \frac{A}{2}\right] = r\cos\frac{A}{2}$$

$$\therefore \quad r = a\frac{\sin\frac{B}{2}\sin\frac{C}{2}}{\cos\frac{A}{2}}$$

Cor. : Since, $a = 2R\sin A = 4R\sin\frac{A}{2}\cos\frac{A}{2}$

we have $\quad r = 4R\sin\frac{A}{2}\sin\frac{B}{2}\sin\frac{C}{2}$

➤ **205.** *To find the value of r_1, the radius of the escribed circle opposite the angle A of the triangle ABC.*

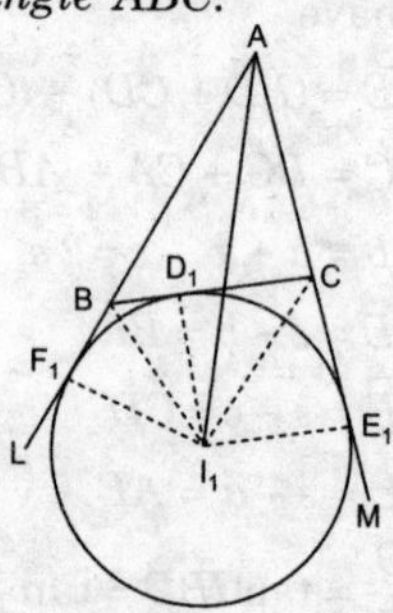

Produce AB and AC to L and M.

Bisect the angles CBL and BCM by the lines BI_1 and CI_1 and let these lines meet in I_1.

Draw I_1D_1, I_1E_1 and I_1F_1 perpendicular to the three sides respectively.

The two triangles I_1D_1B and I_1F_1B are equal in all respects,

so that $\quad I_1F_1 = I_1D_1$

Similarly, $\quad I_1E_1 = I_1D_1$

The three perpendicualrs I_1D_1, I_1E_1 and I_1F_1 being equal, the point I_1 is the centre of the required circle.

Now, the area ABI_1C is equal to the sum of the triangles ABC and I_1BC; it is also equal to the sum of the triangles I_1BA and I_1CA.

Hence, $\quad \Delta ABC + \Delta I_1BC = \Delta I_1CA + \Delta I_1AB$

$$\therefore \quad S + \frac{1}{2}I_1D_1 \cdot BC = \frac{1}{2}I_1E_1 \cdot CA + \frac{1}{2}I_1F_1 \cdot AB$$

i.e., $\quad S + \frac{1}{2}r_1 \cdot a = \frac{1}{2}r_1 \cdot b + \frac{1}{2}r_1 \cdot c$

$$\therefore \quad S = r_1\left[\frac{b+c-a}{2}\right] = r_1\left[\frac{b+c+a}{2} - a\right] = r_1(s-a)$$

$$\therefore \qquad r_1 = \frac{S}{s-a}$$

Similarly it can be shown that

$$r_2 = \frac{S}{s-b'}$$

and
$$r_3 = \frac{S}{s-c}$$

➤ **206.** Since AE_1 and AF_1 are tangents, we have, as in Art. 203, $AE_1 = AF_1$.

Similarly, $BF_1 = BD_1$

and $CE_1 = CD_1$

$$\therefore \qquad 2AE_1 = AE_1 + AF_1 = AB + BF_1 + AC + CE_1$$
$$= AB + BD_1 + AC + CD_1 = AB + BC + CA = 2s$$

$$\therefore \qquad AE_1 = s = AF_1$$

Also, $BD_1 = BF_1 = AF_1 - AB = s - c$

and $CD_1 = CE_1 = AE_1 - AC = s - b$

$$\therefore \qquad I_1E_1 = AE_1 \tan I_1AE_1$$

i.e.,
$$\boldsymbol{r_1 = s \tan \frac{A}{2}}$$

➤ **207.** A third value may be obtained for r_1 in terms of a and the angles B and C.

For, since I_1C bisects the angle BCE_1, we have

$$\angle I_1CD_1 = \frac{1}{2}(180° - C) = 90° - \frac{C}{2}$$

So,
$$\angle I_1BD_1 = 90° - \frac{B}{2}$$

$$\therefore \qquad a = BC = BD_1 + D_1C$$
$$= I_1D_1 \cot I_1BD_1 + I_1D_1 \cot I_1CD_1$$
$$= r_1\left(\tan\frac{B}{2} + \tan\frac{C}{2}\right)$$
$$= r_1\left(\frac{\sin\frac{B}{2}}{\cos\frac{B}{2}} + \frac{\sin\frac{C}{2}}{\cos\frac{C}{2}}\right)$$

$$\therefore \qquad a \cos\frac{B}{2}\cos\frac{C}{2} = r_1\left(\sin\frac{B}{2}\cos\frac{C}{2} + \cos\frac{B}{2}\sin\frac{C}{2}\right)$$

$$= r_1 \sin\left(\frac{B}{2}+\frac{C}{2}\right) = r_1 \sin\left(90° - \frac{A}{2}\right) = r_1 \cos\frac{A}{2}$$

$$\therefore \qquad r_1 = a\frac{\cos\frac{B}{2}\cos\frac{C}{2}}{\cos\frac{A}{2}}$$

Cor: Since $a = 2R\sin A = 4R\sin\frac{A}{2}\cos\frac{A}{2}$

We have $r_1 = 4R\sin\frac{A}{2}\cos\frac{B}{2}\cos\frac{C}{2}$

EXAMPLES XXXVI

1. In a triangle whose sides are 18, 24 and 30 cm. respectively prove that the circumradius, the inradius and the radii of the three escribed circles are respectively 15, 6, 12, 18 and 36 cm.
2. The sides of a triangle are 13, 14 and 15 cm; prove that
   (1) $R = 8.125$ cm,
   (2) $r = 4$ cm
   (3) $r_1 = 10.5$ cm
   (4) $r_2 = 12$ cm, and
   (5) $r_3 = 14$ cm
3. In a triangle ABC if $a = 13$, $b = 4$ and $\cos C = -\frac{5}{13}$, find
   $$R, r, r_1, r_2 \text{ and } r_3.$$
4. In the ambiguous case of the solution of triangles prove that the circumcircles of the two triangles are equal.

   Prove that
5. $r_1(s-a) = r_2(s-b) = r_3(s-c) = rs = S$
6. $\frac{rr_1}{r_2r_3} = \tan^2\frac{A}{2}$
7. $rr_1r_2r_3 = S^2$
8. $r_1r_2r_3 = r^3\cot^2\frac{A}{2}\cot^2\frac{B}{2}\cot^2\frac{C}{2}$
9. $rr_1\cot\frac{A}{2} = S$
10. $r_2r_3 + r_3r_1 + r_1r_2 = s^2$
11. $\frac{1}{r_1}+\frac{1}{r_2}+\frac{1}{r_3}-\frac{1}{r} = 0$
12. $a(rr_1 + r_2r_3) = b(rr_2 + r_3r_1) = c(rr_3 + r_1r_2)$
13. $(r_1 + r_2)\tan\frac{C}{2} = (r_3 - r)\cot\frac{C}{2} = c$

14. $S = 2R^2 \sin A \sin B \sin C$

15. $4R \sin A \sin B \sin C = a\cos A + b\cos B + c\cos C$

16. $S = 4Rr \cos\frac{A}{2} \cos\frac{B}{2} \cos\frac{C}{2}$

17. $\frac{1}{r^2} + \frac{1}{r_1^2} + \frac{1}{r_2^2} + \frac{1}{r_3^2} = \frac{a^2 + b^2 + c^2}{S^2}$

18. $r_1 + r_2 + r_3 - r = 4R$

19. $(r_1 - r)(r_2 - r)(r_3 - r) = 4Rr^2$

20. $\frac{1}{bc} + \frac{1}{ca} + \frac{1}{ab} = \frac{1}{2Rr}$

21. $\frac{r_1}{bc} + \frac{r_2}{ca} + \frac{r_3}{ab} = \frac{1}{r} - \frac{1}{2R}$

22. $r^2 + r_1^2 + r_2^2 + r_3^2 = 16R^2 - a^2 - b^2 - c^2$

➤ 208. Orthocentre and pedal triangle of any triangle.

Let ABC be any triangle and let AK, BL and CM be the perpendiculars from A, B and C upon the opposite sides of the triangle. It can be easily shown, as in most books on Geometry, that these three perpendiculars meet in a common point P. This point P is called the **orthocentre** of the triangle. The triangle KLM, which is formed by joining the feet of these perpendiculars, is called the **pedal triangle** of ABC.

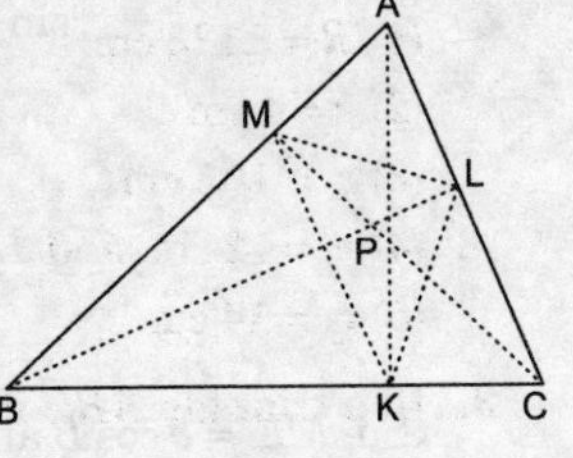

➤ 209. *Distances of the orthocentre from the angular points of the triangle.*

We have $PK = KB \tan PBK = KB \tan(90° - C)$

$$= AB \cos B \cot C = \frac{c}{\sin C} \cos B \cos C$$

$$= 2R \cos B \cos C \qquad \text{(Art. 200.)}$$

Again, $AP = AL \sec KAC$

$$= c \cos A \operatorname{cosec} C$$

$$= \frac{c}{\sin C} \cos A$$

$$= 2R \cos A \qquad \text{(Art. 200)}$$

So, $BP = 2R\cos B$, and $CP = 2R\cos C$

The distances of the orthocentre from the angular points are therefore, $2R\cos A$, $2R\cos B$ and $2R\cos C$; its distances from the sides are $2R\cos B\cos C$, $2R\cos C\cos A$ and $2R\cos A\cos B$.

➤ **210.** To find the sides and angles of the pedal triangle.

Since the angles PKC and PLC are right angles, the points P, L, C and K lie on a circle.

$$\therefore \quad \angle PKL = \angle PCL = 90° - A$$

Similarly, P, K, B and M lie on a circle, and therefore

$$\angle PKM = \angle PBM = 90° - A$$

Hence, $\angle MKL = 180° - 2A$

= the supplement of $2A$

So, $\angle KLM = 180° - 2B$

and $\angle LMK = 180° - 2C$

Again, from the triangle ALM, we have

$$\frac{LM}{\sin A} = \frac{AL}{\sin AML} = \frac{AB\cos A}{\cos PML} = \frac{c\cos A}{\cos PAL} = \frac{c\cos A}{\sin C}$$

$$\therefore \quad LM = \frac{c}{\sin C \sin A \cos A} = a\cos A \qquad \text{(Art. 163)}$$

So, $MK = b\cos B$ and $KL = c\cos C$

The sides of the pedal triangle therefore $a\cos A$, $b\cos B$ and $c\cos C$; also its angles are the supplements of twice the angles of the triangle.

➤ **211.** Let I be the centre of the incircle and I_1, I_2 and I_3 the centre of the escribed circles which are opposite to A, B and C respectively. As in Arts. 202 and 205, IC bisects the angle ACB, and I_1C bisects the angle BCM.

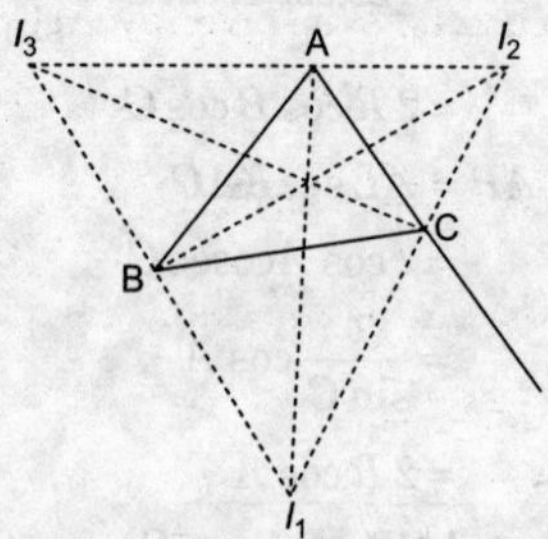

$$\therefore \quad \angle ICI_1 = \angle ICB + \angle I_1CB = \frac{1}{2}\angle ACB + \frac{1}{2}\angle MCB$$

$$= \frac{1}{2}[\angle ACB + \angle MCB]$$

$$= \frac{1}{2} \times 180° = \text{a right angle.}$$

Similarly, $\angle ICI_2$ is a right angle.

Hence, I_1CI_2 is a straight line to which IC is perpendicular.

So, I_2AI_3 is a straight line to which IA is perpendiculars, and I_3BI_1 is a straight line to which IB is perpendicular.

Also, since IA and I_1A both bisect the angle BAC, the three points A, I and I_1 are in a straight line. Similarly, BII_2 and CII_3 are straight lines. Hence, $I_1I_2I_3$ is a triangle, which is such that A, B and C are the feet of the perpendiculars drawn from its vertices upon the opposite sides and such that I is the intersection of these perpendiculars,

i.e., ABC is its pedal triangle and I is its orthocentre.

The triangle $I_1I_2I_3$ is often called the excentric triangle.

➤ 212. Centroid and medians of any triangle.

If ABC be any triangle, and D, E and F respectively the middle points of BC, CA and AB the lines AD, BE and CF are called the **medians** of the triangle.

It is shown in most books on Geometry that the medians meet in a common point G, such that

$$AG = \frac{2}{3}AD, BG = \frac{2}{3}BE$$

and $$CG = \frac{2}{3}CF$$

This point G is called the **centroid** of the triangle.

➤ 213. *Length of the medians.* We have, by Art. 164,

$$AD^2 = AC^2 + CD^2 - 2AC \cdot CD \cos C$$

$$= b^2 + \frac{a^2}{4} - ab\cos C$$

and $$c^2 = b^2 + a^2 - 2ab\cos C.$$

Hence, $$2AD^2 - c^2 = b^2 - \frac{a^2}{2}$$

so that $$AD = \frac{1}{2}\sqrt{2b^2 + 2c^2 - a^2}$$

Hence, also $$AD = \frac{1}{2}\sqrt{b^2 + c^2 + 2bc\cos A}$$ (Art. 164)

So, also $$BE = \frac{1}{2}\sqrt{2c^2 + 2a^2 - b^2} \text{ and } CF = \frac{1}{2}\sqrt{2a^2 + 2b^2 - c^2}$$

➤ **214.** ***Angles that the median AD makes with the sides.***

If the $\angle BAD = \beta$ and $\angle CAD = \gamma$, we have

$$\frac{\sin\gamma}{\sin C} = \frac{DC}{AD} = \frac{a}{2x}$$

$\therefore$ $$\sin\gamma = \frac{a\sin C}{2x} = \frac{a\sin C}{\sqrt{2b^2 + 2c^2 - a^2}}$$

Similarly, $$\sin\beta = \frac{a\sin\beta}{\sqrt{2b^2 + 2c^2 - a^2}}$$

Again, if the $\angle ADC$ be θ, we have

$$\frac{\sin\theta}{\sin C} = \frac{AC}{AD} = \frac{b}{x}$$

$\therefore$ $$\sin\theta = \frac{b\sin C}{x}$$

$$= \frac{2b\sin C}{\sqrt{2b^2 + 2c^2 - a^2}}$$

The angles that AD makes with the sides are therefore found.

➤ **215.** The centroid lies on the line joining the circumcentre to the orthocentre.

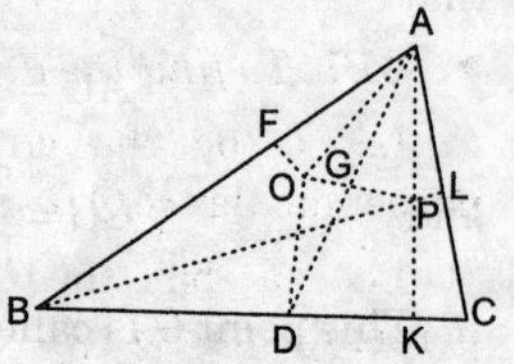

Let O and P be the circumcentre and orthocentre respectively. Draw OD and PK perpendicular to BC.

Let AD and OP meet in G. The triangles OGD and PGA are clearly equiangular.

Also, by Art. 200,

$$OD = R\cos A$$

and, by Art. 209,

$$AP = 2R\cos A$$

Hence, by similar triangles,

$$\frac{AG}{GD} = \frac{AP}{OD} = 2$$

The point G is therefore the centroid of the triangle.

Also, by the same proposition,

$$\frac{OG}{GP} = \frac{OD}{AP} = \frac{1}{2}$$

The centroid therefore lies on the line joining the circumcentre to the orthocentre and divides it in the ratio 1 : 2.

It may be shown by Geometry that the centre of the nine-point circle (which passes through the feet of the perpendiculars, the middle points of the sides, and the middle points of the lines joining the angular points to the orthocentre) lies on OP and bisects it.

The circumcentre, the centroid, the centre of the nine-point circle, and the orthocentre therefore all lie on a straight line.

➤ **216.** *Distance between the circumcentre and the orthocentre.*

If OF be perpendicular to AB, we have

$$\angle OAF = 90° - \angle AOF = 90° - C$$

Also, $$\angle PAL = 90° - C$$

$\therefore$ $$\angle OAP = A - \angle OAF - \angle PAL$$
$$= A - 2(90° - C) = A + 2C - 180°$$
$$= A + 2C - (A + B + C) = C - B$$

Also, $OA = R$ and by Art. 209,

$$PA = 2R \cos A$$

$\therefore$ $$OP^2 = OA^2 + PA^2 - 2\,OA \cdot PA \cos OAP$$
$$= R^2 + 4R^2 \cos^2 A - 4R^2 \cos A \cos(C - B)$$
$$= R^2 + 4R^2 \cos A\,[\cos A - \cos(C - B)]$$
$$= R^2 - 4R^2 \cos A\,[\cos(B + C) + \cos(C - B)] \qquad \text{(Art. 72)}$$
$$= R^2 - 8R^2 \cos A \cos B \cos C$$

$\therefore$ $$OP = R\sqrt{1 - 8 \cos A \cos B \cos C}$$

➤ **217.** *To find the distance between the circumcentre and the incentre.*

Let O be the circumcentre, and OF be perpendicular to AB.

Let I be the incentre, and IE be perpendicular to AC.

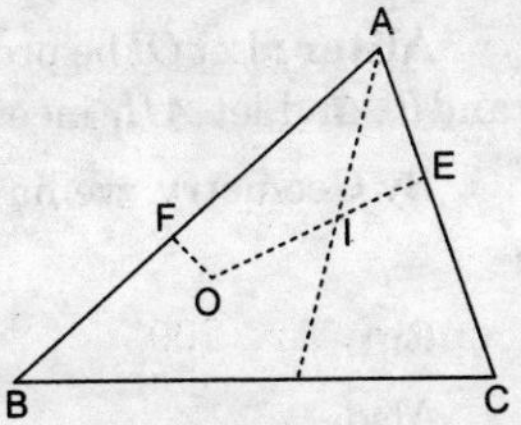

A E F I O B C

Then, as in the previous article,

$$\angle OAF = 90° - C$$

$\therefore$ $$\angle OAI = \angle IAF - \angle OAF$$
$$= \frac{A}{2} - (90° - C)$$
$$= \frac{A}{2} + C - \frac{A + B + C}{2} = \frac{C - B}{2}$$

Also, $$AI = \frac{IE}{\sin\frac{A}{2}} = \frac{r}{\sin\frac{A}{2}} = 4R \sin\frac{B}{2} \sin\frac{C}{2} \qquad \text{(Art. 204, Cor.)}$$

$\therefore$ $$OI^2 = OA^2 + AI^2 - 2\,OA \cdot AI \cos OAI$$

$$R^2 + 16R^2 \sin^2\frac{B}{2}\sin^2\frac{C}{2} - 8R^2 \sin\frac{B}{2}\sin\frac{C}{2}\cos\frac{C-B}{2}$$

$$\therefore \quad \frac{OI^2}{R^2} = 1 + 16\sin^2\frac{B}{2}\sin^2\frac{C}{2}$$

$$- 8\sin\frac{B}{2}\sin\frac{C}{2}\left(\cos\frac{B}{2}\cos\frac{C}{2} + \sin\frac{B}{2}\sin\frac{C}{2}\right)$$

$$= 1 - 8\sin\frac{B}{2}\sin\frac{C}{2}\left(\cos\frac{B}{2}\cos\frac{C}{2} - \sin\frac{B}{2}\sin\frac{C}{2}\right)$$

$$= 1 - 8\sin\frac{B}{2}\sin\frac{C}{2}\cos\frac{B+C}{2}$$

$$= 1 - 8\sin\frac{B}{2}\sin\frac{C}{2}\sin\frac{A}{2} \qquad \text{(Art 69) ...(1)}$$

$$\therefore \quad OI = R\sqrt{1 - 8\sin\frac{B}{2}\sin\frac{C}{2}\sin\frac{A}{2}}$$

Also (1) may be written

$$OI^2 = R^2 - 2R \times 4R\sin\frac{A}{2}\sin\frac{B}{2}\sin\frac{C}{2}$$

$$= R^2 - 2Rr \qquad \text{(Art. 204, Cor)}$$

In a similar manner it may be shown that, if I_1 be the centre of the escribed circle opposite the angle A, we shall have

$$OI_1 = R\sqrt{1 + 8\sin\frac{A}{2}\cos\frac{B}{2}\cos\frac{C}{2}}$$

and hence, $OI_1^2 = R^2 + 2Rr_1$ (Art. 207, Cor.)

Aliter : Let OI be produced to meet the circumcircle of the triangle in S and T, and let AII_1 meet it in H.

By Geometry, we have

$$SI \cdot IT = AI \cdot IH \qquad \text{...(2)}$$

But $SI \cdot IT = (R + OI)(R - OI) = R^2 - OI^2$

Also,

$$\angle HIC = \angle ICA + \angle IAC$$

$$= \angle ICB + \angle HAB$$

$$= \angle ICB + \angle HCB$$

$$= \angle HCI$$

$$\therefore \quad HI = HC = 2R\sin\frac{A}{2} \qquad \text{(Art. 200)}$$

Also,

$$AI = \frac{IE}{\sin\frac{A}{2}} = \frac{r}{\sin\frac{A}{2}}$$

Substituting in (2), we have

$$R^2 - OI^2 = 2\,Rr$$

i.e., $$OI^2 = R^2 - 2\,Rr$$

Similarly, we can show that $I_1H = I_1C$ and hence that

$$I_1O^2 - R^2 = I_1H \cdot I_1A = 2\,R\,r_1$$

i.e., $$I_1O^2 = R^2 + 2\,R\,r_1$$

➤ **218. Bisectors of the angles :** If AD bisect the angle A and divide the base into portions x and y, we have, by Geometry,

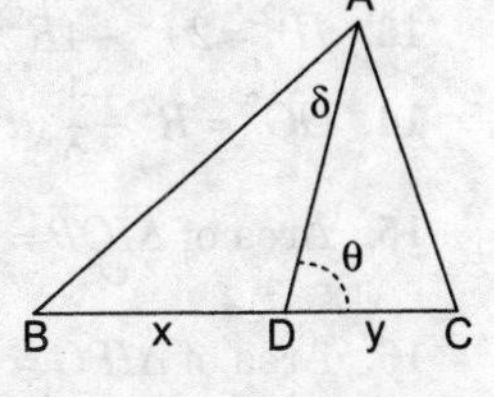

$$\frac{x}{y} = \frac{AB}{AC} = \frac{c}{b}$$

$$\therefore \quad \frac{x}{c} = \frac{y}{b} = \frac{x+y}{b+c} = \frac{a}{b+c} \quad ...(1)$$

giving x and y

Also, if δ be the length of AD and θ the angle it makes with BC, we have

$$\Delta ABD + \Delta ACD = \Delta ABC$$

$$\therefore \quad \frac{1}{2} c\delta \sin\frac{A}{2} + \frac{1}{2} b\delta \sin\frac{A}{2} = \frac{1}{2} bc \sin A$$

i.e., $$\delta = \frac{bc}{b+c} \frac{\sin A}{\sin\frac{A}{2}} = \frac{2bc}{b+c} \cos\frac{A}{2} \quad ...(2)$$

Also, $$\theta = \angle DAB + B = \frac{A}{2} + B \quad ...(3)$$

We thus, have the length of the bisector and its inclination to BC .

EXAMPLES XXXVII

If I, I_1, I_2 and I_3 be respectively the centres of the incircle and the three escribed circles of a triangle ABC, prove that:

1. $AI = r \operatorname{cosec}\frac{A}{2}$
2. $IA \cdot IB \cdot IC = abc \tan\frac{A}{2} \tan\frac{B}{2} \tan\frac{C}{2}$
3. $AI_1 = r_1 \operatorname{cosec}\frac{A}{2}$
4. $II_1 = a \sec\frac{A}{2}$
5. $I_2I_3 = a \operatorname{cosec}\frac{A}{2}$
6. $II_1 \cdot II_2 \cdot II_3 = 16R^2r$
7. $I_2I_3^2 = 4R(r_2 + r_3)$
8. $\angle I_3I_1I_2 = \frac{B+C}{2}$

9. $II_1^2 + I_2I_3^2 = II_2^2 + I_3I_1^2 = II_3^2 + I_1I_2^2$

10. Area of $\Delta I_1I_2I_3 = 8R^2 \cos\frac{A}{2}\cos\frac{B}{2}\cos\frac{C}{2} = \frac{abc}{2r}$

11. $\frac{II_1 \cdot I_2I_3}{\sin A} = \frac{II_2 \cdot I_3I_1}{\sin B} = \frac{II_3 \cdot I_1I_2}{\sin C}$

If I, O and P be respectively the incentre, circumcentre, and orthocentre, and G the centroid of the triangle ABC, prove that.

12. $IO^2 = R^2(3 - 2\cos A - 2\cos B - 2\cos C)$.

13. $IP^2 = 2r^2 - 4R^2 \cos A \cos B \cos C$

14. $OG^2 = R^2 - \frac{1}{9}(a^2 + b^2 + c^2)$

15. Area of $\Delta IOP = 2R^2 \sin\frac{B-C}{2}\sin\frac{C-A}{2}\sin\frac{A-B}{2}$

16. Area of $\Delta IPG = \frac{4}{3}R^2 \sin\frac{B-C}{2}\sin\frac{C-A}{2}\sin\frac{A-B}{2}$

17. Prove that the distance of the centre of the nine-point circle from the angle A is $\frac{R}{2}\sqrt{1 + 8\cos A \sin B \sin C}$.

18. DEF is the pedal triangle of ABC, prove that

(1) its area is $2S\cos A \cos B \cos C$

(2) the radius of its circumcircle is $\frac{R}{2}$ and

(3) the radius of its incircle is $2R\cos A \cos B \cos C$

19. $O_1O_2O_3$ is the triangle formed by the centres of the escribed circles of the triangle ABC; prove that:

(1) its sides are $4R\cos\frac{A}{2}$, $4R\cos\frac{B}{2}$ and $4R\cos\frac{C}{2}$

(2) its angles are $\frac{\pi}{2} - \frac{A}{2}, \frac{\pi}{2} - \frac{B}{2}$ and $\frac{\pi}{2} - \frac{C}{2}$ and

(3) its area is $2Rs$

20. DEF is the triangle formed by joining the points of contact of the incircle with the sides of the triangle ABC; prove that:

(1) its sides are $2r\cos\frac{A}{2}$, $2r\cos\frac{B}{2}$ and $2r\cos\frac{C}{2}$

(2) its angles are $\frac{\pi}{2} - \frac{A}{2}, \frac{\pi}{2} - \frac{B}{2}$ and $\frac{\pi}{2} - \frac{C}{2}$ and

(3) its area is $\frac{2S^2}{abcs}$, *i.e.*, $\frac{1}{2}\frac{r}{R}S$.

21. D, E and F are the middle points of the sides of the triangle ABC; prove that the centroid of the triangle DEF is the same as that of ABC, and that its orthocentre is the circumcentre of ABC.

In any triangle ABC, prove that,

22. The perpendicular from A divides BC into portions which are proportional to the contangents of the adjacent angles, and that it

divides the angle A into portions whose cosines are inversely proportional to the adjacent sides.

23. The median through A divides it into angles whose cotangents are $2\cot A + \cot C$ and $2\cot A + \cot B$ and makes with the base an angle whose cotangent is $\frac{1}{2}(\cot C \sim \cot B)$

24. The distance between the middle point of BC and the foot of the perpendicular from A is $\dfrac{b^2 \sim c^2}{2a}$

25. O is the orthocentre of a triangle ABC; prove that the radii of the circles circumscribing the triangles BOC, COA, AOB and ABC are all equal.

26. AD, BE and CF are the perpendiculars from the angular points of a triangle ABC upon the opposite sides; prove that the diameters of the circumcircles of the triangles AEF, BDF and CDE are respectively $a\cot A$, $b\cos B$, and $c\cot C$ and that the perimeter of the triangles DEF and ABC are in the ratio $r : R$.

27. Prove that the product of the distances of the incentre from the angular points of a triangle is $4Rr^2$.

28. The triangle DEF circumscribes the three escribed circles of the triangle ABC; prove that,

$$\frac{EF}{a\cos A} = \frac{FD}{b\cos B} = \frac{DE}{c\cos C}$$

29. If a circle be drawn touching the inscribed and circumscribed circles of a triangle and the side BC externally, prove that its radius is,

$$\frac{\Delta}{a}\tan^2\frac{A}{2}$$

30. If a, b and c be the radii of three circles which touch one another externally and r_1 and r_2 be the radii of the two circles that can be drawn to touch these three, prove that,

$$\frac{1}{r_1} - \frac{1}{r_2} = \frac{2}{a} + \frac{2}{b} + \frac{2}{c}$$

31. If Δ_0 be the area of the triangle formed by joining the points of contact of the inscribed circle with the sides of the given triangle, whose area is Δ, and Δ_1, Δ_2, and Δ_3 the corresponding areas for the escribed circles, prove that,

$$\Delta_1 + \Delta_2 + \Delta_3 - \Delta_0 = 2\Delta$$

32. If the bisectors of the angles of a triangle ABC meet the opposite sides in A', B', and C', prove that the ratio of the areas of the triangles $A'B'C'$ and ABC is

$$2\sin\frac{A}{2}\sin\frac{B}{2}\sin\frac{C}{2} ; \cos\frac{A-B}{2}\cos\frac{B-C}{2}\cos\frac{C-A}{2}$$

33. Through the angular points of a triangle are drawn straight lines which make the same angle α with the opposite sides of the triangle; prove that the area of the triangle formed by them is to the area of the original triangle as $4\cos^2\alpha : 1$.

34. Two circles, of radii a and b, cut each other at an angle θ. Prove that the length of the common chord is

$$\frac{2ab\sin\theta}{\sqrt{a^2+b^2+2ab\cos\theta}}$$

35. Three equal circles touch one another, find the radius of the circle which touches all three.

36. Three circles, whose radii are a, b and c touch one another externally and the tangents at their points of contact meet in a point; prove that the distance of this point from either of their points of contact is

$$\left(\frac{abc}{a+b+c}\right)^{\frac{1}{2}}$$

37. In the sides BC, CA, AB are taken three points A', B', C' such that $BA' ; A'C = CB' : B'A = AC' ; C'B = m : n$;

prove that if AA', BB' and CC' be joined they will form by their intersections a triangle whose area is to that of the triangle ABC as

$$(m-n)^2 : m^2+mn+n^2$$

38. The circle inscribed in the triangle ABC touches the sides BC, CA and AB in the points A_1, B_1 and C_1 respectively; similarly the circle inscribed in the triangle $A_1B_1C_1$ touches the sides in A_2, B_2, C_2 respectively, and so on; if $A_n\,B_n\,C_n$ be the nth triangle so formed, prove that its angles are

$$\frac{\pi}{3}+(-2)^{-n}\left(A-\frac{\pi}{3}\right), \frac{\pi}{3}+(-2)^{-n}\left(B-\frac{\pi}{3}\right)$$

and

$$\frac{\pi}{3}+(-2)^{-n}\left(C-\frac{\pi}{3}\right)$$

Hence, prove that the triangle so formed is ultimately equilateral.

39. $A_1B_1C_1$ is the triangle formed by joining the feet of the perpendiculars drawn from ABC upon the opposite sides; in like manner $A_2B_2C_2$ is the triangle obtained by joining the feet of the perpendiculars from A_1, B_1 and C_1 on the opposite sides and so on. Find the values of the angles A_n, B_n and C_n in the nth of these triangles.

40. The legs of a tripod are each 10 cm. in length, and their points of contact with a horizontal table on which the tripod stands from a triangle whose sides are 7, 8 ad 9 cm. in length. Find the inclination of the legs to the horizontal and the height of the apex.

16

QUADRILATERALS

➤ **219.** *To find the area of a quadrilateral which is inscribable in a circle.*

Let $ABCD$ be the quadrilateral, the sides being a, b, c and d as marked in the figure.

The area of the quadrilateral

$$= \text{area of } \Delta ABC + \text{area of } \Delta ADC$$

$$= \frac{1}{2}\, ab \sin B + \frac{1}{2}\, cd \sin D \quad \text{(Art. 198)}$$

$$= \frac{1}{2}\,(ab + cd) \sin B,$$

since, by Geometry,

$$\angle B = 180° - \angle D,$$

and therefore, $\quad \sin B = \sin D$

We have to express $\sin B$ in terms of the sides.

We have $\quad a^2 + b^2 - 2ab \cos B = AC^2 = c^2 + d^2 - 2cd \cos D$

But $\quad \cos D = \cos (180° - B) = -\cos B$

Hence, $\quad a^2 + b^2 - 2ab \cos B = c^2 + d^2 + 2cd \cos B,$

so that

$$\cos B = \frac{a^2 + b^2 - c^2 - d^2}{2\,(ab + cd)}$$

Hence, $\quad \sin^2 B = 1 - \cos^2 B$

$$= 1 - \frac{(a^2 + b^2 - c^2 - d^2)^2}{\{2\,(ab + cd)\}^2}$$

$$= \frac{\{2\,(ab + cd)\}^2 - \{a^2 + b^2 - c^2 - d^2\}^2}{4(ab + cd)^2}$$

$$= \frac{\{2\,(ab + cd) + (a^2 + b^2 - c^2 - d^2)\}\{2(ab + cd) - (a^2 + b^2 - c^2 - d^2)\}}{4(ab + cd)^2}$$

$$= \frac{\{(a^2 + 2ab + b^2) - (c^2 - 2cd + d^2)\}\{(c^2 + 2cd + d^2) - (a^2 + b^2 - 2ab)\}}{4(ab + cd)^2}$$

$$= \frac{\{(a+b)^2 - (c-d)^2\}\{(c+d)^2 - (a-b)^2\}}{4(ab+cd)^2}$$

$$= \frac{\{(a+b+c-d)(a+b-c+d)\}\{(c+d+a-b)(c+d-a+b)\}}{4(ab+cd)^2}$$

Let $\quad a+b+c+d = 2s,$

so that $\quad a+b+c-d = (a+b+c+d) - 2d = 2(s-d),$

$\quad a+b-c+d = 2(s-c),$

$\quad a-b+c+d = 2(s-b),$

and $\quad -a+b+c+d = 2(s-a)$

Hence, $\quad \sin^2 B = \dfrac{2(s-d)\times 2(s-c)\times 2(s-b)\times 2(s-a)}{4(ab+cd)^2},$

so that $\quad (ab+cd)\sin B = 2\sqrt{(s-a)(s-b)(s-c)(s-d)}$

Hence, the area of the quadrilateral

$$= \frac{1}{2}(ab+cd)\sin B$$

$$= \sqrt{(\boldsymbol{s}-\boldsymbol{a})(\boldsymbol{s}-\boldsymbol{b})(\boldsymbol{s}-\boldsymbol{c})(\boldsymbol{s}-\boldsymbol{d})}$$

➤ **220.** Since, $\cos B = \dfrac{a^2+b^2-c^2-d^2}{2(ab+cd)},$

we have $\quad AC^2 = a^2 + b^2 - 2ab\cos B$

$$= a^2 + b^2 - ab\,\frac{a^2+b^2-c^2-d^2}{ab+cd}$$

$$= \frac{(a^2+b^2)\,cd + ab\,(c^2+d^2)}{ab+cd}$$

$$= \frac{(ac+bd)(ad+bc)}{ab+cd}.$$

Similarly, it could be proved that

$$BD^2 = \frac{(ab+cd)(ac+bd)}{ad+bc}.$$

We thus have the lengths of the diagonals of the quadrilateral. It follows by multiplication that

$$AC^2 \cdot BD^2 = (ac+bd)^2,$$

i.e., $\quad AC \cdot BD = AB \cdot CD + BC \cdot AD$

This is a well-known proposition in Geometry.

Again, the radius of the circle circumscribing the quadrilateral

$$= \frac{1}{2} \frac{AC}{\sin B}$$

$$= \sqrt{\frac{(ac+bd)(ad+bc)}{ab+cd}} \div 4\sqrt{\frac{(s-a)(s-b)(s-c)(s-d)}{(ab+cd)^2}}$$

$$= \frac{1}{4}\sqrt{\frac{(ab+cd)(ac+bd)(ad+bc)}{(s-a)(s-b)(s-c)(s-d)}}$$

➤ **221.** If we have any quadrilateral, not necessarily inscribable in a circle, we can express its area in terms of its sides and the sum of any two opposite angles.

For let the sum of the two angles B and D be denoted by 2α, and denote the area of the quadrilateral by Δ.

$$\Delta = \text{area of } ABC + \text{area of } ACD$$

$$= \frac{1}{2} ab \sin B + \frac{1}{2} cd \sin D,$$

so that $$4\Delta = 2ab \sin B + 2cd \sin D \quad \ldots(1)$$

Also $$a^2 + b^2 - 2ab \cos B = c^2 + d^2 - 2cd \cos D,$$

so that $$a^2 + b^2 - c^2 - d^2 = 2\,ab \cos B - 2\,cd \cos D \quad \ldots(2)$$

Squaring (1) and (2) and adding, we have

$$16\Delta^2 + (a^2 + b^2 - c^2 - d^2)^2 = 4a^2b^2 + 4c^2d^2 - 8abcd\,(\cos B \cos D - \sin B \sin D)$$

$$= 4a^2b^2 + 4c^2d^2 - 8abcd \cos (B + D)$$

$$= 4a^2b^2 + 4c^2d^2 - 8abcd \cos 2\alpha$$

$$= 4a^2b^2 + 4c^2d^2 - 8abcd\,(2\cos^2 \alpha - 1)$$

$$= 4(ab + cd)^2 - 16abcd \cos^2 \alpha,$$

so that,

$$16\Delta^2 = 4(ab + cd)^2 - (a^2 + b^2 - c^2 - d^2)^2 - 16abcd \cos^2 \alpha \quad \ldots(3)$$

But, as in Art. 219, we have

$$4(ab + cd)^2 - (a^2 + b^2 - c^2 - d^2) = 2\,(s-a)\cdot 2\,(s-b)\cdot 2\,(s-c)\cdot 2\,(s-d)$$

$$= 16(s-a)(s-b)(s-c)(s-d)$$

Hence, (3) becomes

$\Delta^2 = (s-a)(s-b)(s-c)(s-d) - abcd \cos^2 \alpha$, giving the required area.

Cor. 1: If d be zero, the quadrilateral becomes a triangle, and the formula above becomes that of Art. 198.

Cor. 2: If the sides of the quadrilateral be given in length, we know a, b, c, d and therefore, s. The area Δ is hence, greatest when $abcd \cos^2 \alpha$ is least, that is when $\cos^2 \alpha$ is zero, and then $\alpha = 90°$. In this case the sum of two opposite angles of the quadrilateral is 180° and the figure inscribable in a circle.

The quadrilateral, whose sides are given, has therefore the greatest area when it can be inscribed in a circle.

➤ 222.

EXAMPLE *Find the area of a quadrilateral which can have a circle inscribed in it.*

If the quadrilateral $ABCD$ can have a circle inscribed in it so as to touch the sides AB, BC, CD, and DA in the points P, Q, R, and S, we should have

$$AP = AS, BP = BQ, CQ = CR, \text{ and } DR = DS.$$

$$\therefore \quad AP + BP + CR + DR = AS + BQ + CQ + DS,$$

i.e., $$AB + CD = BC + DA,$$

i.e., $$a + c = b + d$$

Hence, $s = \dfrac{a+b+c+d}{2} = a + c = b + d.$

$$\therefore \quad s - a = c, s - b = d, s - c = a, \text{ and } s - d = b$$

The formula of the previous article therefore, gives in this case

$$\Delta^2 = abcd - abcd \cos^2 \alpha = abcd \sin^2 \alpha,$$

i.e., the area required $= \sqrt{abcd} \sin \alpha$.

If in addition the quadrilateral be also inscribable in the circle, we have $2\alpha = 180°$, so that $\sin \alpha = \sin 90° = 1$,

Hence, the area of a quadrilateral which can be both inscribed in a circle and circumscribed about another circle is $\sqrt{abcd}$.

EXAMPLES XXXVIII

1. Find the area of a quadrilateral, which can be inscribed in a circle, whose sides are
   (1) 3, 5, 7 and 9 cm; and (2) 7, 10, 5, and 2 cm.
2. The sides of a quadrilateral are respectively 3, 4, 5, and 6 cm, and the sum of a pair of opposite angles is 120°; prove that the area of the quadrilateral is $3\sqrt{30}$ sq. cm.
3. The sides of a quadrilateral which can be inscribed in a circle are 3, 3, 4, and 4 cm; find the radii of the incircle and circumcircle.
4. Prove that the area of any quadrilateral is one-half the product of the two diagonals and the sine of the angle between them.

5. If a quadrilateral can be inscribed in one circle and circumscribed about another circle, prove that its area is $\sqrt{abcd}$, and that the radius of the latter circle is

$$\frac{2\sqrt{abcd}}{a+b+c+d}.$$

6. A quadrilateral $ABCD$ is described about a circle; prove that

$$AB \sin\frac{A}{2}\sin\frac{B}{2} = CD \sin\frac{C}{2}\sin\frac{D}{2}$$

7. a, b, c and d are the sides of a quadrilateral taken in order, and α is the angle between the diagonals opposite to b or d; prove that the area of the quadrilateral is

$$\frac{1}{4}(a^2 - b^2 + c^2 - d^2)\tan\alpha$$

8. If a, b, c and d be the sides and x and y the diagonals of a quadrilateral, prove that its area is

$$\frac{1}{4}[4x^2y^2 - (b^2 + d^2 - a^2 - c^2)^2]^{1/2}$$

9. If a quadrilateral can be inscribed in a circle, prove that the angle between its diagonals is

$$\sin^{-1}[2\sqrt{(s-a)(s-b)(s-c)(s-d)} \div (ac+bd)]$$

If the same quadrilateral can also be circumscribed about a circle, prove that this angle is then

$$\cos^{-1}\frac{ac-bd}{ac+bd}$$

10. The sides of a quadrilateral are divided in order in the ratio $m : n$, and a new quadrilateral is formed by joining the points of division; prove that its area is to the area of the original figure as $m^2 + n^2$ to $(m+n)^2$.

11. If $ABCD$ be a quadrilateral inscribed in a circle, prove that

$$\tan\frac{B}{2} = \sqrt{\frac{(s-a)(s-b)}{(s-c)(s-d)}},$$

and that the product of the segments into which one diagonal is divided by the other diagonal is

$$\frac{abcd\,(ac+bd)}{(ab+cd)(ad+bc)}.$$

12. If a, b, c and d be the sides of a quadrilateral, taken in order, prove that

$$d^2 = a^2 + b^2 + c^2 - 2ab\cos\alpha - 2bc\cos\beta - 2ca\cos\gamma,$$

where α, β, and γ denote the angles between the sides a and b, b and c, and c and a respectively.

➤ **223. Regular Polygons.** A regular polygon is a polygon which has all its sides equal and all its angles equal.

If the polygon have n angles we have, by Geometry, n times its angle + 4 right angles = twice as many right angles as the figure has sides = $2n$ right angles.

Hence, each angle $= \dfrac{2n-4}{n}$ right angles $= \dfrac{2n-4}{n} \times \dfrac{\pi}{2}$ radians.

➤ **224.** *Radii of the inscribed and circumscribing circles of a regular polygon.*

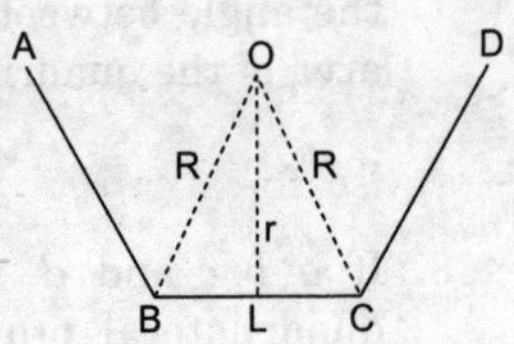

Let AB, BC and CD be three successive sides of the polygon, and let n be the number of its sides.

Bisect the angles ABC and BCD by the lines BO and CO which meet in O, and draw OL perpendicular to BC.

It is easily seen that O is the centre of both the incircle and the circumcircle of the polygon, and that BL equals LC.

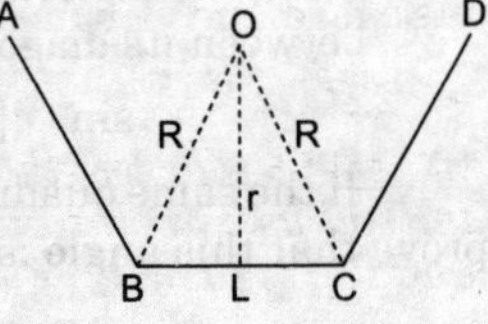

Hence, we have $OB = OC = R$, the radius of the circumcircle, and $OL = r$, the radius of the incircle.

The angle BOC is $\dfrac{1}{n}$ th of the sum of all the angles subtended at O by the sides, *i.e.*,

$$\angle BOC = \frac{4 \text{ right angles}}{n}$$

$$= \frac{2\pi}{n} \text{ radians.}$$

Hence, $\quad \angle BOL = \dfrac{1}{2} \angle BOC = \dfrac{\pi}{2}.$

If a be a side of the polygon, we have

$$a = BC = 2BL$$

$$= 2R \sin BOL = 2R \sin \frac{\pi}{n}$$

$$\therefore \qquad R = \frac{a}{2 \sin \frac{\pi}{n}} = \frac{a}{2} \operatorname{cosec} \frac{\pi}{n} \qquad \ldots(1)$$

Again, $a = 2\,BL = 2\,OL \tan BOL = 2\,r \tan \dfrac{\pi}{n}.$

$$\therefore \qquad r = \frac{a}{2\tan\frac{\pi}{n}} = \frac{a}{n}\cot\frac{\pi}{n} \qquad \text{...(2)}$$

➤ 225. Area of a Regular Polygon.

The area of the polygon is n times the area of the triangle BOC. Hence, the area of the polygon

$$= n \times \frac{1}{2} OL \cdot BC = n \cdot OL \cdot BL = n \cdot BL \cot LOB \cdot BL$$

$$= n \cdot \frac{a^2}{4} \cot\frac{\pi}{n} \qquad \text{...(1)}$$

an expression for the area in terms of the side.

Also, the area $= n \cdot OL \cdot BL = n \cdot OL \cdot OL \tan BOL = nr^2 \tan\frac{\pi}{n}$ ... (2)

Again, the area $= n \cdot OL \cdot BL = n \cdot OB \cos LOB \cdot OB \sin LOB$

$$= nR^2 \cos\frac{\pi}{n} \sin\frac{\pi}{n} = \frac{n}{2} R^2 \sin\frac{2\pi}{n} \qquad \text{... (3)}$$

The formulae (2) and (3) give the area in terms of the radius of the inscribed and circumscribed circles.

➤ 226.

EXAMPLE *The length of each side of a regular dodecagon is 20 cm; find* (1) *the radius of its inscribed circle,* (2) *the radius of its circumscribing circle, and* (3) *its area.*

The angle subtended by a side at the centre of the polygon

$$= \frac{360°}{12} = 30°$$

Hence, we have $\quad 10 = r \tan 15° = R \sin 15°$

$$\therefore \qquad r = 10 \cot 15°$$

$$= \frac{10}{2-\sqrt{3}} \qquad \text{(Art. 101)}$$

$$= 10(2+\sqrt{3}) = 37.32 \ldots \text{cm}$$

Also,

$$R = \frac{10}{\sin 15°} = 10 \times \frac{2\sqrt{2}}{\sqrt{3}-1} \qquad \text{(Art. 106)}$$

$$= 10 \cdot \sqrt{2}\,(\sqrt{3}+1) = 10(\sqrt{6}+\sqrt{2})$$

$$= 10(2.4495\ldots + 1.4142\ldots) = 38.637 \ldots \text{cm}$$

Again, $\quad$ the area $= 12 \times r \times 10$ sq cm

$$= 1200(2+\sqrt{3}) = 4478.46 \ldots \text{sq cm}$$

EXAMPLES XXXIX

1. Find, correct to 0.01 of a cm, the length of the perimeter of a regular decagon which surrounds a circle of radius 12 cm [$\tan 18° = 0.32492$.]
2. Find to 3 places of decimals the length of the side of a regular polygon of 12 sides which is circumscribed to a circle of unit radius.
3. Find the area of (1) a pentagon, (2) a hexagon, (3) an octagon, (4) a decagon and (5) a dodecagon, each being a regular figure of side 1 metre [$\cot 18° = 3.07768\ldots$; $\cot 36° = 1.37638\ldots$]
4. Find the difference between the areas of a regular octagon and a regular hexagon if the perimeter of each is 24 cm.
5. A square, whose side is 2 cm, has its corners cut away so as to form a regular octagon; find its area.
6. Compare the areas, and perimeters of octagons which are respectively inscribed in and circumscribed to a given circle, and show that the area of the inscribed hexagon and octagon are as $\sqrt{27}$ to $\sqrt{32}$.
7. Prove that the radius of the circle described about a regular pentagon is nearly $\frac{17}{20}$ ths of the side of the pentagon.
8. If an equilateral triangle and a regular hexagon have the same perimeter, prove that their areas are as $2:3$.
9. If a regular pentagon and a regular decagon have the same perimeter, prove that their areas are as $2:\sqrt{5}$.
10. Prove that the sum of the radii of the circles, which are respectively inscribed in and circumscribed about a regular polygon of n sides, is $\frac{a}{2}\cot\frac{\pi}{2n}$, where a is a side of the polygon.
11. Of two regular polygons of n sides, one circumscribes and the other is inscribed in a given circle. Prove that the perimeters of the circumscribing polygon, the circle, and the inscribed polygon are in the ratio

$$\sec\frac{\pi}{n} : \frac{\pi}{n}\operatorname{cosec}\frac{\pi}{n} : 1$$

and that the areas of the polygons are in the ratio $\cos^2\frac{\pi}{n} : 1$.
12. Given that the area of a polygon of n sides circumscribed about a circle is to the area of the circumscribed polygon of $2n$ sides as $3:2$, find n.
13. Prove that the area of a regular polygon of $2n$ sides inscribed in a circle is a mean proportional between the areas of the regular inscribed and circumscribed polygons of n sides.

14. The area of a regular polygon of n sides inscribed in a circle is to that of the same number of sides circumscribing the same circle as 3 is to 4. Find the value of n.

15. The interior angles of a polygon are in A.P.; the least angle is 120° and the common difference is 5°; find the number of sides.

16. There are two regular polygons, the number of sides in one being double the number in the other, and an angle of one polygon is to an angle of the other, as 9 to 8; find the number of sides of each polygon.

17. Show that there are eleven pairs of regular polygons such that the number of degrees in the angle of the one is to the number in the angle of the other as 10 : 9. Find the number of sides in each.

18. The side of a base of a square pyramid is a metres and its vertex is at a height of h metres about the centre of the base; if θ and ϕ be respectively the inclinations of any face to the base, and of any two faces to one another, prove that

$$\tan\theta = \frac{2h}{a} \text{ and } \tan\frac{\phi}{2} = \sqrt{1 + \frac{a^2}{2h^2}}.$$

19. A pyramid stands on a regular hexagon as base. The perpendicular from the vertex of the pyramid on the base passes through the centre of the hexagon, and its length is equal to that of a side of the base. Find the tangent of the angle between the base and any face of the pyramid, and also of half the angle between any two side faces.

20. A regular pyramid has for its base a polygon of n sides, and each slant face consists of an isosceles triangle of vertical angle 2α. If the slant faces are each inclined at an angle β to the base, and at an angle 2γ to one another, show that

$$\cos\beta = \tan\alpha \cot\frac{\pi}{n},$$

and

$$\sin\gamma = \sec\alpha \cos\frac{\pi}{n}.$$

17

TRIGONOMETRICAL RATIOS OF $\sin\theta < \theta < \tan\theta$ SMALL ANGLES

➤ **227.** *If θ be the number of radians in any angle, which is less than a right angle, then $\sin\theta, \theta,$ and $\tan\theta$ are in ascending order of magnitude.*

Let *TOP* be any angle which is less than a right angle.

With centre *O* and any radius *OP*, describe an arc *PAP′* meeting *OT* in *A*.

Draw *PN* perpendicular to *OA*, and produce it to meet the arc of the circle in *P′*.

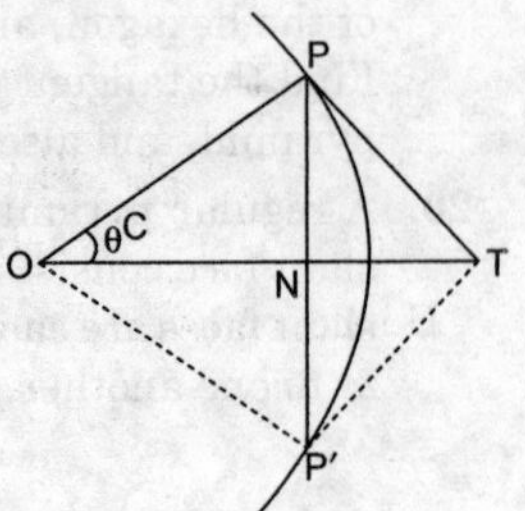

Draw the tangent *PT* at *P* to meet *OA* in *T*, and join *TP′*.

The triangles *PON* and *P′ON* are equal in all respects, so that

$$PN = NP' \text{ and arc } PA = \text{arc } AP'.$$

Also the triangles *TOP* and *TOP′* are equal in all respects, so that

$$TP = TP'.$$

The straight line *PP′* is less than the arc *PAP′*, so that *NP* is < arc *PA*.

We shall assume that the arc *PAP′* is less than the sum of *PT* and *TP′*, so that arc *PA* < *PT*.

Hence, *NP*, the arc *AP*, and *PT* are in ascending order of magnitude.

$$\sin\theta < \theta < \tan\theta$$

Therefore, $\dfrac{NP}{OP}, \dfrac{\text{arc } AP}{OP}$, and $\dfrac{PT}{OP}$ are in ascending order of magnitude.

But $\dfrac{NP}{OP} = \sin AOP = \sin\theta$,

$$\frac{\text{arc } AP}{OP} = \text{number of radians in } \angle AOP = \theta \qquad \text{(Art. 21)},$$

and $\dfrac{PT}{OP} = \tan POT = \tan AOP = \tan\theta$.

Hence, $\sin\theta$, θ and $\tan\theta$ are in ascending order of magnitude, provided that $\theta < \dfrac{\pi}{2}$.

The assumption made in the previous article may be proved as follows:

Divide the arc PP' into a large number, n, of equal parts, and let the points of division be $A_1, A_2, A_3, \ldots A_{n-1}$.

Let PA_1 meet TP' in B_1, let A_1A_2 meet it in B_2, A_2A_3 in B_3, ... and finally let $A_{n-2}A_{n-1}$ meet it in B_{n-1}.

Since two sides of a triangle are always greater than the third, we have

$$PT + TB_1 > PB_1, \textit{ i.e.}, > PA_1 + A_1B_1,$$

$$A_1B_1 + B_1B_2, > A_1B_2 \textit{ i.e.}, > A_1A_2 + A_2B_2,$$

$$A_2B_2 + B_2B_3 > A_2A_3 + A_3B_3,$$

$$\ldots \quad \ldots \quad \ldots$$

$$A_{n-2}B_{n-2} + B_{n-2}B_{n-1} > A_{n-2}A_{n-1} + A_{n-1}B_{n-1},$$

and $$A_{n-1}B_{n-1} + B_{n-1}P' > A_{n-1}P'.$$

Hence, on adding and cancelling like quantities, we have

$$PT + TB_1 + B_1B_2 + B_2B_3 + \ldots + B_{n-1}P'$$
$$> PA_1 + A_1A_2 + A_2A_3 + \ldots A_{n-1}P',$$

i.e., $$PT + TP' > PA_1 + A_1A_2 + A_2A_3 + \ldots + A_{n-1}P' \qquad \ldots (1)$$

Now, let the number, n, of subdivisions be indefinitely increased; the right-hand side of (1) becomes ultimately equal to the arc PP', and we thus have

$$PT + TP' > \text{the arc } PP'.$$

➤ **228.** Since, $\sin\theta < \theta < \tan\theta$, we have, by dividing each by the positive quantity $\sin\theta$,

$$1 < \frac{\theta}{\sin\theta} < \frac{1}{\cos\theta}.$$

Hence, $\dfrac{\theta}{\sin\theta}$ always lies between 1 and $\dfrac{1}{\cos\theta}$.

This holds however small θ may be.

Now, when θ is very small, $\cos\theta$ is very nearly unity, and the smaller θ becomes, the more nearly does $\cos\theta$ become unity, and hence the more nearly does $\frac{1}{\cos\theta}$ become unity.

Hence, when θ is very small, the quantity $\frac{\theta}{\sin\theta}$ lies between 1 and a quantity which differs from unity by an indefinitely small quantity. In other words, when θ is made indefinitely small the quantity $\frac{\theta}{\sin\theta}$, and therefore $\frac{\sin\theta}{\theta}$, is ultimately equal to unity, *i.e.*, the smaller an angle becomes the more nearly is its sine equal to the number of radians in it.

This is often shortly expressed thus:

$$\sin\theta = \theta, \qquad \text{when } \theta \text{ is very small.}$$

So also

$$\tan\theta = \theta, \qquad \text{when } \theta \text{ is very small.}$$

Cor. : Putting $\theta = \frac{\alpha}{n}$, it follows that, when θ is indefinitely small, n is indefinitely great.

Hence, $\dfrac{\sin\frac{\alpha}{n}}{\frac{\alpha}{n}}$ is unity,

when n is indefinitely great.

So, $n\sin\frac{\alpha}{n} = \alpha$, when n is indefinitely great.

Similarly, $n\tan\frac{\alpha}{n} = \alpha$, when n is indefinitely great.

➤ **229.** In the preceding article it must be particularly noticed that θ is the number of radians in the angle considered.

The value of $\sin\alpha°$, when α is small, may be found. For, since $\pi° = 180°$, we have

$$\alpha° = \left(\pi\frac{\alpha}{180}\right)^{\circ}.$$

$$\therefore \qquad \sin\alpha° = \sin\left(\frac{\pi\alpha}{180}\right)^{\circ} = \frac{\pi\alpha}{180},$$

by the result of the previous article.

➤ **230.** From the tables it will be seen that the sine of an angle and its circular measure agree to 7 places of decimals so long as the angle is not greater than 18′. The agree to the 5th place of decimals so long as the angle is less than about 2°.

➤ **231.** If θ *be the number of radians in an angle, which is less than a right angle,* then $\sin\theta$ is $> \theta - \frac{\theta^2}{4}$ and $\cos\theta$ is $> 1 - \frac{\theta^2}{2}$.

By Art. 227,we have

$$\tan\frac{\theta}{2} > \frac{\theta}{2}.$$

$$\therefore \quad \sin\frac{\theta}{2} > \frac{\theta}{2}\cos\frac{\theta}{2}.$$

Hence, since $\sin\theta = 2\sin\frac{\theta}{2}\cos\frac{\theta}{2}$,

We have, $\sin\theta > \theta\cos^2\frac{\theta}{2}$, i.e., $> \theta\left(1 - \sin^2\frac{\theta}{2}\right)$.

But since, by Art. 227,

$$\sin\frac{\theta}{2} < \frac{\theta}{2}$$

therefore, $1 - \sin^2\frac{\theta}{2} > 1 - \left(\frac{\theta}{2}\right)^2$, *i.e.*, $> 1 - \frac{\theta^2}{4}$.

$\therefore \quad \sin\theta > \theta\left(1 - \frac{\theta^2}{4}\right)$, *i.e.*, $> \theta - \frac{\theta^2}{4}$.

Again, $\cos\theta = 1 - 2\sin^2\frac{\theta}{2}$;

therefore, since $\sin^2\frac{\theta}{2} < \left(\frac{\theta}{2}\right)^2$,

we have $1 - 2\sin^2\frac{\theta}{2} > 1 - 2\left(\frac{\theta}{2}\right)^2$, *i.e.*, $\cos\theta > 1 - \frac{\theta^2}{2}$.

From the results of Part II, Arts. 32 and 33, it will follow that $\sin\theta > \theta - \frac{\theta^2}{6}$, and $\cos\theta < 1 - \frac{\theta^2}{2} + \frac{\theta^4}{24}$.

➤ **232.**

EXAMPLE 1 *Find the values of* sin 10′ *and* cos 10′.

Since, $10' = \frac{1^\circ}{6} = \frac{\pi^\circ}{180 \times 6}$

we have $\sin 10' = \sin\left(\frac{\pi}{180 \times 6}\right)^\circ = \frac{\pi}{180 \times 6}$

$$= \frac{3.14159265\ldots}{180 \times 6} = 0.0029089 \text{ (nearly)}$$

Also, $\cos 10' = \sqrt{1 - \sin^2 10'}$

$$= [1 - 0.000008468\ldots]^{1/2}$$

$$= 1 - \frac{1}{2}[0.000008468\ldots],$$

approximately by the Binomial theorem,

$$= 1 - 0.000004234\ldots = 0.9999958\ldots$$

EXAMPLE 2 *Solve approximately the equation*

$$\sin\theta = 0.52$$

Since $\sin\theta$ is very nearly equal to $\frac{1}{2}$, θ must be nearly equal to $\frac{\pi}{6}$.

Let then $\theta = \frac{\pi}{6} + x$, where x is small.

$$\therefore \quad 0.52 = \sin\left(\frac{\pi}{6} + x\right) = \sin\frac{\pi}{6}\cos x + \cos\frac{\pi}{6}\sin x$$

$$= \frac{1}{2}\cos x + \frac{\sqrt{3}}{2}\sin x.$$

Since, x is very small, we have

$$\cos x = 1 \text{ and } \sin x = x \text{ nearly.}$$

$$\therefore \quad 0.52 = \frac{1}{2} + \frac{\sqrt{3}}{2}x$$

$$\therefore \quad x = 0.02 \times \frac{2}{\sqrt{3}} \text{ radians} = \frac{\sqrt{3}^c}{75} = 1.32^\circ \text{ nearly.}$$

Hence, $\theta = 31^\circ 19'$ nearly.

EXAMPLES XL

$$\left[\pi = 3.14159265; \frac{1}{\pi} = 0.31831\ldots\right]$$

Find, to 5 places of decimals, the value of

1. $\sin 7'$ **2.** $\sin 15''$ **3.** $\sin 1'$

4. $\cos 15'$ **5.** $\operatorname{cosec} 8''$ **6.** $\sec 5'$

Solve approximately the equations

7. $\sin\theta = 0.01$ **8.** $\sin\theta = 0.48$

9. $\cos\left(\frac{\pi}{3}+\theta\right)=0.49$

10. $\cos\theta=0.999$

11. Find approximately the distance at which a coin, which is 1 cm in diameter, must be placed so as to just hide the moon, the angular diameter of the moon, that is the angle its diameter subtends at the observer eye, being taken to be 30′.

12. A person walks in a straight line toward a very distant object, and observes that at three points A, (,) B and C the angles of elevation of the top of the object are $a, 2a$, and $3a$ respectively; prove that

$$AB = 3BC \text{ nearly}$$

13. If θ be the number of radians in an angle which is less than a right angle, prove that

$$\cos\theta \text{ is} < 1-\frac{\theta^2}{2}+\frac{\theta^4}{16}.$$

14. Prove the theorem of Euler, *viz.* that

$$\sin\theta=\theta\cos\frac{\theta}{2}\cdot\cos\frac{\theta}{2^2}\cdot\cos\frac{\theta}{2^3}\ldots\text{ ad inf.}$$

[We have $\sin\theta=2\sin\frac{\theta}{2}\cos\frac{\theta}{2}=2^2\sin\frac{\theta}{2^2}\cos\frac{\theta}{2^2}\cos\frac{\theta}{2}$

$$=2^3\sin\frac{\theta}{2^3}\cos\frac{\theta}{2^3}\cos\frac{\theta}{2^2}\cos\frac{\theta}{2}=\ldots$$

$$=2^n\sin\frac{\theta}{2^n}\times\cos\frac{\theta}{2}\cdot\cos\frac{\theta}{2^2}\cdot\cos\frac{\theta}{2^3}\ldots\cos\frac{\theta}{2^n}.$$

Make n indefinitely great so that, by Art. 228 Cor.,

$$2^n\sin\frac{\theta}{2^n}=\theta.$$

Hence, $\sin\theta=\theta\cos\frac{\theta}{2}\cos\frac{\theta}{2^2}\cdot\cos\frac{\theta}{2^3}\ldots\text{ ad inf.}$]

15. Prove that

$$\left(1-\tan^2\frac{\theta}{2}\right)\left(1-\tan^2\frac{\theta}{2^2}\right)\left(1-\tan^2\frac{\theta}{2^3}\right)\ldots\text{ ad inf.}=\theta\cdot\cot\theta$$

➤ **233. Area of a circle:** By Art. 225, the area of a regular polygon of n sides, which is inscribed in a circle of radius R, is

$$\frac{n}{2}R^2\sin\frac{2\pi}{n}.$$

Let now the number of sides of this polygon be indefinitely increased, the polygon always remaining regular.

It is clear that the perimeter of the polygon must more and more approximate to the circumference of the circle.

Hence, when the number of sides of the polygon is infinitely great, the area of the circle must be the same as that of the polygon.

$$\text{Now, } \frac{n}{2}R^2\sin\frac{2\pi}{n} = \frac{n}{2}R^2\cdot\frac{2\pi}{n}\cdot\frac{\sin\frac{2\pi}{n}}{\frac{2\pi}{n}} = \pi/R^2\cdot\frac{\sin\frac{2\pi}{n}}{\frac{2\pi}{n}}$$

$$= \pi R^2\cdot\frac{\sin\theta}{\theta} \quad \text{where } \theta = \frac{2\pi}{n}$$

When n is made infinitely great, the value of θ becomes infinitely small, and then, by Art. 228, $\frac{\sin\theta}{\theta}$ is unity.

The area of the circle therefore $= \pi R^2 = \pi$ times the square of its radius.

234. *Area of the sector of a circle.*

Let O be the centre of a circle, AB the bounding arc of the sector, and let $\angle AOB = \alpha$ radians.

By Geometry, since sectors are to one another as the arcs on which they stand, we have

$$\frac{\text{area of sector } AOB}{\text{area of whole circle}} = \frac{\text{arc } AB}{\text{circumference}}$$

$$= \frac{R\alpha}{2\pi R} = \frac{\alpha}{2\pi}$$

$$\therefore \quad \text{area of sector } AOB = \frac{\alpha}{2\pi}\times\text{area of whole circle}$$

$$= \frac{\alpha}{2\pi}\times\pi R^2 = \frac{1}{2}R^2\cdot\alpha$$

EXAMPLES XLI

[Assume that $\pi = 3.14159\ldots, \frac{1}{\pi} = 0.31831$ and $\log\pi = 0.49715$]

1. Find the area of a circle whose circumference is 74 metres.
2. The diameter of a circle is 10 cm.; find the area of a sector whose arc is $22\frac{1}{2}^\circ$.
3. The area of a certain sector of a circle is 10 square cm; if the radius of the circle be 3 cm., find the angle of the sector.
4. The perimeter of a certain sector of a circle is 10 cm.; if the radius of the circle be 3 cm., find the area of the sector.

5. A strip of paper, two km. long and 0.003 of a cm. thick, is rolled up into a solid cylinder; find approximately the radius of the circular ends of the cylinder.
6. A strip of paper, one km. long, is rolled tightly up into a solid cylinder, the diameter of whose circular ends is 10 cm. find the thickness of the paper.
7. Given two concentric circles of radii r and $2r$, two parallel tangents to the inner circle cut off an arc from the outer circle; find its length.
8. The circumference of a semicircle is divided into two arcs such that the chord of one is double that of the other. Prove that the sum of the areas of the two segments cut off by these chords is to the area of the semicircle as 27 is to 55.

$$\left[\pi = \frac{22}{7}\right]$$

9. If each of three circles, of radius a, touch the other two, prove that the area included between them in nearly equal to $\frac{4}{25}a^2$.
10. Six equal circles, each of radius a, are placed so that each touches two others, their centres being all on the circumference of another circle, prove that the area which they enclose is

$$2a^2(3\sqrt{3} - \pi).$$

11. From the vertex A of a triangle a straight line AD is drawn making an angle θ with the base and meeting it at D. Prove that the area common to the circumscribing circles of the triangles ABD and ACD is

$$\frac{1}{4}(b^2\gamma + c^2\beta - bc\sin A)\operatorname{cosec}^2\theta$$

where β and γ are the number of radians in the angles B and C respectively.

➤ **235. Dip of the Horizon:** Let O be a point at a distance h above the earth's surface. Draw tangents, such as OT and OT', to the surface of the earth. The ends of all these tangents all clearly lie on a circle. This circle is called the **Offing or Visible Horizon**. The angle that each of the these tangents OT makes with a horizontal plane POQ is called the **Dip** of the Horizon.

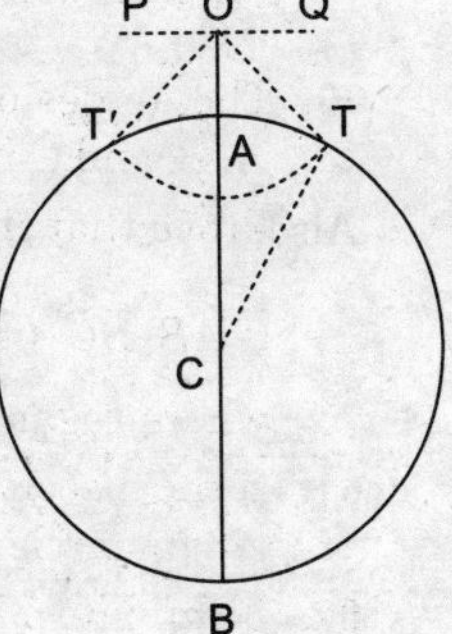

Let r be the radius of the earth, and let B be the other end of the diameter through A.

We then have

$$OT^2 = OC^2 - CT^2 = (r + h)^2 - r^2 = h(2r + h),$$

so that,
$$OT = \sqrt{h\,(2r + h)}$$

This gives an accurate value for OT.

In all practical cases, however, h is very small compared with r.

[$r = 4000$ miles nearly, and h is never greater, and generally is very considerably less, than 5 miles.]

Hence h^2 is very small compared with hr.

As a clos approximation, we have then

$$OT = \sqrt{2hr}$$

$$\text{The dip} = \angle TOQ$$

$$= 90° - \angle COT = \angle OCT$$

Also,
$$\tan OCT = \frac{OT}{CT} = \frac{\sqrt{2hr}}{r} = \sqrt{\frac{2h}{r}},$$

so that, very approximately, we have

$$\angle OCT = \sqrt{\frac{2h}{r}} \text{ radians}$$

$$= \left(\sqrt{\frac{2h}{r}}\,\frac{180}{\pi}\right)^{\circ} = \left[\frac{180 \times 60 \times 60}{\pi}\sqrt{\frac{2h}{r}}\right]^{\pi}$$

➤ **236.** <u>EXAMPLE</u> *Taking the radius of the earth as 6400 km., find the dip at the top of a lighthouse which is 45 metres above the sea, and the distance of the offing.*

Here $r = 6400$ km, and $h = 45$ metres $= \frac{45}{1000}$ km.

Hence h is very small compared with r so that

$$OT = \sqrt{\frac{2 \times 45 \times 6400}{1000}}$$

$$= \sqrt{9 \times 64} = 24 \text{ km}$$

Also,
$$\text{the dip} = \sqrt{\frac{2h}{r}} \text{ radians}$$

$$= \sqrt{\frac{48}{6400}} \text{ radians}$$

$$= \frac{\sqrt{3}}{20} \times \frac{180}{\pi} \text{ degree}$$

$$= 4°57'43'' \text{ nearly.}$$

EXAMPLES XLII

[*Radius of earth* = 6400*km*]

1. Find in degrees, minutes, seconds, the dip of the horizon from the top of a mountain 3200 m. high, the earth's radius being 6400 km.
2. The lamp of a lighthouse is 50 metres high; how far off can it be seen?
3. Find the height of a balloon when the dip is 1°.
   Find also the dip when the balloon is 2 km. high.
4. From the top of the mast of a ship, which is 20 m. above the sea, the light of a lighthouse which is known to be 45 m. high can just be seen; prove that its distance is 40 km.
5. From the top of mast 20 m. above the sea, the top of the mast of another ship can just be seen at a distance of 32 km.; prove that the heights of the mast are the same.
6. From the top of the mast of a ship which is 44 metres above the sea-level, the light of a lighthouse can just be seen; after sailing for 15 minutes the light can just be seen from the deck which is 11 metres above the sea-level; prove that the rate of sailing of the ship is neartly 47.48 km. per hour towards the lighthouse.
7. Prove that, if the height of the place of observation be n metres, the distance that the observer can see is $8\dfrac{\sqrt{n}}{5}$ km. nearly.
8. Find approximately the distance at which the top of the Eiffel Tower should be visible, its height being 300 metres.

18

INVERSE CIRCULAR FUNCTIONS

➤ **237.** If $\sin\theta = a$, where a is a known quantity, we know, from Art. 82, that θ is not definitely known. We only know that θ is some one of a definite series of angles.

The symbol "$\sin^{-1} a$" is used to denote the *smallest* angle, whether positive or negative that has a for its sine.

The symbol "$\sin^{-1} a$" is read in words as "sine minus one a", and must be carefully distinguished from $\frac{1}{\sin a}$ which would be written, if so desired, in the form $(\sin a)^{-1}$.

It will therefore be carefully noted that "$\sin^{-1} a$" is an angle, and denotes the **smallest numerical** angle whose sine is a.

So "$\cos^{-1} a$" means the smallest numerical angle whose cosine is a. Similarly "$\tan^{-1} a$", "$\cot^{-1} a$", "$\text{cosec}^{-1} a$", "$\sec^{-1} a$", "$\text{vers}^{-1} a$", and "$\text{covers}^{-1} a$", are defined.

Hence, $\sin^{-1} a$ and $\tan^{-1} a$ (and therefore $\text{cosec}^{-1} a$ and $\cot^{-1} a$) always lie between $-90°$ and $+90°$.

But $\cos^{-1} a$ (and therefore $\sec^{-1} a$) always lies between $0°$ and $180°$.

➤ **238.** The quantities $\sin^{-1} a, \cos^{-1} a, \tan^{-1} a, \ldots$ are called Inverse Circular Functions.

The symbol $\sin^{-1} a$ is often, especially in foreign mathematical books, written as "arc sin a", similarly $\cos^{-1} a$ is written "arc cos a", and so for the other inverse ratios.

➤ **239.** When a is positive, $\sin^{-1} a$ clearly lies between $0°$ and $90°$; when a is negative, it lies between $-90°$ and $0°$.

EXAMPLE $\sin^{-1}\frac{1}{2} = 30°;\ \sin^{-1}\left(\frac{-\sqrt{3}}{2}\right) = -60°$

When a is positive, there are two angles, one lying between $0°$ and $90°$ and the other lying between $-90°$ and $0°$, each of which has its cosine equal to a. [For example both $30°$ and $-30°$ have their cosine equal to $\frac{\sqrt{3}}{2}$.] In this case we take the smallest *positive* angle. Hence $\cos^{-1} a$, when a is positive, lies between 0° and 90°.

So $\cos^{-1} a$, when a is negative, lies between 90° and 180°.

EXAMPLE $\cos^{-1}\dfrac{1}{\sqrt{2}} = 45°;\ \cos^{-1}\left(\dfrac{1}{2}\right) = 120°$

When a is positive, the angle $\tan^{-1} a$ lies between 0° and 90°; when a is negative, it lies between – 90° and 0°.

EXAMPLE $\tan^{-1}\sqrt{3} = 60°;\ \tan^{-1}(-1) = -45°$

➤ 240.

EXAMPLE 1 Prove that, $\sin^{-1}\dfrac{3}{5} - \cos^{-1}\dfrac{12}{13} = \sin^{-1}\dfrac{16}{65}$

Let $\sin^{-1}\dfrac{3}{5} = \alpha$, so that $\sin\alpha = \dfrac{3}{5}$,

and therefore $\cos\alpha = \sqrt{1 - \dfrac{9}{25}} = \dfrac{4}{5}$

Let $\cos^{-1}\dfrac{12}{13} = \beta$, so that $\cos\beta = \dfrac{12}{13}$

and therefore, $\sin\beta = \sqrt{1 - \dfrac{144}{169}} = \dfrac{5}{13}$

Let $\sin^{-1}\dfrac{16}{65} = \gamma$, so that, $\sin\gamma = \dfrac{16}{65}$

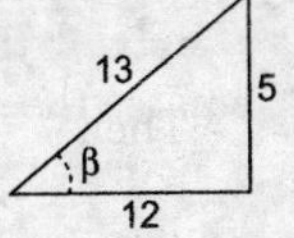

We have then to prove that

$$\alpha - \beta = \gamma$$

i.e. to show that $\sin(\alpha - \beta) = \sin\gamma$

Now, $\sin(\alpha - \beta) = \sin\alpha\cos\beta - \cos\alpha\sin\beta$

$$= \frac{3}{5}\cdot\frac{12}{13} - \frac{4}{5}\cdot\frac{5}{13} = \frac{36-20}{65} = \frac{16}{35} = \sin\gamma$$

Hence the relation is proved.

EXAMPLE 2 Prove that $2\tan^{-1}\dfrac{1}{3} + \tan^{-1}\dfrac{1}{7} = \dfrac{\pi}{4}$

Let $\tan^{-1}\dfrac{1}{3} = \alpha$, so that $\tan\alpha = \dfrac{1}{3}$,

and let $\tan^{-1}\dfrac{1}{7} = \beta$, so that $\tan\beta = \dfrac{1}{7}$

We have then to show that

$$2a + \beta = \frac{\pi}{4}$$

Now, $$\tan 2\alpha = \frac{2\tan\alpha}{1-\tan^2\alpha}$$

$$= \frac{\frac{2}{3}}{1-\frac{1}{9}} = \frac{6}{8} = \frac{3}{4}$$

Also, $$\tan(2\alpha+\beta) = \frac{\tan 2\alpha + \tan\beta}{1-\tan 2\alpha\tan\beta}$$

$$= \frac{\frac{3}{4}+\frac{1}{7}}{1-\frac{3}{4}\cdot\frac{1}{7}} = \frac{21+4}{28-3} = \frac{25}{25} = 1 = \tan\frac{\pi}{4}$$

$\therefore$ $$2\alpha+\beta = \frac{\pi}{4}$$

EXAMPLE 3 *Prove that*

$$4\tan^{-1}\frac{1}{5} - \tan^{-1}\frac{1}{239} = \frac{\pi}{4}$$

Let $$\tan^{-1}\frac{1}{5} = \alpha, \text{ so that } \tan\alpha = \frac{1}{5}$$

Then, $$\tan 2\alpha = \frac{2\tan\alpha}{1-\tan^2\alpha} = \frac{\frac{2}{5}}{1-\frac{1}{25}} = \frac{5}{12}$$

and $$\tan 4\alpha = \frac{\frac{10}{12}}{1-\frac{25}{144}} = \frac{120}{119}$$

so that $\tan 4\alpha$ is nearly unity, and 4α therefore, nearly $\frac{\pi}{4}$.

Let $$4\alpha = \frac{\pi}{4} + \tan^{-1}x$$

$\therefore$ $$\frac{120}{119} = \tan\left(\frac{\pi}{4}+\tan^{-1}x\right) = \frac{1+x}{1-x} \qquad \text{(Art. 100)}$$

$\therefore$ $$x = \frac{1}{239}$$

Hence, $$4\tan^{-1}\frac{1}{5} - \tan^{-1}\frac{1}{239} = \frac{\pi}{4}$$

EXAMPLE 4 *Prove that*

$$\tan^{-1}a + \tan^{-1}b = \tan^{-1}\frac{a+b}{1-ab}$$

Let $\tan^{-1} a = \alpha$, so that $\tan\alpha = a$,

and let $\tan^{-1} b = \beta$, so that $\tan\beta = b$

Also, let $\tan^{-1}\left(\dfrac{a+b}{1-ab}\right) = \gamma$ so, that $\tan\gamma = \dfrac{a+b}{1-ab}$

We have then to prove that

$$\alpha + \beta = \gamma$$

Now $$\tan(\alpha+\beta) = \frac{\tan\alpha + \tan\beta}{1-\tan\alpha\tan\beta} = \frac{a+b}{1-ab} = \tan\gamma$$

so, that the relation is proved.

The above relation is merely the formula

$$\tan(x+y) = \frac{\tan x + \tan y}{1 - \tan x \tan y}$$

expressed in inverse notation.

For put $\tan x = a$, so that $x = \tan^{-1} a$,

and $\tan y = b$, so that $y = \tan^{-1} b$

Then, $$\tan(x+y) = \frac{a+b}{1-ab}$$

$\therefore$ $$x + y = \tan^{-1}\frac{a+b}{1-ab}$$

i.e. $$\tan^{-1} a + \tan^{-1} b = \tan^{-1}\frac{a+b}{1-ab}$$

In the above we have tacitly assumed that $ab < 1$, so that $\dfrac{a+b}{1-ab}$ is positive, and therefore $\tan^{-1}\dfrac{a+b}{1-ab}$ lies between 0° and 90°.

If, however, ab be > 1, then $\dfrac{a+b}{1-ab}$ is negative, and therefore according to our definition $\tan^{-1}\dfrac{a+b}{1-ab}$ is a negative angle. Here γ is therefore a negative angle and, since $\tan(\pi+\gamma) = \tan\gamma$, the formula should be

$$\tan^{-1} a + \tan^{-1} b = \pi + \tan^{-1}\frac{a+b}{1-ab}$$

EXAMPLE 5 *Prove that*

$$\cos^{-1}\frac{63}{65} + 2\tan^{-1}\frac{1}{5} = \sin^{-1}\frac{3}{5}$$

Since, $(65)^2 - (63)^2 = (16)^2$,

we have $$\cos^{-1}\frac{63}{65} = \tan^{-1}\frac{16}{63}$$

65 16 63

Also, as in Ex. 1, $\qquad \sin^{-1}\dfrac{3}{5} = \tan^{-1}\dfrac{3}{4}$

We have therefore to show that

$$\tan^{-1}\frac{16}{63} + 2\tan^{-1}\frac{1}{5} = \tan^{-1}\frac{3}{4}$$

Now,

$$\tan\left[2\tan^{-1}\frac{1}{5}\right] = \frac{2\tan\left[\tan^{-1}\frac{1}{5}\right]}{1-\tan^2\left[\tan^{-1}\frac{1}{5}\right]} = \frac{\frac{2}{5}}{1-\frac{1}{25}} = \frac{5}{12}$$

so that

$$2\tan^{-1}\frac{1}{5} = \tan^{-1}\frac{5}{12}$$

Thus, $\tan\left[\tan^{-1}\dfrac{16}{63} + 2\tan^{-1}\dfrac{1}{5}\right] = \tan\left[\tan^{-1}\dfrac{16}{63} + \tan^{-1}\dfrac{5}{12}\right]$

$$= \frac{\frac{16}{63}+\frac{5}{12}}{1-\frac{16}{63}\cdot\frac{5}{12}} = \frac{192+315}{756-80} = \frac{507}{676} = \frac{3}{4}$$

i.e.

$$\tan^{-1}\frac{16}{63} + 2\tan^{-1}\frac{1}{5} = \tan^{-1}\frac{3}{4}$$

EXAMPLE 6 *Solve the equation*

$$\tan^{-1}\frac{x+1}{x-1} + \tan^{-1}\frac{x-1}{x} = \tan^{-1}(-7)$$

Taking the tangents of both sides of the equation, we have

$$\frac{\tan\left[\tan^{-1}\frac{x+1}{x-1}\right] + \tan\left[\tan^{-1}\frac{x-1}{x}\right]}{1-\tan\left[\tan^{-1}\frac{x+1}{x-1}\right]\tan\left[\tan^{-1}\frac{x-1}{x}\right]} = \tan\{\tan^{-1}(-7)\} = -7$$

i.e.,

$$\frac{\frac{x+1}{x-1}+\frac{x-1}{x}}{1-\frac{x+1}{x-1}\,\frac{x-1}{x}} = -7$$

i.e.,

$$\frac{2x^2-x+1}{1-x} = -7$$

so, that $\qquad x = 2$

This value makes the left-hand side of the given equation positive, so that there is no value of x strictly satisfying the given equation.

The value $x = 2$ is a solution of the equation

$$\tan^{-1}\frac{x+1}{x-1} + \tan^{-1}\frac{x-1}{x} = \pi + \tan^{-1}(-7)$$

EXAMPLES XLIII

[*The student should verify the results of some of the following examples (e.g. Nos.* 1—4, 8, 9, 12, 13) *by an accurate graph.*]

Prove that

1. $\sin^{-1}\frac{3}{5}+\sin^{-1}\frac{8}{17}=\sin^{-1}\frac{77}{85}$
2. $\sin^{-1}\frac{5}{13}+\sin^{-1}\frac{7}{25}=\cos^{-1}\left(\frac{253}{325}\right)$
3. $\cos^{-1}\frac{4}{5}+\tan^{-1}\frac{3}{5}=\tan^{-1}\frac{27}{11}$
4. $\cos^{-1}\frac{4}{5}+\cos^{-1}\frac{12}{13}=\cos^{-1}\frac{33}{65}$
5. $\cos^{-1}x=2\sin^{-1}\sqrt{\frac{1-x}{2}}=2\cos^{-1}\sqrt{\frac{1+x}{2}}$
6. $2\cos^{-1}\frac{3}{\sqrt{13}}+\cot^{-1}\frac{16}{63}+\frac{1}{2}\cos^{-1}\frac{7}{25}=\pi$
7. $\tan^{-1}\frac{1}{2}+\tan^{-1}\frac{1}{3}=\sin^{-1}\frac{1}{\sqrt{5}}+\cot^{-1}3=45°$
8. $\tan^{-1}\frac{1}{7}+\tan^{-1}\frac{1}{13}=\tan^{-1}\frac{2}{9}$
9. $\tan^{-1}\frac{2}{3}=\frac{1}{2}\tan^{-1}\frac{12}{5}$
10. $\tan^{-1}\frac{1}{4}+\tan^{-1}\frac{2}{9}=\frac{1}{2}\cos^{-1}\frac{3}{5}$
11. $2\tan^{-1}\frac{1}{5}+\tan^{-1}\frac{1}{7}+2\tan^{-1}\frac{1}{8}=\frac{\pi}{4}$
12. $\tan^{-1}\frac{3}{4}+\tan^{-1}\frac{3}{5}-\tan^{-1}\frac{8}{19}=\frac{\pi}{4}$
13. $\tan^{-1}\frac{1}{3}+\tan^{-1}\frac{1}{5}+\tan^{-1}\frac{1}{7}+\tan^{-1}\frac{1}{8}=\frac{\pi}{4}$
14. $3\tan^{-1}\frac{1}{4}+\tan^{-1}\frac{1}{20}=\frac{\pi}{4}-\tan^{-1}\frac{1}{1985}$
15. $4\tan^{-1}\frac{1}{5}-\tan^{-1}\frac{1}{70}+\tan^{-1}\frac{1}{99}=\frac{\pi}{4}$
16. $\tan^{-1}\frac{120}{119}=2\sin^{-1}\frac{5}{13}$
17. $\tan^{-1}\frac{m}{n}-\tan^{-1}\frac{m-n}{m+n}=\frac{\pi}{4}$

18. $\tan^{-1} t + \tan^{-1} \dfrac{2t}{1-t^2} = \tan^{-1} \dfrac{3t - t^3}{1 - 3t^2}$, t being positive if $t < \dfrac{1}{\sqrt{3}}$ or $> \sqrt{3}$

and $= \pi + \tan^{-1} \dfrac{3t - t^3}{1 - 3t^2}$ if $t > \dfrac{1}{\sqrt{3}}$ and $< \sqrt{3}$.

Prove that

19. $\tan^{-1} \sqrt{\dfrac{a(a+b+c)}{bc}} + \tan^{-1} \sqrt{\dfrac{b(a+b+c)}{ca}} + \tan^{-1} \sqrt{\dfrac{c(a+b+c)}{ab}} = \pi$

20. $\cot^{-1} \dfrac{ab+1}{a-b} + \cot^{-1} \dfrac{bc+1}{b-c} + \cot^{-1} \dfrac{ca+1}{c-a} = 0$

21. $\tan^{-1} n + \cot^{-1}(n+1) = \tan^{-1}(n^2 + n + 1)$

22. $\cos\left(2\tan^{-1} \dfrac{1}{7}\right) = \sin\left(4\tan^{-1} \dfrac{1}{3}\right)$

23. $2\tan^{-1}\left[\tan(45° - \alpha)\tan \dfrac{\beta}{2}\right] = \cos^{-1}\left[\dfrac{\sin 2\alpha + \cos\beta}{1 + \sin 2\alpha \cos\beta}\right]$

24. $\tan^{-1} x = 2\tan^{-1}[\operatorname{cosec} \tan^{-1} x - \tan \cot^{-1} x]$

25. $2\tan^{-1}\left[\tan \dfrac{\alpha}{2} \tan\left(\dfrac{\pi}{4} - \dfrac{\beta}{2}\right)\right] = \tan^{-1} \dfrac{\sin\alpha \cos\beta}{\sin\beta + \cos\alpha}$

26. Show that

$$\cos^{-1} \sqrt{\frac{a-x}{a-b}} = \sin^{-1} \sqrt{\frac{x-b}{a-b}} = \cot^{-1} \sqrt{\frac{a-x}{x-b}}$$

$$= \frac{1}{2} \sin^{-1} \frac{2\sqrt{(a-x)(x-b)}}{a-b}$$

27. If $\cos^{-1} \dfrac{x}{a} + \cos^{-1} \dfrac{y}{b} = \alpha$ prove that

$$\frac{x^2}{a^2} - \frac{2xy}{ab} \cos\alpha + \frac{y^2}{b^2} = \sin^2\alpha$$

Solve the equations

28. $\tan^{-1} \dfrac{\sqrt{1+x^2} - \sqrt{1-x^2}}{\sqrt{1+x^2} + \sqrt{1-x^2}} = \beta$

29. $\tan^{-1} 2x + \tan^{-1} 3x = \dfrac{\pi}{4}$

30. $\tan^{-1} \dfrac{x-1}{x-2} + \tan^{-1} \dfrac{x+1}{x+2} = \dfrac{\pi}{4}$

31. $\tan^{-1}(x+1) + \cot^{-1}(x-1) = \sin^{-1} \dfrac{4}{5} + \cos^{-1} \dfrac{3}{5}$

32. $\tan^{-1}(x+1) + \tan^{-1}(x-1) = \tan^{-1} \dfrac{8}{31}$

33. $2\tan^{-1}(\cos x) = \tan^{-1}(2 \operatorname{cosec} x)$

34. $\tan^{-1} x + 2\cot^{-1} x = \frac{2}{3}\pi$

35. $\tan\cos^{-1} x = \sin\cot^{-1}\frac{1}{2}$

36. $\cot^{-1} x - \cot^{-1}(x+2) = 15°$

37. $\cos^{-1}\frac{x^2-1}{x^2+1} + \tan^{-1}\frac{2x}{x^2-1} = \frac{2\pi}{3}$

38. $\cot^{-1} x + \cot^{-1}(n^2 - x + 1)$
$= \cot^{-1}(n-1)$

39. $\sin^{-1} x + \sin^{-1} 2x = \frac{\pi}{3}$

40. $\sin^{-1}\frac{5}{x} + \sin^{-1}\frac{12}{x} = \frac{\pi}{2}$

41. $\tan^{-1}\frac{a}{x} + \tan^{-1}\frac{b}{x} + \tan^{-1}\frac{c}{x} + \tan^{-1}\frac{d}{x} = \frac{\pi}{2}$

42. $\sec^{-1}\frac{x}{a} - \sec^{-1}\frac{x}{b} = \sec^{-1} b - \sec^{-1} a$

43. $\text{cosec}^{-1} x = \text{cosec}^{-1} a + \text{cosec}^{-1} b$

44. $2\tan^{-1} x = \cos^{-1}\frac{1-a^2}{1+a^2} - \cos^{-1}\frac{1-b^2}{1+b^2}$

Draw the graphs of

45. $\sin^{-1} x$. [N. B. If $y = \sin^{-1} x$, then $x = \sin y$ and the graph bears the same relation to OY that the curve in Art. 62 bears to OX.]

46. $\cos^{-1} x$

47. $\tan^{-1} x$

48. $\cot^{-1} x$

49. $\text{cosec}^{-1} x$

50. $\sec^{-1} x$

51. By obtaining the intersections of the graphs of $\tan x$ and $2x$, show that the least positive solution of the equation $\tan^{-1} 2x = x$ is the circular measure of an angle of approximately 67°.

52. By means of graphs, show that the solutions of the equations,

(1) $\sin x = \frac{1}{100} x$ (2) $\sin x = \frac{1}{2} x$ (3) $\cos x = x^2$

are respectively the circular measures of angles of 178°, 109° and 47° approximately.

53. By using the tables at the end of this book, show that nearer approximations to the results of the previous example are the circular measures of angles of 178° 13′, 108° 36′ and 47°13′ respectively.

19

SUMMATION OF SOME SIMPLE TRIGONOMETRICAL SERIES

➤ **241.** *To find the sum of sines of a series of angles, the angles being in arithmetical progression.*

Let the angles be

$$\alpha, \alpha + \beta, \alpha + 2\beta, \ldots, \{\alpha + (n-1)\beta\}$$

Let

$$S \equiv \sin\alpha + \sin(\alpha + \beta) + \sin(\alpha + 2\beta) + \ldots + \sin\{\alpha + (n-1)\beta\}$$

By Art. 97 we have

$$2\sin\alpha\sin\frac{\beta}{2} = \cos\left(\alpha - \frac{\beta}{2}\right) - \cos\left(\alpha + \frac{\beta}{2}\right),$$

$$2\sin(\alpha + \beta)\sin\frac{\beta}{2} = \cos\left(\alpha + \frac{\beta}{2}\right) - \cos\left(\alpha + \frac{3\beta}{2}\right),$$

$$2\sin(\alpha + 2\beta)\sin\frac{\beta}{2} = \cos\left(\alpha + \frac{3\beta}{2}\right) - \cos\left(\alpha + \frac{5\beta}{2}\right)$$

$$\ldots \quad \ldots \quad \ldots \quad \ldots$$

$$2\sin\{\alpha + (n-2)\beta\}\sin\frac{\beta}{2} = \cos\left\{\alpha + \left(n - \frac{5}{2}\right)\beta\right\} - \cos\left\{\alpha + \left(n - \frac{3}{2}\right)\beta\right\}$$

and $$2\sin\{\alpha + (n-1)\beta\}\sin\frac{\beta}{2} = \cos\left\{\alpha + \left(n - \frac{3}{2}\right)\beta\right\} - \cos\left\{\alpha + \left(n - \frac{1}{2}\right)\beta\right\}$$

By adding together these n lines, we have

$$2\sin\frac{\beta}{2}\cdot S = \cos\left(\alpha - \frac{\beta}{2}\right) - \cos\left\{\alpha + \left(n - \frac{1}{2}\right)\beta\right\},$$

the other terms on the right-hand sides cancelling one another.

Hence, by Art, 94, we have

$$2\sin\frac{\beta}{2}\cdot S = 2\sin\left\{\alpha + \left(\frac{n-1}{2}\right)\beta\right\}\sin\frac{n\beta}{2}$$

i.e.,

$$S = \frac{\sin\left\{\alpha + \left(\frac{n-1}{2}\right)\beta\right\}\sin\frac{n\beta}{2}}{\sin\frac{\beta}{2}}$$

<u>**EXAMPLE**</u> By putting $\beta = 2\alpha$, we have

$$\sin\alpha + \sin 3\alpha + \sin 5\alpha + \cdots + \sin(2n-1)\alpha$$

$$= \frac{\sin\{\alpha + (n-1)\alpha\}\sin n\alpha}{\sin\alpha} = \frac{\sin^2 n\alpha}{\sin\alpha}$$

➤ **242.** *To find the sum of the cosines of a series of angles, the angles being in arithmetical progression.*

Let the angles be

$$\alpha, \alpha+\beta, \alpha+2\beta, \ldots \alpha+(n-1)\beta$$

Let $S \equiv \cos\alpha + \cos(\alpha+\beta) + \cos(\alpha+2\beta) + \cdots + \cos\{\alpha+(n-1)\beta\}$

By Art. 97, we have

$$2\cos\alpha\sin\frac{\beta}{2} = \sin\left(\alpha + \frac{\beta}{2}\right) - \sin\left(\alpha - \frac{\beta}{2}\right),$$

$$2\cos(\alpha+\beta)\sin\frac{\beta}{2} = \sin\left(\alpha + \frac{3\beta}{2}\right) - \sin\left(\alpha + \frac{\beta}{2}\right),$$

$$2\cos(\alpha+2\beta)\sin\frac{\beta}{2} = \sin\left(\alpha + \frac{5\beta}{2}\right) - \sin\left(\alpha + \frac{3\beta}{2}\right),$$

$$\cdots \quad \cdots \quad \cdots \quad \cdots$$

$$2\cos\{\alpha+(n-2)\beta\}\sin\frac{\beta}{2} = \sin\left\{\alpha + \left(n - \frac{3}{2}\right)\beta\right\} - \sin\left\{\alpha + \left(n - \frac{5}{2}\right)\beta\right\}$$

$$2\cos\{\alpha+(n-1)\beta\}\sin\frac{\beta}{2} = \sin\left\{\alpha + \left(n - \frac{1}{2}\right)\beta\right\} - \sin\left\{\alpha + \left(n - \frac{3}{2}\right)\beta\right\}$$

By adding together these n lines, we have

$$2S\times\sin\frac{\beta}{2} = \sin\left\{\alpha + \left(n - \frac{1}{2}\right)\beta\right\} - \sin\left\{\alpha - \frac{\beta}{2}\right\}$$

the other terms on the right-hand sides cancelling one another.

Hence, by Art. 94, we have

$$2S\times\sin\frac{\beta}{2} = 2\cos\left\{\alpha + \frac{n-1}{2}\beta\right\}\sin\frac{n\beta}{2}$$

i.e.,
$$S = \frac{\cos\left\{\alpha + \frac{n-1}{2}\beta\right\}\sin\frac{n\beta}{2}}{\sin\frac{\beta}{2}}$$

➤ **243.** Both the expression for S in Arts. 241 and 242 vanish when $\sin\frac{n\beta}{2}$ is zero, *i.e.* when $\frac{n\beta}{2}$ is equal to any multiple of π,

i.e., when
$$\frac{n\beta}{2} = p\pi$$

where p is any integer,

i.e., when
$$\beta = p\cdot\frac{2\pi}{n}$$

Hence, the sum of the sines (or cosines) of n angles, which are in arithmetical progression, vanishes when the common difference of the angles in any multiple of $\frac{2\pi}{n}$.

EXAMPLE $\cos\alpha + \cos\left(\alpha + \frac{2\pi}{n}\right) + \cos\left(\alpha + \frac{4\pi}{n}\right) + \dots$ to n terms $= 0$

and $\sin\alpha + \sin\left(\alpha + \frac{4\pi}{n}\right) + \sin\left(\alpha + \frac{8\pi}{n}\right) + \cdots$ to n terms $= 0$.

➤ **244.**

EXAMPLE 1 *Find the sum of*

$$\sin\alpha - \sin(\alpha + \beta) + \sin(\alpha + 2\beta) - \dots \textit{ to n terms.}$$

We have, by Art. 73,

$$\sin(\alpha + \beta + \pi) = -\sin(\alpha + \beta)$$
$$\sin(\alpha + 2\beta + 2\pi) = \sin(\alpha + 2\beta)$$
$$\sin(\alpha + 3\beta + 3\pi) = -\sin(\alpha + 3\beta)$$
$$\dots\dots\dots\dots\dots\dots$$

Hence the series $= \sin\alpha + \sin(\alpha + \beta + \pi) + \sin\{\alpha + 2(\beta + \pi)\} + \sin\{\alpha + 3(\beta + \pi)\} + \cdots$

$$= \frac{\sin\left\{\alpha + \frac{n-1}{2}(\beta + \pi)\right\}\sin\frac{n(\beta + \pi)}{2}}{\sin\frac{\beta + \pi}{2}} \quad \text{[by Art. 241]}$$

$$= \frac{\sin\left\{\alpha + \frac{n-1}{2}(\beta + \pi)\right\}\sin\frac{n(\beta + \pi)}{2}}{\cos\frac{\beta}{2}}$$

EXAMPLE 2 *Find the sum of series*

$$\cos^3\alpha + \cos^3 2\alpha + \cos^3 3\alpha + \ldots \text{ to } n \text{ terms.}$$

By Art. 107, we have

$$\cos 3\alpha = 4\cos^3\alpha - 3\cos\alpha$$

so that $$4\cos^2\alpha = 3\cos\alpha + \cos 3\alpha$$

So $$4\cos^3 2\alpha = 3\cos 2\alpha + \cos 6\alpha$$

$$4\cos^3 3\alpha = 3\cos 3\alpha + \cos 9\alpha$$

$$\ldots \ldots \ldots \ldots \ldots \ldots$$

Hence, if S be the given series, we have

$$4S = (3\cos\alpha + \cos 3\alpha) + (3\cos 2\alpha + \cos 6\alpha) + (3\cos 3\alpha + \cos 9\alpha) + \ldots$$

$$= 3(\cos\alpha + \cos 2\alpha + \cos 3\alpha + \ldots) + (\cos 3\alpha + \cos 6\alpha + \cos 9\alpha + \ldots)$$

$$= 3\frac{\cos\left\{\alpha + \frac{n-1}{2}\alpha\right\}\sin\frac{n\alpha}{2}}{\sin\frac{\alpha}{2}} + \frac{\cos\left\{3\alpha + \frac{n-1}{2}\cdot 3\alpha\right\}\sin\frac{n\cdot 3\alpha}{2}}{\sin\frac{3\alpha}{2}}$$

$$= 3\frac{\cos\frac{n+1}{2}\alpha\sin\frac{n\alpha}{2}}{\sin\frac{\alpha}{2}} + \frac{\cos\frac{3(n+1)}{2}\alpha\sin\frac{3n\alpha}{2}}{\sin\frac{3\alpha}{2}}$$

In a similar manner we can obtain the sum of the cubes of the sines of a series of angles in A.P.

Since, $2\sin^2\alpha = 1 - \cos 2\alpha$, and $2\cos^2\alpha = 1 + \cos 2\alpha$

we can similarly obtain the sum of squares

Since again $8\sin^4\alpha = 2\,[1 - \cos 2\alpha]^2$

$$= 2 - 4\cos 2\alpha + 2\cos^2 2\alpha$$

$$= 3 - 4\cos 2\alpha + \cos 4\alpha$$

we can obtain the sum of the 4th powers of the sines. Similarly for the cosines.

EXAMPLE 3 *Sum to n terms the series*

$$\cos\alpha\sin\beta + \cos 3\alpha\sin 2\beta + \cos 5\alpha\sin 3\beta + \ldots \textit{ to n terms.}$$

Let S denote the series

Then $2S = \{\sin(\alpha + \beta) - \sin(\alpha - \beta)\} + \{\sin(3\alpha + 2\beta) - \sin(3\alpha - 2\beta)\}$

$$+ \{\sin(5\alpha + 3\beta) - \sin(5\alpha - 3\beta)\} + \cdots$$

$$= \{\sin(\alpha + \beta) + \sin(3\alpha + 2\beta) + \sin(5\alpha + 3\beta) + \ldots \text{ to } n \text{ terms}\}$$

$$- \{\sin(\alpha - \beta) + \sin(3\alpha - 2\beta) + \sin(5\alpha - 3\beta) + \ldots \text{ to } n \text{ terms}\}$$

$$= \frac{\sin\left\{(\alpha+\beta)+\frac{n-1}{2}(2\alpha+\beta)\right\}\sin n\frac{2\alpha+\beta}{2}}{\sin\frac{2\alpha+\beta}{2}}$$

$$- \frac{\sin\left\{(\alpha+\beta)+\frac{n-1}{2}(2\alpha+\beta)\right\}\sin n\frac{2\alpha-\beta}{2}}{\sin\frac{2\alpha-\beta}{2}} \quad \text{[by Art, 241]}$$

$$= \frac{\sin\left\{n\alpha+\frac{n+1}{2}\beta\right\}\sin\frac{n\,(2\alpha+\beta)}{2}}{\sin\frac{2\alpha+\beta}{2}} - \frac{\sin\left\{n\alpha-\frac{n+1}{2}\beta\right\}\sin\frac{2\,(2\alpha+\beta)}{2}}{\sin\frac{2\alpha-\beta}{2}}$$

EXAMPLE 4 *$A_1A_2 \ldots An$ is a regular polygon of n sides inscribed in a circle, whose centre is O, and P is any point on the arc A_nA_1 such that the angle POA_1 is θ; Find the sum of the lengths of the lines joining P to the angular points of the polygon.*

Each of the angles $A_1OA_2, A_2OA_3, \ldots A_nOA_1$ is $\frac{2\pi}{n}$, so that the angles $POA_1, POA_2, \ldots$ are respectively

$$\theta, \theta+\frac{2\pi}{n}, \theta+\frac{4\pi}{n}, \ldots$$

Hence, if r be the radius of the circle, we have

$$PA_1 = 2r\sin\frac{POA_1}{2} = 2r\sin\frac{\theta}{2}$$

$$PA_2 = 2r\sin\frac{POA_2}{2} = 2r\sin\left(\frac{\theta}{2}+\frac{\pi}{n}\right)$$

$$PA_3 = 2r\sin\frac{POA_3}{2} = 2r\sin\left(\frac{\theta}{2}+\frac{2\pi}{n}\right)$$

$$\ldots\ \ldots\ \ldots\ \ldots\ \ldots\ \ldots$$

Hence the required sum

$$= 2r\left[\sin\frac{\theta}{2}+\sin\left(\frac{\theta}{2}+\frac{\pi}{n}\right)+\sin\left(\frac{\theta}{2}+\frac{2\pi}{n}\right)+\ldots \text{ to } n \text{ terms}\right]$$

$$= 2r\,\frac{\sin\left[\frac{\theta}{2}+\frac{n-1}{2}\cdot\frac{\pi}{n}\right]\sin\frac{n}{2}\cdot\frac{\pi}{n}}{\sin\frac{\pi}{2n}} \quad \text{(Art. 241)}$$

$$= 2r\ \text{cosec}\,\frac{\pi}{2n}\sin\left[\frac{\pi}{2}+\frac{\theta}{2}-\frac{\pi}{2n}\right]$$

$$= 2r\ \text{cosec}\,\frac{\pi}{2n}\cos\left(\frac{\theta}{2}-\frac{\pi}{2n}\right)$$

EXAMPLES XLIV

Sum the series :

1. $\cos\theta + \cos 3\theta + \cos 5\theta + \ldots$ to n terms.
2. $\cos\frac{A}{2} + \cos 2A + \cos\frac{7A}{2} + \ldots$ to n terms.

Prove that

3. $\dfrac{\sin\alpha + \sin 2\alpha + \sin 3\alpha + \cdots + \sin n\alpha}{\cos\alpha + \cos 2\alpha + \cdots + \cos n\alpha} = \tan\dfrac{n+1}{2}\alpha$
4. $\dfrac{\sin\alpha + \sin 3\alpha + \sin 5\alpha + \ldots + \sin(2n-1)\alpha}{\cos\alpha + \cos 3\alpha + \cos 5\alpha + \ldots + \cos(2n-1)\alpha} = \tan n\alpha$
5. $\dfrac{\sin\alpha - \sin(\alpha+\beta) + \sin(\alpha+2\beta) + \ldots \text{ to } n \text{ terms}}{\cos\alpha - \cos(\alpha+\beta) + \cos(\alpha+2\beta) + \ldots \text{ to } n \text{ terms}}$

$$= \tan\left\{\alpha + \frac{n-1}{2}(\pi+\beta)\right\}$$

Sum the following series :

6. $\cos\frac{\pi}{2n+1} + \cos\frac{3\pi}{2n+1} + \cos\frac{5\pi}{2n+1} + \ldots$ to n terms
7. $\cos\alpha - \cos(\alpha+\beta) + \cos(\alpha+2\beta) - \ldots$ to $2n$ terms
8. $\sin\theta + \sin\frac{n-4}{n-2}\theta + \sin\frac{n-6}{n-2}\theta + \ldots$ to n terms
9. $\cos x + \sin 3x + \cos 5x + \sin 7x + \ldots + \sin(4n-1)x$
10. $\sin\alpha\sin 2\alpha + \sin 2\alpha\sin 3\alpha + \sin 3\alpha\sin 4\alpha + \ldots$ to n terms
11. $\cos\alpha\sin 2\alpha + \sin 2\alpha\cos 3\alpha + \cos 3\alpha\sin 4\alpha + \sin 4\alpha\cos 5\alpha + \ldots$ to $2n$ terms
12. $\sin\alpha\sin 3\alpha + \sin 2\alpha\sin 4\alpha + \sin 3\alpha\sin 5\alpha + \ldots$ to n terms.
13. $\cos\alpha\cos\beta + \cos 3\alpha\cos 2\beta + \cos 5\alpha\cos 3\beta + \ldots$ to n terms
14. $\sin^2\alpha + \sin^2 2\alpha + \sin^2 3\alpha + \ldots$ to n terms
15. $\sin^2\theta + \sin^2(\theta+\alpha) + \sin^2(\theta+2\alpha) \ldots$ to n terms
16. $\sin^3\alpha + \sin^3 2\alpha + \sin^3 3\alpha + \ldots$ to n terms
17. $\sin^4\alpha + \sin^4 2\alpha + \sin^4 3\alpha + \ldots$ to n terms
18. $\cos^4\alpha + \cos^4 2\alpha + \cos^4 3\alpha + \ldots$ to n terms
19. $\cos\theta\cos 2\theta\cos 3\theta + \cos 2\theta\cos 3\theta\cos 4\theta + \ldots$ to n terms.
20. $\sin\alpha\sin(\alpha+\beta) - \sin(\alpha+\beta)\sin(\alpha+2\beta) + \ldots$ to $2n$ terms
21. From the sum of the series

$$\sin\alpha + \sin 2\alpha + \sin 3\alpha + \ldots \text{to } n \text{ terms}$$

deduce (by making a very small) the sum of the series

$$1 + 2 + 3 + \ldots + n$$

22. From the result of the example of Art. 241 deduce the sum of

$$1 + 3 + 5 + \dots \text{ to } n \text{ terms}$$

23. If $\alpha = \dfrac{2\pi}{17}$

prove that $2(\cos\alpha + \cos 2\alpha + \cos 4\alpha + \cos 8\alpha)$

and $2(\cos 3\alpha + \cos 5\alpha + \cos 6\alpha + \cos 7\alpha)$

are the roots of the equation

$$x^2 + x - 4 = 0$$

24. $ABCD\dots$ is a regular polygon of n sides which is inscribed in a circle, whose centre is O and whose radius is r, and P is any point on the arc AB such that POA is θ. Prove that

$$PA \cdot PB + PA \cdot PC + PA \cdot PD + \dots + PB \cdot PC + \dots$$
$$= r^2\left[2\cos^2\left(\frac{\theta}{2} - \frac{\pi}{2n}\right)\operatorname{cosec}^2\frac{\pi}{2n} - n\right]$$

25. Two regular polygons, each of n sides, are circumscribed to and inscribed in a given circle. If an angular point of one of them be joined to each of the angular points of the other, then the sum of the squares of the straight lines so drawn is to the sum of the areas of the polygons as

$$2 : \sin\frac{2\pi}{n}$$

26. $A_1, A_2 \dots A_{2n+1}$ are the angular points of a regular polygon inscribed in a circle, and O is any point on the circumference between A_1 and A_{2n+1}; prove that

$$OA_1 + OA_3 + \dots + OA_{2n+1} = OA_2 + OA_4 + \dots + OA_{2n}$$

27. If perpendiculars be drawn on the sides of a regular polygon of n sides from any point on the inscribed circle whose radius is a, prove that

$$\frac{2}{n}\Sigma\left(\frac{p}{a}\right)^2 = 3, \quad \text{and} \quad \frac{2}{n}\Sigma\left(\frac{p}{a}\right)^3 = 5$$

20

ELIMINATION

➤ **245.** It sometimes happens that we have two equations each containing one unknown quantity. In this case there must clearly be a relation between the constants of the equations in order that the same value of the unknown quantity may satisfy both. For example, suppose we knew that an unknown quantity x satisfied both of the equations

$$ax + b = 0 \text{ and } cx^2 + dx + e = 0$$

From the first equation, we have

$$x = -\frac{b}{a}$$

and this satisfies the second, if

$$c\left(-\frac{b}{a}\right)^2 + d\left(-\frac{b}{a}\right) + e = 0$$

i.e., if $$b^2c - abd + a^2e = 0$$

This latter equation is the result of eliminating x between the above two equations and is often called their eliminant.

➤ **246.** Again, suppose we knew that an angle θ satisfied both of the equations

$$\sin^3\theta = b, \text{ and } \cos^3\theta = c$$

so, that $$\sin\theta = b^{\frac{1}{3}} \text{ and } \cos\theta = c^{\frac{1}{3}}$$

Now, we always have, for all values of θ

$$\sin^2\theta + \cos^2\theta = 1$$

so that in this case $$b^{2/3} + c^{2/3} = 1$$

This is the result of eliminating θ.

➤ **247.** Between any two equations involving one unknown quantity we can, in theory, always eliminate that quantity. In practice, a considerable amount of artifice and ingenuity is often required in seemingly simple cases.

So, between any three equations involving two unknown quantities, we can theoretically eliminate both of the unknown quantities.

➤ **248.** Some examples of elimination are appended.

EXAMPLE 1 *Eliminate θ from the equations*

$$a\cos\theta + b\sin\theta = c$$

and
$$d\cos\theta + e\sin\theta = f$$

Solving for $\cos\theta$ and $\sin\theta$ by cross multiplication, or otherwise, we have

$$\frac{\cos\theta}{bf - ce} = \frac{\sin\theta}{cd - af} = \frac{1}{bd - ae}$$

$$\therefore \qquad 1 = \cos^2\theta + \sin^2\theta = \frac{(bf - ce)^2 + (cd - af)^2}{(bd - ae)^2}$$

so that $(bf - ce)^2 + (cd - af)^2 = (bd - ae)^2$

EXAMPLE 2 *Eliminate θ between*

$$\frac{ax}{\cos\theta} - \frac{by}{\sin\theta} = a^2 - b^2 \qquad \ldots(1)$$

and
$$\frac{ax\sin\theta}{\cos^2\theta} + \frac{by\cos\theta}{\sin^2\theta} = 0 \qquad \ldots(2)$$

From (2) we have $ax\sin^3\theta = -\,by\cos^3\theta$

$$\therefore \qquad \frac{\sin\theta}{-(by)^{1/3}} = \frac{\cos\theta}{(ax)^{1/3}} = \frac{\sqrt{\sin^2\theta + \cos^2\theta}}{\sqrt{(by)^{2/3} + (ax)^{2/3}}} = \frac{1}{\sqrt{(by)^{2/3} + (ax)^{2/3}}}$$

Hence,
$$\frac{1}{\sin\theta} = -\frac{\sqrt{(by)^{2/3} + (ax)^{2/3}}}{(by)^{1/3}}$$

and
$$\frac{1}{\cos\theta} = \frac{\sqrt{(by)^{2/3} + (ax)^{2/3}}}{(ax)^{1/3}}$$

so that (1) becomes

$$a^2 - b^2 = \sqrt{(by)^{2/3} + (ax)^{2/3}}\left[ax.\frac{1}{(ax)^{1/3}} - by\left\{-\frac{1}{(by)^{1/3}}\right\}\right]$$

$$= \sqrt{(by)^{\frac{2}{3}} + (ax)^{\frac{2}{3}}}\,\{(ax)^{\frac{2}{3}} + (by)^{\frac{2}{3}}\}$$

$$= \{(ax)^{\frac{2}{3}} + (by)^{\frac{2}{3}}\}^{\frac{3}{2}}$$

i.e., $\quad (ax)^{\frac{2}{3}} + (by)^{\frac{2}{3}} = (a^2 - b^2)^{\frac{2}{3}}$

The student who shall afterwards become acquainted with Analytical Geometry will find that the above is the solution of an important problem concerning normals to an ellipse.

EXAMPLE 3 *Eliminate θ from the equations*

$$\frac{x}{a}\cos\theta - \frac{y}{b}\sin\theta = \cos 2\theta \qquad ...(1)$$

and

$$\frac{x}{a}\sin\theta + \frac{y}{b}\cos\theta = 2\sin\theta \qquad ...(2)$$

Multiplying (1) by $\cos\theta$, (2) by $\sin\theta$ and adding, we have

$$\frac{x}{a} = \cos\theta\cos 2\theta + 2\sin\theta\sin 2\theta$$

$$= \cos\theta + \sin\theta\sin 2\theta = \cos\theta + 2\sin^2\theta\cos\theta \qquad ...(3)$$

Multiplying (2) by $\cos\theta$ (1) by $\sin\theta$, and subtracting, we have

$$\frac{y}{b} = 2\sin 2\theta\cos\theta - \cos 2\theta\sin\theta$$

$$= \sin 2\theta\cos\theta + \sin\theta = \sin\theta + 2\sin\theta\cos^2\theta \qquad ...(4)$$

Adding (3) and (4) we have

$$\frac{x}{a} + \frac{y}{b} = (\sin\theta + \cos\theta)[1 + 2\sin\theta\cos\theta]$$

$$= (\sin\theta + \cos\theta)[\sin^2\theta + \cos^2\theta + 2\sin\theta\cos\theta]$$

$$= (\sin\theta + \cos\theta)^3$$

so that

$$\sin\theta + \cos\theta = \left(\frac{x}{a} + \frac{y}{b}\right)^{\frac{1}{3}} \qquad ...(5)$$

Subtracting (4) from (3), we have

$$\frac{x}{a} - \frac{y}{b} = (\cos\theta - \sin\theta)(1 - 2\sin\theta\cos\theta)$$

$$= (\cos\theta - \sin\theta)^3$$

so, that

$$\cos\theta - \sin\theta = \left(\frac{x}{a} - \frac{y}{b}\right)^{\frac{1}{3}} \qquad ...(6)$$

Squaring and adding (5) and (6) we have

$$2 = \left(\frac{x}{a} + \frac{y}{b}\right)^{\frac{2}{3}} + \left(\frac{x}{a} - \frac{y}{b}\right)^{\frac{2}{3}}$$

EXAMPLES XLV

Eliminate θ from the equations

1. $a\cos\theta + b\sin\theta = c$, and $b\cos\theta - a\sin\theta = d$
2. $x = a\cos(\theta - \alpha)$, and $y = b\cos(\theta - \beta)$
3. $a\cos 2\theta = b\sin\theta$, and $c\sin 2\theta = d\cos\theta$
4. $a\sin\alpha - b\cos\alpha = 2b\sin\theta$, and $a\sin 2\alpha - b\cos 2\theta = a$

5. $x\sin\theta - y\cos\theta = \sqrt{x^2+y^2}$, and $\dfrac{\sin^2\theta}{a^2} + \dfrac{\cos^2\theta}{b^2} = \dfrac{1}{x^2+y^2}$

6. $\dfrac{x\cos\theta}{a} + \dfrac{y\sin\theta}{b} = 1$

and $x\sin\theta - y\cos\theta = \sqrt{a^2\sin^2\theta + b^2\cos^2\theta}$

7. $\sin\theta - \cos\theta = p$, and $\operatorname{cosec}\theta - \sin\theta = q$

8. $x = a\cos\theta + b\cos 2\theta$ and $y = a\sin\theta + b\sin 2\theta$

9. If $m = \operatorname{cosec}\theta - \sin\theta$, and $n = \sec\theta - \cos\theta$

prove that $m^{\frac{2}{3}} + n^{\frac{2}{3}} = (mn)^{-\frac{2}{3}}$

10. Prove that the result of eliminating θ from the equations

$x\cos(\theta+\alpha) + y\sin(\theta+\alpha) = \alpha\sin 2\theta$

and $y\cos(\theta+\alpha) - x\sin(\theta+\alpha) = 2\alpha\cos 2\theta$

$(x\cos\alpha + y\sin\alpha)^{\frac{2}{3}} + (x\sin\alpha - y\cos\alpha)^{\frac{2}{3}} = (2\alpha)^{\frac{2}{3}}$

Eliminate θ and ϕ from the equations

11. $\sin\theta + \sin\phi = a$, $\cos\theta + \cos\phi = b$ and $\theta - \phi = \alpha$

12. $\tan\theta + \tan\phi = x$, $\cot\theta + \cot\phi = y$, and $\theta + \phi = \alpha$

13. $a\cos^2\theta + b\sin^2\theta = c$, $b\cos^2\phi + a\sin^2\phi = d$ and $a\tan\theta = b\tan\phi$

14. $\cos\theta + \cos\phi = a$, $\cot\theta + \cot\phi = b$, and $\operatorname{cosec}\theta + \operatorname{cosec}\phi =$

15. $a\sin\theta = b\sin\phi$, $a\cos\theta + b\cos\phi = c$, and $x = y\tan(\theta+\phi)$

16. $\dfrac{x}{a}\cos\theta + \dfrac{y}{b}\sin\theta = 1$, $\dfrac{x}{a}\cos\phi + \dfrac{y}{b}\sin\phi = 1$

and $\quad a^2\sin\dfrac{\theta}{2}\sin\dfrac{\phi}{2} + b^2\cos\dfrac{\theta}{2}\cos\dfrac{\phi}{2} = c^2$

21

PROJECTIONS

➤ **249.** Let PQ be any straight line, and from its ends, P and Q, let perpendiculars be drawn to a fixed straight line OA. Then MN is called the projection of PQ on OA.

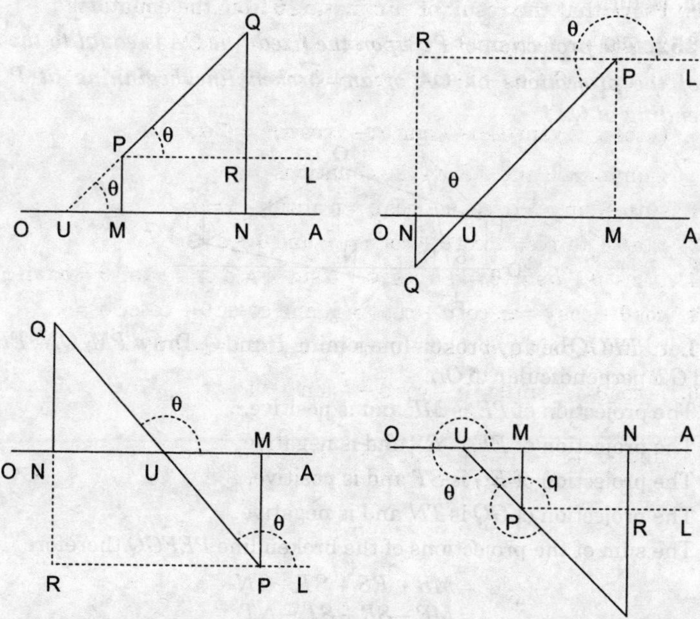

If MN be in the same direction as OA, it is positive; if in the opposite direction, it is negative.

➤ **250.** *If θ be the angle between any straight line PQ and a fixed line OA, the projection of PQ on OA is PQ* $\cos\theta$.

Whatever be the direction of PQ draw, through P a straight line PL parallel to OA and let it and QN, both produced if necessary, meet in R.

Then, in each figure, the angle LPQ or the angle AUQ is equal to θ.

Also, $$MN = PR = PQ \cos LPQ = PQ \cos\theta,$$

by the definitions of Art 50.

Similarly, the projection of PQ on a line perpendicular to $OA = RQ$.

$$= PQ \sin LPQ = PQ \sin \theta$$

The projections of any line PQ on a line to which PQ is inclined at any angle θ and on a perpendicular line, are therefore $PQ \cos \theta$ and $PQ \sin \theta$.

➤ **251.** We might therefore, in Art. 50 have defined the cosine as the ratio to OP of the projection of OP on the initial line, and similarly, the sine as the ratio to OP of the projection of OP on a line perpendicular to the initial line.

This method of looking upon the definition of the cosine and sine is often useful.

➤ **252.** *The projection of PQ upon the fixed line OA is equal to the sum of the projections on OA of any broken line beginning at P and ending at Q.*

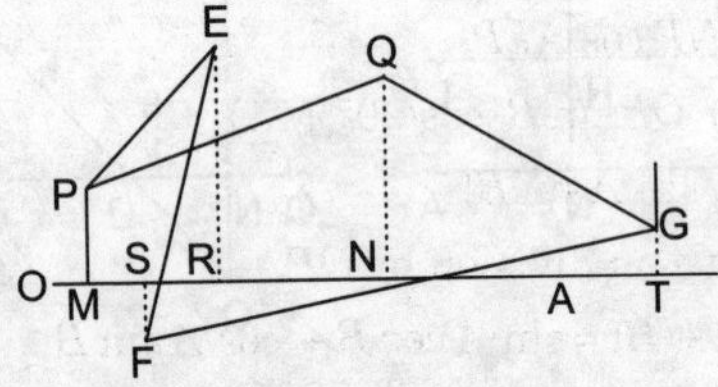

Let $PEFGQ$ be any broken line joining P and Q. Draw PM, QN, ER, FS and GT perpendicular to OA.

The projection of PE is MR and is positive.

The projection of EF is RS and is negative.

The projection of EG is ST and is positive.

The projection of GQ is TN and is negative.

The sum of the projections of the broken line $PEFGQ$ therefore

$$= MR + RS + ST + TN$$
$$= MR - SR + ST - NT$$
$$= MS + SN$$
$$= MN.$$

A similar proof will hold whatever be the positions of P and Q, and however broken the lines joining them may be.

Cor. : The sum of the projections of any broken line, joining P to Q, is equal to the sum of the projections of any other broken line joining the same two points; for each sum is equal to the projection of the straight line PQ.

➤ **253.** *General Proofs, by Projections, of the Addition and Subtraction Theorems.*

Let AOB be the angle A and BOC the angle B. On OC, the bounding line of the angle $A + B$, take any point P, and draw PN perpendicular to OB and produce it to meet OA in L.

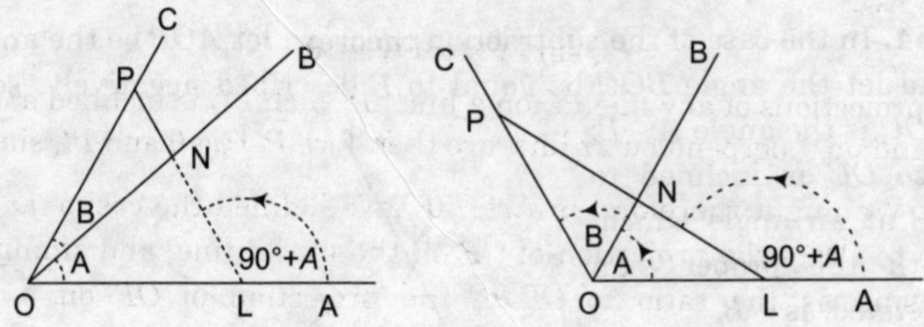

Then, $\angle ALP = \angle LNO + \angle AOB = 90° + A$

(i) *To prove* $\cos(A + B) = \cos A \cos B - \sin A \sin B$

$$OP \cdot \cos(A + B) = OP \cdot \cos AOP$$

$=$ projection of OP on OA (Art. 250)

$=$ projection of ON on OA + projection of NP on OA (Art. 252)

$= ON \cos AON + NP \cos ALP$ (Art. 250)

$= OP \cos B \cdot \cos A + OP \sin B \cdot \cos(90° + A)$

$= OP[\cos A \cos B - \sin A \sin B]$ (Art. 70)

Hence, the result (i) on division by OP.

(ii) *To prove* $\sin(A + B) = \sin A \cos B + \cos A \sin B$

$$OP \cdot \sin(A + B) = OP \cdot \sin AOP$$

$=$ projection of OP on a perpendicular to OA (Art 250)

$=$ sum of the projections of ON, NP on the perpendiculars to OA

(Art. 252)

$= ON \sin A + NP \sin ALP$ (Art. 250)

$= OP \cos B \cdot \sin A + OP \sin B \cdot \sin(90° + A)$ (Art. 250)

$= OP[\sin A \cos B + \cos A \sin B]$ (At. 70)

Hence, the result (ii)

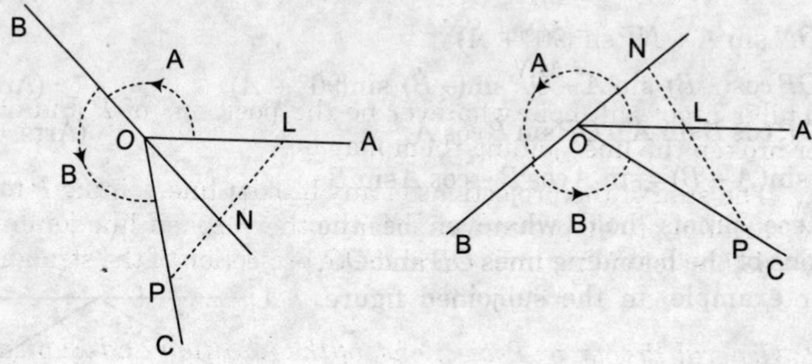

The above proof holds, as in the subjoined figures, for all positions of the bounding lines OB and OC.

➤ **254.** In the case of the subtraction theorem, let AOB be the angle A, and let the angle BOC be equal to B described negatively, so that AOC is the angle $A - B$; also OC is inclined to OB at an angle which, with the proper sign prefixed, is $-B$.

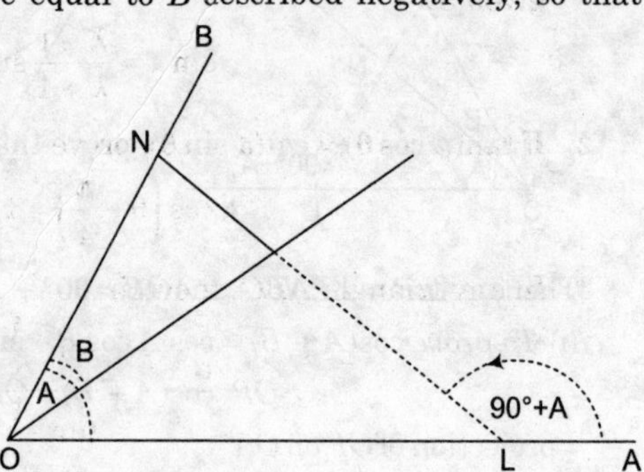

In OC, the bounding line of the angle we are considering, take any point P; draw PN perpendicular to OB and produce it to meet OA in L.

(i) *To prove* $\cos(A - B) = \cos A \cos B + \sin A \sin B$

$$OP \cdot \cos(A - B) = OP \cdot \cos AOC$$

$=$ projection of OP on OA (Art. 250)

$=$ projection of ON on OA + projection of NP on OA (Art. 252)

$= ON \cos A + NP \cos(90° + A)$ (Art. 250)

$= OP \cos(-B) \cdot \cos A + OP \sin(-B) \cdot \cos(90° + A)$ (Art. 250)

$= OP \cos B \cos A + OP(-\sin B)(-\sin A)$ (Arts. 68, 70)

$= OP[\cos A \cos B + \sin A \sin B]$

Hence $\cos(A - B) = \cos A \cos B + \sin A \sin B$.

(ii) *To prove* $\sin(A - B) = \sin A \cos B - \cos A \sin B$

$$OP \cdot \sin(A - B) = OP \cdot \sin AOC$$

$=$ projection of OP on a perpendicular to OA (Art. 250)

$=$ sum of the projections of ON, NP on the perpendicular to OA (Art. 252)

$= ON \sin A + NP \sin(90° + A)$

$= OP \cos(-B) \cdot \sin A + OP \sin(-B) \cdot \sin(90° + A)$ (Art. 250)

$= OP \cos B \sin A - OP \sin B \cos A$ (Arts. 68, 70)

$\therefore \sin(A - B) = \sin A \cos B - \cos A \sin B$

These proofs hold whatever be the positions of the bounding lines OB and OC, as, for example, in the subjoined figure.

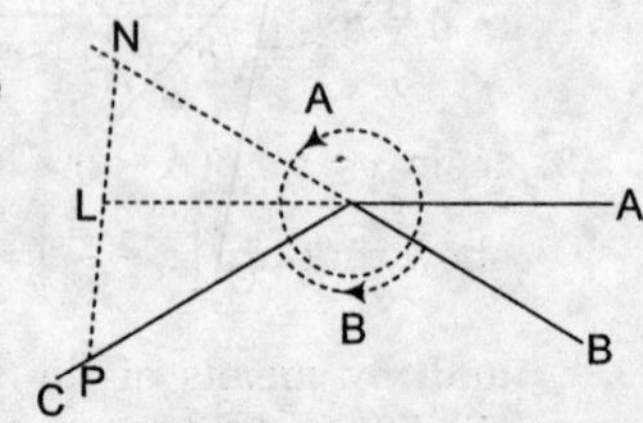

MISCELLANEOUS EXAMPLES.

1. Show that if an angle a be divided into two parts, so that the ratio of tangents of the parts is λ, the difference x between the parts is given by

$$\sin x = \frac{\lambda - 1}{\lambda + 1} \sin \lambda.$$

2. If $\tan(\pi \cos \theta) = \cot(\pi \sin \theta)$, prove that

$$\cos\left(\theta - \frac{\pi}{4}\right) = \pm \frac{1}{2\sqrt{2}}$$

3. In any triangle ABC, show that

$$\frac{a-b}{c} = \frac{\tan\frac{A}{2} - \tan\frac{B}{2}}{\tan\frac{A}{2} + \tan\frac{B}{2}}$$

and
$$\frac{a+b}{c} = \frac{1 + \tan\frac{A}{2}\tan\frac{B}{2}}{1 - \tan\frac{A}{2}\tan\frac{B}{2}}$$

4. An aeroplane is travelling east with a constant velocity of 180 km. per hour at a constant height above the ground. At a certain time a man observes it due north of him at an angle of elevation of 9°30′. At the end of one minute he sees it in a direction 62° east of north. At what height is the aeroplane travelling, and what is the angle of elevation at which the man sees it in the second observed position?

5. If the sides of a triangle are 51, 35 and 26 cm., find the sides of a triangle, on a base of 41 cm., which shall have the same area and

6. Prove that

$$\sin \cot^{-1} \cos \tan^{-1} x = \sqrt{\frac{x^2 + 1}{x^2 + 2}}$$

7. Eliminate θ from the equations

$$\sin(\theta + a) = a, \cos^2(\theta + \beta) = b.$$

8. Show that, whatever be the value of θ, the expression

$$a \sin^2\theta + b \sin\theta \cos\theta + c \cos^2\theta$$

lies between

$$\frac{a+c}{2} + \frac{1}{2}\sqrt{b^2 + (a-c)^2} \text{ and } \frac{a+c}{2} - \frac{1}{2}\sqrt{b^2 + (a-c)^2}$$

9. If $\sin x = k \sin(A - x)$,

show that $\tan\left(x - \frac{A}{2}\right) = \frac{k-1}{k+1} \tan\frac{A}{2}$.

and, by means of the tables, solve the equation when $k = 3$ and $A = 50°$

10. Express

$$\tan\theta + \tan\left(\theta + \frac{\pi}{3}\right) + \tan\left(\theta + \frac{2\pi}{3}\right)$$

in terms of $\tan 3\theta$.

Hence, or otherwise, solve the equation

$$\tan\theta + \tan\left(\theta + \frac{\pi}{3}\right) + \tan\left(\theta + \frac{2\pi}{3}\right) = 3$$

11. In a triangle ABC, if $\tan\frac{A}{2}$, $\tan\frac{B}{2}$, and $\tan\frac{C}{2}$ are in arithmetic progression, then $\cos A, \cos B, \cos C$ are also in arithmetic progression.

12. A man standing on the sea shore observes two buoys in the same direction, the line through them making an angle α with the shore. He then walks along the shore a distance a, when he finds the buoys subtend an angle α at his eye; and on walking a further distance b he finds that they again subtend an angle α at his eye. Show that the distance between the buoys is $\left(a + \frac{b}{2}\right)\sec\alpha - \frac{2a(a+b)}{2a+b}\cos\alpha$, assuming the shore to be straight, and neglecting the height of the man's eye above the sea.

13. The bisectors of the angles of a triangle ABC meet its circumcircle in the points D, E, F respectively. Show that the area of the triangle DEF is to that of ABC as $R:2r$.

14. The alternate angles of a regular pentagon are joined forming another regular pentagon; find the ratio of the areas of the two pentagons.

15. If $\phi = \tan^{-1}\frac{x\sqrt{3}}{2k - x}$ and $\theta = \tan^{-1}\frac{2x - k}{k\sqrt{3}}$, prove that one value of $\phi - \theta$ is 30°.

16. If
$$m^2 + m'^2 + 2mm'\cos\theta = 1,$$
$$n^2 + n'^2 + 2nn'\cos\theta = 1,$$
and
$$nm + m'n' + (mn' + m'n)\cos\theta = 0,$$
prove that
$$m^2 + n^2 = \operatorname{cosec}^2\theta.$$

17. If x be real, prove that

$$\frac{x^2 - 2x\cos\alpha + 1}{x^2 - 2x\cos\beta + 1} \text{ lies between } \frac{\sin^2\frac{\alpha}{2}}{\sin^2\frac{\beta}{2}} \text{ and } \frac{\cos^2\frac{\alpha}{2}}{\cos^2\frac{\beta}{2}}.$$

18. Prove that the area of circle exceeds the area of a regular polygon of n sides and of equal perimeter in the ratio of

$$\tan\frac{\pi}{n} : \frac{\pi}{n}.$$

19. If $\frac{\sin(2\alpha - \theta)}{\sin\theta} = 1 + x$, where x is very small, show that

$\frac{\cos\theta}{\cos\alpha} = 1 + \frac{1}{2} x \tan^2\alpha$, approximately.

20. If $2\sigma = \alpha + \beta + \gamma + \delta$,

prove that $\cos(\sigma - \alpha)\cos(\sigma - \beta)\cos(\sigma - \gamma)\cos(\sigma - \delta) + \sin(\sigma - \alpha)$
$\sin(\sigma - \beta)\sin(\sigma - \gamma)\sin(\sigma - \delta)$
$= \cos\alpha\cos\beta\cos\gamma\cos\delta + \sin\alpha\sin\beta\sin\gamma\sin\delta$.

21. Solve completely the equations

(i) $\tan\alpha\tan(\theta - a) + \tan\beta\tan(\theta - \beta) = \tan\frac{\beta - \alpha}{2}(\tan\alpha - \tan\beta)$, and

(ii) $\sin 3\theta = 4\sin\theta\sin 2\theta\sin 4\theta$

22. *OA* is a crank 2 metres long which rotates about *O*; *AB* is a connecting rod to *B* which moves on a straight line passing through *O*. Find the angles that the crank *OA* makes with *OB* when *B* has described respectively $\frac{1}{4}, \frac{1}{2}$, and $\frac{3}{4}$ of its total travel from its extreme position, the length of *AB* being 5 metres.

23. From the top of a cliff, 200 metres high, two ships are observed at sea. The angle of depression of the one is 9°10′ and it is seen in a direction 30° north of east; the angle of depression of the other is 7 °30′ and it is seen in a direction 25° south of east. What is the distance between the ships, and what is the bearing of the one as seen from the other?

24. Show that the radius of the circle, passing through the centre of the inscribed circle of a triangle and any two of the centres of the escribed circles, is equal to the diameter of the circumscribed circle of the triangle.

25. If $\tan\left(\frac{\pi}{4} + \frac{y}{2}\right) = \tan^3\left(\frac{\pi}{4} + \frac{x}{2}\right)$,

$$\text{prove that } \sin y = \sin x \frac{3 + \sin^2 x}{1 + 3\sin^2 x}.$$

26. Prove that $\sin\beta\sin\gamma\cos^2\alpha\sin(\beta - \gamma)$ + two similar expressions
$= -\sin(\beta - \gamma)\sin(\gamma - \alpha)\sin(\alpha - \beta)$.

27. The legs of a pair of compasses are each 7 cm. long, and the pencil leg has a joint at 4 cm. from the common end of the two legs. The compasses are used to describe a circle of radius 4 cm, and the pencil leg is bent at the joint so that the pencil is perpendicular to the paper. Show that the angles of inclination of the two legs to the vertical are 19°5′ and 25°20′ approximately.

28. A tower stands in a field, whose shape is that of an equilateral triangle and whose side is 30 metres. It subtends angles at the three corners whose tangents are respectively $\sqrt{3}+1$, $\sqrt{2}$, $\sqrt{2}$. Find its height.

29. Two circles of radii r_1 and r_2 out at an angle α show that the area common to them is

$$(r_1^2 - r_2^2)\tan^{-1}\frac{r_2\sin\alpha}{r_2 + r_2\cos\alpha} + r_2^3\,a - r_1 r_2 \sin\alpha$$

30. Find the simplest values of

$$\tan^{-1}\frac{\sqrt{1+x^2}-1}{x}, \text{ and } \tan\left(\frac{1}{2}\sin^{-1}\frac{2x}{1+x^2} + \frac{1}{2}\cos^{-1}\frac{1-y^2}{1+y^2}\right).$$

31. Eliminate α and β from the equations

$$\sin\alpha + \sin\beta = l,$$

$$\cos\alpha + \cos\beta = m,$$

and $$\tan\frac{\alpha}{2}\tan\frac{\beta}{2} = n$$

32. Find, by drawing graphs, how many real roots of the equation $x^2 \tan x = 1$ lie between 0 and 2π?

33. Show that $\cos 2\alpha = 2\sin^2\beta + 4\cos(\alpha+\beta)\sin\alpha\sin\beta + \cos 2(\alpha+\beta)$.

34. Prove that $\sin\dfrac{\pi}{14}\sin\dfrac{3\pi}{14}\sin\dfrac{5\pi}{14} = \dfrac{1}{8}$

35. Solve the equations

$$\sqrt{3}\sin 2A = \sin 2B,$$

$$\sqrt{3}\sin^2 A + \sin^2 B = \frac{1}{2}(\sqrt{3}-1).$$

36. If the tangents of the angles of a triangle are in arithmetic progression, prove that the squares of the sides are in the ratio

$$x^2(x^2+9) : (3+x^2)^2 : 9(1+x^2),$$

where x is the least or greatest tangent.

37. A, B, C are three points on a horizontal plane in the same straight line, AB being 100 metres and BC 150 metres. The angles of elevation of a balloon observed simultaneously from A, B, C are α, β, γ. Show that the height h of the balloon in metres is given by

$$h^2(3\cot^2\alpha + 2\cot^2\gamma - 5\cot^2\beta) = 75{,}000.$$

38. If p, q, r are the perpendiculars from the vertices of a triangle upon any straight line meeting the sides externally in D, E, F, prove that

$$a^2(p-q)(p-r) + b^2(q-r)(q-p) + c^2(r-p)(r-q) = 4\Delta^2,$$

where Δ is the area of the triangle.

Prove also that $EF = \dfrac{2p\Delta}{(p-q)(p-r)}$.

39. The length of the side of a regular polygon of n sides is $2l$ and the areas of the polygon and of the inscribed and circumscribed circles are A, A_1 and A_2; prove that

$$A_2 - A_1 = \pi l^2 \text{ and } n^2 l^2 A_1 = \pi \Delta^3.$$

40. Prove that in the triangle whose sides are 31, 56 and 64, one of the angles differs from a right angle by rather less than a minute of angle.

41. Show that

$$\frac{1+\sin A}{\cos A} + \frac{\cos B}{1-\sin B} = \frac{2\sin A - 2\sin B}{\sin(A-B) + \cos A - \cos B}.$$

42. Prove that

$$(1+\sec 2\theta)(1+\sec 4\theta)(1+\sec 8\theta)\ldots(1+\sec 2^n\theta) = \tan 2^n\theta \cdot \cot\theta$$

43. If the sides of a triangle are in arithmetic progression, and if its greatest angle exceeds the least angle by α, show that the sides are in the ratio $1-x:1:1+x$, where $x = \sqrt{\dfrac{1-\cos\alpha}{7-\cos\alpha}}$.

44. A tower stands on the edge of a circular lake $ABCD$. The foot of the tower is at D and the angles of elevation of its top at A, B, C are respectively α, β and γ. If the angles BAC, ACB are each θ, show that $2\cos\theta\cos\beta = \cot\alpha + \cot\gamma$.

45. The internal bisectors of the angles of a triangle ABC meet the sides in D, E, and F. Show that the area of the triangle DEF is equal to $\dfrac{2\Delta abc}{(b+c)(c+a)(a+b)}$.

46. If $\cos^{-1} x + \cos^{-1} y + \cot^{-1} z = \pi$,
prove that $x^2 + y^2 + z^2 + 2xyz = 1$.

47. Eliminate θ from the equations

$$\lambda\cos 2\theta = \cos(\theta + \alpha),$$

and

$$\lambda\sin 2\theta = 2\sin(\theta + \alpha)$$

48. A circle is described whose diameter is 6 metres; find an equation to determine the angle subtended at the centre by an arc which is such that the sum of the arc and its chord is 8 metres and solve the equation by a graphic method.

49. Simplify

$$\left\{\frac{\cos(\alpha+\beta)}{\cos(\alpha-\beta)} - \frac{\cos(\alpha+\gamma)}{\cos(\alpha-\gamma)}\right\}^2 + \left[\frac{\sin(\alpha+\beta)}{\cos(\alpha-\beta)} - \frac{\sin(\alpha+\gamma)}{\cos(\alpha-\gamma)}\right]^2.$$

50. Show that

$$\sin^2 12° + \sin^2 21° + \sin^2 39° + \sin^2 48° = 1 + \sin^2 9° + \sin^2 18°.$$

51. If a, b, c are the sides of a triangle, $\lambda a, \lambda b, \lambda c$ the sides of a similar triangle inscribed in the former and θ the angle between the sides a and λc, prove that $2\lambda \cos\theta = 1$.

52. The top of a hill is observed from two stations A and B on the same level; A is south of the hill and B is north-east of A. If the angles of elevation from A and B are $9°30'$ and $7°30'$, find the compass bearing of B from the hill.

53. The tangents at B and C to the circumcircle of a triangle ABC meet in A', and O is the circumcentre. If the angle OAA' is θ, prove that $2\tan\theta = \cot B \sim \cot C$.

54. Find by a geometrical construction the number of values of $\cos\left(\frac{1}{3}\sin^{-1} a\right)$. Show that their product is $-\frac{1}{16}(1-a^2)$.

55. Show that the expression $\frac{\tan(x+\alpha)}{\tan(x-\alpha)}$ cannot lie between the values $\tan^2\left(\frac{\pi}{4}-\alpha\right)$ and $\tan^2\left(\frac{\pi}{4}+\alpha\right)$.

56. Show that

$$\cos^4\theta + \cos^4\left(\theta + \frac{2\pi}{n}\right) + \cos^4\left(\theta + \frac{4\pi}{n}\right) + \dots \text{ to } n \text{ terms} = \frac{3n}{8}.$$

57. If $\{\sin(\alpha-\beta) + \cos(\alpha+2\beta)\sin\beta\}^2 = 4\cos\alpha\sin\beta\sin(\alpha+\beta)$, prove that

$$\tan\alpha = \tan\beta\left\{\frac{1}{(\sqrt{2}\cos\beta - 1)^2} - 1\right\},$$

α and β being each less than a right angle.

58. Find all the values of x which satisfy the equation

$$\tan(x+\beta)\tan(x+\gamma) + \tan(x+\gamma)\tan(x+\alpha) + \tan(x+\alpha)\tan(x+\beta) = 1.$$

59. ABC is a triangle and D is the foot of the perpendicular from A upon BC. If $BC = 117$ cm, $\angle B = 43°14'$, and $\angle C = 61°27'$, find the length of AD.

60. The angles of elevation of the top of a mountain from three points A, B, and C in a base line are observed to be α, β, γ respectively. Prove that the height of the mountain is

$$(-AB \cdot BC \cdot CA)^{\frac{1}{2}}(BC\cot^2\alpha + CA\cot^2\beta + AB\cot^2\gamma)^{-\frac{1}{2}},$$

where regard is paid to the sense of the lines.

61. If the bisector of the angle C of a triangle ABC cuts AB in D and the circumcircle in E, prove that $CE : DE = (a+b)^2 : c^2$.

62. Eliminate θ from the equations

$a\tan\theta + b\cot 2\theta = c$,

and $a\cot\theta - b\tan 2\theta = c$.

63. Find, by a graph, an approximate value, correct to half a degree, of the equation $\cot x = \cos 2x$.

64. A man setting out a tennis court uses three strings of lengths 3m., 4 m. and 4.94 m. respectively to construct the right angles. Find the errors be makes in the angles of the court.

65. If $n^2 \sin^2(\alpha + \beta) = \sin^2 \alpha + \sin^2 \beta - 2 \sin \alpha \sin \beta \cos(\alpha - \beta)$,

show that $\tan \alpha = \dfrac{1 \pm n}{1 \mp n} \tan \beta$.

66. If the expression $\dfrac{A \cos(\theta + \alpha) + B \sin(\theta + \beta)}{A' \sin(\theta + \alpha) + B' \cos(\theta + \beta)}$

retain the same value for all values of θ, show that

$$AA' - BB' = (A'B - AB') \sin(\alpha - \beta).$$

67. Show that the values of θ which are the roots of the equation $\sin 2\theta \cos^2(\alpha - \beta) - \sin 2\alpha \cos^2(\beta + \theta) - \sin 2\beta \sin^2(\alpha + \theta) = 0$

are given by $(2n + 1)\dfrac{\pi}{2} - \beta$ and $n\pi + \alpha$, when n is any positive or negative integer.

68. The three medians of a triangle ABC make angles α, β, γ with each other. Prove that

$\cot \alpha + \cot \beta + \cot \gamma + \cot A + \cot B + \cot C = 0$.

69. From each of two points, distant $2a$ apart, on one bank of a river the angular elevation of the top of a tower on the opposite bank is a, and from the point midway between these two points the angular elevation of the top of the tower is β. Find in terms of a, α, β the height of the tower.

70. If D, E, F are the points of contact of the inscribed circle with the sides BC, CA, AB of a triangle, show that if the squares of AD, BE, CF are in arithmetic progression, then the sides of the triangle are in harmonic progression.

71. Show that half the side of the equilateral triangle inscribed in a circle differs from the side of the regular inscribed heptagon by the less than $\dfrac{1}{500}$th of the radius.

72. Show that the quantity

$\cos \theta \{\sin \theta + \sqrt{\sin^2 \theta + \sin^2 \alpha}\}$

always lies between the values $\pm \sqrt{1 + \sin^2 \alpha}$.

73. Express $8 \sin \alpha \sin \beta \sin \gamma \sin \delta$ as a series of eight cosines.

74. If $\sin^2 \phi = \dfrac{\cos 2\alpha \cos 2\beta}{\cos^2(\alpha + \beta)}$, prove that $$\tan^2\frac{\phi}{2} = \frac{\tan\left(\frac{\pi}{4} \pm \alpha\right)}{\tan\left(\frac{\pi}{4} \pm \beta\right)}.$$

75. Given the base a of a triangle, the opposite angle A, and the product k^2 of the other two sides, solve the triangle and show that there is no such triangle if $a < 2k\sin\frac{A}{2}$.

76. At a point O on a horizontal plane the angles of elevation of two points P and Q on the side of a hill are found to be 38° and 25°; the distance of A, the foot of the hill, from O is 500 metres and the distance AQ is 320 metres, the whole figure being in a vertical plane. Prove that the distance PQ is 329 metres approximately, and find the slope of the hill.

77. I_1, I_2 and I_3 are the centres of the circles escribed to ABC, and ρ_1, ρ_2, ρ_3 are the radii of the circles inscribed in the triangles BI_1O, OI_2A, AI_3B. Show that
$$\rho_1 : \rho_2 : \rho_3 :: \sin\frac{A}{2} : \sin\frac{B}{2} : \sin\frac{C}{2}.$$

78. Two circles, the sum of whose radii is a, are placed in the same plane with their centres at a distance $2a$, and an endless string is fully stretched so as partly to surround the circles and to cross between them. Show that the length of the string is $\left(\frac{4\pi}{3} + 2\sqrt{3}\right)a$.

79. Show that
$$2\tan^{-1}\frac{\sqrt{x^2+a^2} - x + b}{\sqrt{a^2-b^2}} + \tan^{-1}\frac{x\sqrt{a^2-b^2}}{b\sqrt{x^2+a^2}+a^2} + \tan^{-1}\frac{\sqrt{a^2-b^2}}{b} = n\pi.$$

80. Given that -2.45 is an approximate value of x satisfying the equation $3\sin x = 2x + 3$, find a closer approximation.
[Assume that 2.45 radians = 140°22′30″.]

81. Show that
$$\sin A = \sin(36° + A) - \sin(36° - A) - \sin(72° + A) + \sin(72° - A).$$

82. Find the complete solution of the equations
$\tan 3\theta + \tan 3\phi = 2$,
and $\tan\theta + \tan\phi = 4$.

83. If ABC be a triangle, and if
$$\sin^3\theta = \sin(A-\theta)\sin(B-\theta)\sin(C-\theta),$$
then $\cot\theta = \cot A + \cot B + \cot C$.

84. A ship steaming at a speed of 15 km. per hour towards a harbour A was observed from a station B, 10 km. due west of A, to lie 42° N of E.

If the ship reached the harbour after three-quarters of an hour, find its distance from B when first observed.

85. Show that the radius of the circle inscribed in the triangle formed by joining the centres of the escribed circles of a triangle ABC is

$$\frac{4R\cos\frac{A}{2}\cos\frac{B}{2}\cos\frac{C}{2}}{\cos\frac{A}{2}\cos\frac{B}{2}+\cos\frac{C}{2}}.$$

86. A polygon of n sides inscribed in a circle is such that its sides subtend angles $2\alpha, 4\alpha, 6\alpha, \ldots 2n\alpha$ at the centre; prove that its area is to the area of the regular inscribed polygon of n sides in the ratio $\sin n\alpha : n\sin\alpha$.

87. Express the equation

$$\cot^{-1}\left\{\frac{y}{\sqrt{1-x^2-y^2}}\right\}=2\tan^{-1}\sqrt{\frac{3-4x^2}{4x^2}}-\tan^{-1}\sqrt{\frac{3-4x^2}{x^2}}$$

as a rational integral equation between x and y.

88. If x_1, x_2, x_3, x_4 are the roots of the equation

$$x^4 - x^3\sin 2\beta + x^2\cos 2\beta - x\cos\beta - \sin\beta = 0,$$

prove that $\tan^{-1}x_1 + \tan^{-1}x_2 + \tan^{-1}x_3 + \tan^{-1}x_4 = n\pi + \frac{\pi}{2} - \beta$,

where n is an integer.

89. If $\dfrac{\sin(\theta-\beta)\cos\alpha}{\sin(\phi-\alpha)\cos\beta}+\dfrac{\cos(\alpha+\theta)\sin\beta}{\cos(\phi-\beta)\sin\alpha}=0$

and $\dfrac{\tan\theta\tan\alpha}{\tan\phi\tan\beta}+\dfrac{\cos(\alpha-\beta)}{\cos(\alpha+\beta)}=0,$

show that $\tan\theta=\frac{1}{2}(\tan\beta+\cot\alpha)$ and $\tan\phi=\frac{1}{2}(\tan\alpha-\cot\beta)$.

90. If $\cos 3x = -\frac{3}{8}\sqrt{6}$, show that the three values of $\cos x$ are

$\frac{1}{2}\sqrt{6}\sin\frac{\pi}{10}, \frac{1}{2}\sqrt{6}\sin\frac{\pi}{6}$ and $-\frac{1}{2}\sqrt{6}\sin\frac{3\pi}{10}$.

91. The base a of a triangle and the ratio $r(<1)$ of the sides are given. Show that the altitude h of the triangle cannot exceed $\frac{ar}{1-r^2}$, and that when h has this value the vertical angle of the triangle is $\frac{\pi}{2}-2\tan^{-1}r$.

92. A railway-curve, in the shape of a quadrant of a circle, has n telegraph posts at its ends and at equal distances along the curve. A man stationed at a point on one of the extreme radii produced sees the pth and qth posts from the end nearest him in a straight line.

Show that the radius of the curve is $\frac{a}{2}\cos(p+q)\phi \operatorname{cosec} q\phi$, where $\phi = \frac{\pi}{4(n-1)}$, and a is the distance from the man to the nearest end of the curve.

93. Show that the radii of the three escribed circles of a triangle are the roots of the equation

$$x^3 - x^2(4R + r) + xs^2 - rs^2 = 0.$$

94. Eliminate x and y from the equations

$$\cos x + \cos y = a,$$
$$\cos 2x + \cos 2y = b,$$

and
$$\cos 3x + \cos 3y = c$$

giving the result in a rational form.

95. Sum the series

$\sin\theta \sin 2\theta \sin 3\theta + \sin 2\theta \sin 3\theta \sin 4\theta + \sin 3\theta \sin 4\theta \sin 5\theta + \ldots$ to n terms.

96. In a circle of radius 5 cm. the area of a certain segment is 25 sq.cm. Find graphically the angle that is subtended at the centre by the arc of the segment.

97. Prove that

$$4\sin 27° = (5+\sqrt{5})^{1/2} - (3-\sqrt{5})^{1/2}$$

98. If $\cos(\beta-\gamma) + \cos(\gamma-\alpha) + \cos(\alpha-\beta) + 1 = 0$,
show that $\beta-\gamma$, $\gamma-a$ or $\alpha-\beta$ is a multiple of π.

99. Given the product p of the sines of the angles of a triangle, and the product q of their cosines, show that the tangents of the angles are the roots of the equation

$$qx^3 + px^2 + (1+q)x - p = 0.$$

If $p = \frac{1}{8}(3+\sqrt{3})$ and $q = \frac{1}{8}(\sqrt{3}-1)$, show that the angles of the triangle are 45°, 60° and 75°.

100. Observations on the positions of a ship are made from a fixed station. At one instant the bearing of the ship is α_1 west of north. Ten minutes later the ship is due north and after a further interval of ten minutes its bearing is α_2 east of north. Assuming that the speed and direction of motion of the ship have not changed, show that its course is θ east of north where

$$\tan\theta = \frac{2\sin\alpha_1 \sin\alpha_2}{\sin(\alpha_1-\alpha_2)}.$$

101. A hill on a level plane has the form of a portion of a sphere. At the bottom the surface slopes at an angle α and from a point on the plain distant a from the foot of the hill the elevation of the highest visible point is β. Prove that the height of the hill above the plain is

$$\frac{a \sin\beta \sin^2\frac{\alpha}{2}}{\sin^2\frac{\alpha-\beta}{2}}.$$

102. If D, E, F be the foot of the perpendiculars from ABC on the opposite sides and $\rho, \rho_1, \rho_2, \rho_3$ be the radii of the circles inscribed in the triangles DEF, AEF, BFD, ODE, prove that $r^3\rho = 2R\rho\rho_1\rho_2\rho_3$.

103. O is the centre of a circular field and A any point on its boundary; a horse, tethered by a rope fastened at one end at A, can graze over $\frac{1}{n}$th of the field; if B be the farthest point of the boundary that he can reach and $\angle AOB = \theta$, prove that

$$\sin\theta + (\pi - \theta)\cos\theta = \left(1 - \frac{1}{n}\right)\pi.$$

104. Solve the equation

$$\theta = \tan^{-1}(2\tan^2\theta) - \frac{1}{2}\sin^{-1}\frac{3\sin 2\theta}{5 + 4\cos 2\theta}$$

105. If $\cos^2\theta = \dfrac{m^2-1}{3}$ and $\tan^3\dfrac{\theta}{2} = \tan\alpha$,

prove that $$\cos^{2/3}\alpha + \sin^{2/3}\alpha = \left(\frac{2}{m}\right)^{2/3}.$$

106. A man walks on a horizontal plane a distance a, and then through a distance a at an angle α with his previous direction. After he has done this n times, the change of his direction being always in the same sense, show that he is distant

$$\frac{a \sin\frac{n\alpha}{2}}{\sin\frac{\alpha}{2}}$$

from his starting point, and that this distance makes an angle $(n-1)\dfrac{\alpha}{2}$ with his original direction.

107. Prove that

$$\frac{\tan(\gamma-\delta)}{\tan(\alpha-\beta)} + \frac{\tan(\delta-\beta)}{\tan(\alpha-\gamma)} + \frac{\tan(\beta-\gamma)}{\tan(\alpha-\delta)} + \frac{\tan(\gamma-\delta)\tan(\delta-\beta)\tan(\beta-\gamma)}{\tan(\alpha-\beta)\tan(\alpha-\gamma)\tan(\alpha-\delta)} = 0.$$

108. A meteor moving in a straight line passes vertically above two points, A and B, in a horizontal plane, 1 km. apart. When above A it has altitude 50° as seen from B, and when above B it has altitude 40°

as seen from A. Find the distance from A at which it will strike the plane, correct to the nearest metre.

109. The face of a hill is a plane inclined at an angle θ to the horizontal. From two points at the foot of the hill two men walk up it along straight paths lying in vertical planes perpendicular to one another. If they meet after having walked distances a and b respectively, show that they are then at a vertical height h given by the smaller root of the quadratic

$$(2-\sin^2\theta)h^4-(a^2+b^2)h^2+a^2b^2\sin^2\theta=0.$$

110. Show that, if $\alpha, \beta, \gamma, \delta$ are roots of

$$\tan\left(\theta+\frac{\pi}{4}\right)=3\tan 3\theta,$$

no two of which have equal tangents, then

$$\tan\alpha+\tan\beta+\tan\gamma+\tan\delta=0.$$

111. If $\theta_1, \theta_2, \theta_3, \theta_4$ be roots of the equation

$$\sin(\theta+\alpha)=k\sin 2\theta,$$

no two of which differ by a multiple of 2π, prove that

$$\theta_1+\theta_2+\theta_3+\theta_4=(2n+1)\pi.$$

112. Prove, by means of projections, the theorems of Art. 243.

113. Prove the identities

(i) $\sin\alpha+\sin\beta+\sin\gamma-\sin(\alpha+\beta+\gamma)$

$$=4\sin\frac{\beta+\gamma}{2}\sin\frac{\gamma+\alpha}{2}\sin\frac{\alpha+\beta}{2}$$

(ii) $\cos^2\alpha\sin 2(\beta-\gamma)+\cos^2\beta\sin 2(\gamma-\alpha)+\cos^2\gamma\sin 2(\alpha-\beta)$

$$+2\sin(\beta-\gamma)\sin(\gamma-\alpha)\sin(\alpha-\beta)=0.$$

114. Show that the equation

$$\sec\theta+\operatorname{cosec}\theta=c$$

has two roots between 0 and 2π, if $c^2<8$, and four roots if $c^2>8$.

115. If the external bisectors of the angles of the triangle ABC form a triangle $A_1B_1C_1$, and if the external bisectors of the triangle $A_1B_1C_1$ form a triangle $A_2B_2C_2$ and so on, show that the angle A_n of the nth derived triangle is $\frac{\pi}{3}+\left(-\frac{1}{2}\right)^n\left(A-\frac{\pi}{3}\right)$, and that the triangles tend to become equilateral.

116. From a certain station A the angular elevation of a mountain peak P, to the north of A, is α. A hill, of height h above A, is amended. From B, the top of this hill, the angular elevation of P is β, the bearing of A is δ west of south, and the bearing of P is γ north of A. Show that the height of P above A is

$$\frac{h \tan\alpha \sin\gamma}{\tan\alpha \sin\gamma - \tan\beta \sin\delta}.$$

117. A man at the bottom of a hill observes an object, 880 metres distant, at the same level as himself. He then walks 200 metres up the hill and observes that the angle of depression of the object is 2°30′ and that the direction to it makes an angle of 75° with the direction to his starting point. Find to the nearest minute the angle which his path makes with the horizontal.

118. If $2\phi, 2\phi_2, 2\phi_3$ are the angles subtended by the circle escribed to the side a of a triangle at the centres of the inscribed circle and the other two escribed circles, prove that

$$\sin\phi_1, \sin\phi_2, \sin\phi_3 = \frac{r_1^2}{16R^2}.$$

119. A regular polygon of n sides is placed with one side in contact with a fixed straight line and is turned about one extremity of this side until the next side is in contact with the straight line and so on for a complete revolution; show that the length of the path described by any one of the angular points of the polygon is $\frac{4\pi R}{n}\cot\frac{\pi}{2n}$, where R is the radius of the circle circumscribing the polygon.

Show also that the sum of the areas of the sectors of the circles described by the angular point is $2\pi R^2$.

120. Eliminate θ and ϕ from the equations

$$\frac{x}{a}\cos\theta + \frac{y}{b}\sin\theta = 1,$$

$$\frac{x}{a}\cos\phi + \frac{y}{b}\sin\phi = 1$$

and $$\frac{\cos\theta\cos\phi}{a^2} + \frac{\sin\theta\sin\phi}{b^2} = 0.$$

121. If $S \equiv \sin\theta + 2\sin 2\theta + 3\sin 3\theta + \ldots + n\sin n\theta$,

and $C \equiv \cos\theta + 2\cos 2\theta + 2\cos 3\theta + \ldots + n\cos n\theta$,

prove that $4\sin^2\frac{\theta}{2}\cdot S = (n+1)\sin n\theta - n\sin(n+1)\theta$,

and $$4\sin^2\frac{\theta}{2}\cdot C = -1 + (n+1)\cos n\theta - n\cos(n+1)\theta.$$

122. Prove that

$$\frac{\sin(\theta-\gamma-\alpha)}{\sin(\beta-\alpha)\sin(\gamma-\alpha)} + \frac{\sin(\theta-\alpha-\beta)\sin(\theta-\beta-\gamma)}{\sin(\gamma-\beta)\sin(\alpha-\beta)}$$

$$\frac{\sin(\theta-\beta-\gamma)\sin(\theta-\gamma-\alpha)}{\sin(\alpha-\gamma)\sin(\beta-\gamma)} = 1.$$

123. If

$(\sin^2\phi - \sin^2\psi)\cot\theta + (\sin^2\psi - \sin^2\theta)\cot\phi +$
$(\sin^2\theta - \sin^2\phi)\cot\psi = 0$ then either the difference of two angles or the sum of all three is a multiple of π.

124. A hill, standing on a horizontal plane, has a circular base and forms part of a sphere. At two points on the plane, distant a and b from the base, the angular elevations of the highest visible points on the hill are θ and ϕ. Prove that the height of the hill is

$$2\left[\frac{\left(b\cot\frac{\phi}{2}\right)^{\frac{1}{2}} - \left(a\cot\frac{\phi}{2}\right)^{\frac{1}{2}}}{\cot\frac{\phi}{2} - \cot\frac{\phi}{2}}\right]$$

125. There is a hemispherical dome on the top of a tower; on the top of the dome stands a cross; at a certain point the elevation of the cross is observed to be α, and that of the dome to be β; at a distance a nearer the done, the cross is seen just above the dome, when its elevation is observed to be γ; prove that the height of the centre of the dome above the ground is

$$\frac{a\sin\gamma}{\sin(\gamma-\alpha)}\cdot\frac{\cos\alpha\sin\beta - \sin\alpha\cos\gamma}{\cos\beta - \cos\gamma}.$$

126. If $\sin^2 A + \sin^2 B + \sin^2 C = 1$, show that the circumscribed circle of the triangle ABC cuts its nine-point circle orthogonally.

127. A point O is situated on a circle of radius R, and with centre O another circle of radius $\frac{3R}{2}$ is described. Inside the crescent-shaped area intercepted between these circles a circle of radius $\frac{1}{8}R$ is placed. Show that if the small circle moves in contact with the original circle of radius R, the length of arc described by its centre in moving from one extreme position to the other is $\frac{7}{12}\pi R$.

128. Eliminate x and y from the equations

$$\sin x + \sin y = a,$$
$$\cos x + \cos y = b,$$

and $$\tan x + \tan y = c.$$

129. If $2\cos n\theta$ be denoted by u_n, show that

$$u_{n+1} = u_1 u_n - u_{n-1}.$$

Hence, show that

$$2\cos 7\theta = u_1^7 - 7\mu_1^5 + 14u_1^3 - 7u_1.$$

130. Show by a graph that 0.74 is an approximate solution of the equation $\cos x = x$ (where x is measured in radians), and prove that this is the only real root.

Further, by putting $x = 0.74 + y$, where y is small, prove that a still nearer value of x is 0.7391, so that the angle required is 42°21′ to the nearest minute.

131. Show that

$$\frac{\sin(x-\beta)\sin(x-\gamma)}{\sin(\alpha-\beta)\sin(\alpha-\gamma)}\sin 2(x-\alpha) + \text{two similar terms} = 0.$$

132. If ABC is a triangle, prove that

$$\sin^3 A\cos(B-C) + \sin^3 B\cos(C-A) + \sin^3 C\cos(A-B) = 3\sin A\sin B\sin C.$$

133. A man notices two objects in a straight line due west. After walking a distance c due north he observes that the objects subtend an angle α at his eye; and, after walking a further distance c due north, an angle β. Show that the distance between the objects is

$$\frac{3c}{2\cot\beta - \cot\alpha}.$$

134. The side of a hill is plane and inclined at an angle α to the horizon; a road on it is in a vertical plane making an angle β with the vertical plane through the line of greatest slope; prove that the inclination of the road to the horizontal is $\tan^{-1}(\tan\alpha\cos\beta)$.

If the road is inclined at an angle γ to the line of greatest slope on the hill, show that its inclination is $\sin^{-1}(\sin\alpha\cos\gamma)$.

135. Show that the line joining the incentre to the circumcentre of a triangle ABC is inclined to BC at an angle

$$\tan^{-1}\left(\frac{\cos B + \cos C - 1}{\sin B \sim \sin C}\right).$$

136. Eliminate θ from the equations

$$x\sin\theta - y\cos\theta = -\sin 4\theta,$$

and

$$x\cos\theta + y\sin\theta = \frac{5}{2} - \frac{3}{2}\cos 4\theta.$$

137. A regular polygon is inscribed in a circle; show that the arithmetic mean of the squares of the distances of its corners from any point (not necessarily in its plane) is equal to the arithmetic mean of the sum of the squares of the longest and shortest distances of the point from the circle.

138. Three points A, B, C lie in a straight line and AB is to BC as m to n. Through A, B, C are drawn parallel straight line AX, BY, CZ. A point P moves on AX and a point R on CZ so that at any time t the distance AP is equal to $a_1 + a_2\sin(nt+\alpha)$ and the distance OR is equal to $c_1 + c_2 \sin(nt + \gamma)$, and the straight line PR cuts BY in Q. Express the distance BQ in a similar form.

139. Prove that

$$\sin(\beta - \gamma)\sin 3\alpha + \sin(\gamma - \alpha)\sin 3\beta + \sin(\alpha - \beta)\sin 3\gamma$$
$$= 4\sin(\beta - \gamma)\sin(\gamma - \alpha)\sin(\alpha - \beta)\sin(\alpha + \beta + \gamma).$$

140. Prove that

$$\sin(\beta - \gamma)\cos 3\alpha + \sin(\gamma - \alpha)\cos 3\beta + \sin(\alpha - \beta)\cos 3\gamma$$
$$= 4\sin(\beta - \gamma)\sin(\gamma - \alpha)\sin(\alpha - \beta)\cos(\alpha + \beta + \gamma).$$

141. If

$$\sin(x + 3\alpha)\sin(\beta - \gamma) + \sin(x + 3\beta)\sin(\gamma - \alpha) + \sin(x + 3\gamma)\sin(\alpha - \beta)$$
$$= 4\sin(\beta - \gamma)\sin(\gamma - \alpha)\sin(\alpha - \beta),$$

prove that $x + \alpha + \beta + \gamma = \left(2n + \frac{1}{2}\right)\pi$.

142. If $A + B + C = 2\pi$, show that

$$\sin^3 A + \sin^3 B + \sin^3 C = 3\sin\frac{A}{2}\sin\frac{B}{2}\sin\frac{C}{2} - \sin\frac{3A}{2}\sin\frac{3B}{2}\sin\frac{3C}{2}.$$

143. A man walks in a horizontal circle round the foot of a flagstaff, which is inclined to the vertical, the foot of the flagstaff being the centre of the circle. The greatest and least angles which the flagstaff subtends at his eye are α and β; and when he is midway between the corresponding positions the angle is θ. If the man's height be neglected, prove that

$$\tan\theta = \frac{\sqrt{\sin^2(\alpha - \beta) + 4\sin^2\alpha\sin^2\beta}}{\sin(\alpha + \beta)}.$$

144. Two lines, inclined at an angle γ, are drawn on an inclined plane and their inclinations to the horizon are found to be α and β respectively; show that the inclination of the plane to the horizon is

$$\sin^{-1}\{\operatorname{cosec}\gamma\sqrt{\sin^2\alpha + \sin^2\beta - 2\sin\alpha\sin\beta\cos\gamma}\},$$

and that the angle between one of the given pair of lines and the line of greatest slope on the inclined plane is

$$\tan^{-1}\left\{\frac{\sin\beta - \sin\alpha\cos\gamma}{\sin\alpha\sin\gamma}\right\}.$$

145. Show that the line joining the orthocentre to the circumcentre of a triangle ABC is inclined to BC at an angle

$$\tan^{-1}\left(\frac{3 - \tan B\tan C}{\tan B - \tan C}\right).$$

146. Eliminate θ from the equations

$$\frac{\cos(\alpha - 3\theta)}{\cos^3\theta} = \frac{\sin(\alpha - 3\theta)}{\sin^3\theta} = m.$$

147. $A_1A_2A_3 \ldots A_n$ is a regular polygon of n sides circumscribed to a circle of centre O and radius a. P is any point distant c from O. Show that the sum of the squares of the perpendiculars from P on the sides of the polygon is $n\left(a^2+\frac{c^2}{2}\right)$

148. AB is an arc of a circle which subtends an angle of 2θ at its centre, and the tangents at A and B meet in T. By graphic methods find the value of θ to the nearest degree.

(i) when the area between TA, TB and the arc AB is equal to the area of the circle;

(ii) when the sum of the lengths of TA and TB is equal to the sum of the lengths of the arc AB and the chord AB.

149. Show that the angles of a triangle satisfy the relations

(i) $\sin^3 A+\sin^3 B+\sin^3 C$

$$=3\cos\frac{A}{2}\cos\frac{B}{2}\cos\frac{C}{2}+\cos\frac{3A}{2}\cos\frac{3B}{2}\cos\frac{3C}{2};$$

(ii) $\sin^4 A+\sin^4 B+\sin^4 C$

$$=\frac{3}{2}+2\cos A\cos B\cos C+\frac{1}{2}\cos 2A\cos 2B\cos 2C.$$

150. From a point O a man is observed to be walking in a straight path up a hill, and from two sets of observations on his apparent size, made as he passes two points P, Q, it is found that $OP/OQ=\lambda$, and the angle $POQ=\gamma$. The elevations of P and Q above O being α and β, prove that the inclination ϕ of the path to the horizon is given by

$$\sin^2\phi=(\lambda\sin\alpha-\sin\beta)^2/(\lambda^2-2\lambda\cos\gamma+1).$$

151. Eliminate θ from the equations

$$x+a=a(2\cos\theta-\cos 2\theta),$$

and $$y=a(2\sin\theta-\sin 2\theta).$$

152. If from any point in the plane of a regular polygon perpendiculars are drawn on the sides, show that the sum of the squares of these perpendiculars is equal to the sum of the squares on the lines joining the feet of the perpendiculars with the centre of the polygon.

153. A horse is tied to a peg in the centre of a rectangular field of sides a and $2a$; if he can graze over just half of the field, show that the length of the rope by which he is tethered is approximately $0.583a$.

154. Show that the equation

$$\sin(\theta+\lambda)=a\sin 2\theta+b$$

has four roots whose sum is an odd multiple of two right angles.

155. If θ is a positive acute angle, show that $\frac{\theta}{\sin\theta}$ continually increases, and $\frac{\theta}{\tan\theta}$ continually decreases, as θ increases.

156. If $\sin x = m \sin y$ where m is greater than unity, show that as x increases from zero to a right angle $\frac{\tan x}{\tan y}$ continually increases, and that its values, when x is zero and a right angle, are m and ∞ respectively.

157. Prove that

$$\sin^3(\beta-\gamma)\sin^3(\alpha-\delta)+\sin^3(\gamma-\alpha)\sin^3(\beta-\delta)+\sin^3(\alpha-\beta)\sin^3(\gamma-\delta)$$
$$=3\sin(\alpha-\beta)\sin(\beta-\gamma)\sin(\gamma-\alpha)\sin(\alpha-\delta)\sin(\beta-\delta)\sin(\gamma-\delta).$$

158. Prove that,

$$\Sigma\cos(3\alpha-\beta-\gamma-\delta)$$
$$=4\cos(\alpha+\beta-\gamma-\delta)\cos(\alpha+\gamma-\beta-\delta)\cos(\alpha+\delta-\beta-\gamma).$$

159. Show that

$$\sin(\alpha+\beta+\gamma)\cos\alpha\sin\beta\sin\gamma+\cos(\alpha+\beta+\gamma)\sin\alpha\sin\beta\sin\gamma$$
$$-\sin(\alpha+\beta+\gamma)\cos\alpha\cos\beta\cos\gamma-\cos(\alpha+\beta+\gamma)\sin\alpha\cos\beta\cos\gamma$$
$$+\sin(\alpha+\beta)\cos(\beta+\gamma)\cos(\gamma+\alpha)+\cos(\alpha+\beta)\cos(\beta+\gamma)\sin(\gamma+\alpha)=0$$

160. Show that

$$\sin^2\alpha\sin(\beta-\gamma)\sin(\gamma-\delta)\sin(\delta-\beta)$$
$$-\sin^2\beta\sin(\gamma-\delta)\sin(\delta-\alpha)\sin(\alpha-\gamma)$$
$$+\sin^2\gamma\sin(\delta-\alpha)\sin(\alpha-\beta)\sin(\beta-\delta)$$
$$-\sin^2\delta\sin(\alpha-\beta)\sin(\beta-\gamma)\sin(\gamma-\alpha)=0.$$

161. Simplify the expression $PQ - RS$, where

$$P = x\cos(\alpha+\beta)+y\sin(\alpha+\beta)-\cos(\alpha-\beta),$$
$$Q = x\cos(\gamma+\delta)+y\sin(\gamma+\delta)-\cos(\gamma-\delta),$$
$$R = x\cos(\alpha+\gamma)+y\sin(\alpha+\gamma)-\cos(\alpha-\gamma),$$

and
$$S = x\cos(\beta+\delta)+y\sin(\beta+\delta)-\cos(\beta-\delta).$$

162. If
$$a^2+b^2-2ab\cos\alpha = c^2+d^2-2cd\cos\gamma,$$
$$b^2+c^2-2bc\cos\beta = a^2+d^2-2ad\cos\delta,$$

and
$$ab\sin\alpha+cd\sin\gamma = bc\sin\beta+ad\sin\delta$$

show that $\cos(\alpha+\gamma)=\cos(\beta+\delta)$.

163. Show that the solution of the equation

$$\begin{vmatrix} 1, & \cos\theta, & 0, & 0 \\ \cos\theta, & 1, & \cos\alpha, & \cos\beta \\ 0, & \cos\alpha, & 1, & \cos\gamma \\ 0, & \cos\beta, & \cos\gamma, & 1 \end{vmatrix} = 0$$

is
$$\theta = n\pi + (-1)^n \sin^{-1}\left\{\frac{\sqrt{\cos^2\alpha+\cos^2\beta-2\cos\alpha\cos\beta\cos\gamma}}{\sin\gamma}\right\}$$

164. In any triangle ABC, show that

$\cos mA + \cos mB + \cos mC - 1 = \pm 4 \sin \frac{mA}{2} \sin \frac{mB}{2} \sin \frac{mC}{2}$ according as m is of the form $4n + 1$ or $4n + 3$.

165. Show that, in any triangle ABC,

(i) $a^3 \cos B \cos C + b^3 \cos C \cos A + c^3 \cos A \cos B$

$$= abc(1 - 2 \cos A \cos B \cos C),$$

and

(ii) $\sin 2mA + \sin 2mB + \sin 2mC$

$$= (-1)^{m+1} \cdot 4 \sin mA \sin mB \sin mC.$$

166. If A, B, C are the angles of a triangle, prove that

$$\tan^{-1}(\cot B \cot C) + \tan^{-1}(\cot C \cot A) + \tan^{-1}(\cot A \cot B)$$

$$= \tan^{-1}\left\{1 + \frac{8 \cos A \cos B \cos C}{\sin^2 2A + \sin^2 2B + \sin^2 2C}\right\}$$

167. Through the angular points A, B, C of a triangle straight lines are drawn making the same angle α with AB, BC, CA respectively; show that the sides of the triangle thus, formed bear to the sides of the triangle ABC the ratio

$$\cos \alpha - \sin \alpha (\cot A + \cot B + \cot C) : 1.$$

168. A cylindrical tower is surmounted by a cone from a point on the ground the angles of elevation of the nearest point of the top of the tower and of the top of the cone are α and β, and from a point nearer to the tower by a distance a these angles are γ and δ. Show that the heights above the ground of the tops of the tower and cone are

$a \sin \alpha \sin \gamma \operatorname{cosec}(\gamma - \alpha)$ and $a \sin \beta \sin \delta \operatorname{cosec}(\delta - \beta)$

and that the diameter of the tower is

$$2a \sin \beta \cos \delta \operatorname{cosec}(\delta - \beta) - 2a \sin \alpha \cos \gamma \operatorname{cosec}(\gamma - \alpha).$$

169. In order to find the dip of a stratum of coal below the surface of the ground, vertical borings are made from the angular points A, B, C of a triangle ABC which is a horizontal plane; the depths of the stratum at these points are found to be $x, x + y$, and $x + z$ respectively. Show that the dip, θ, of the stratum, which is assumed to be a plane, is given by

$$\tan \theta \sin A = \sqrt{\frac{y^2}{c^2} + \frac{z^2}{b^2} - \frac{2yz}{bc} \cos A}.$$

170. A tunnel is to be bored from A to B, which are two places on the opposite sides of a mountain. From A and B the elevations of a distant point C are found to be α and β, and the angle ACB is found to be γ; also the lengths AC, BC are known to be a and b. Show that the height (h) of B above A is $a \sin \alpha - b \sin \beta$, that the length ($k$) of AB is

$\sqrt{a^2 + b^2 - 2ab\cos\gamma}$, and that AB is inclined at $\sin^{-1}\dfrac{h}{k}$ to the horizontal and at $\sin^{-1}\dfrac{b\sin\gamma}{k}$ to the line AC.

171. A man walks up a hill of elevation ϕ in a direction making an angle λ with the line of greatest slope; when he has walked up a distance m he observes that α is the angle of depression of an object situated in the horizontal plane through the foot of the hill and in the vertical plane through the path he is taking; after walking a further distance n, he observes that the angle of depression of the same object is β. Show that the elevation ϕ is given by the equation

$$\left\{\frac{m}{n}(\cot\beta - \cot\alpha) + \cot\beta\right\}^2 + 1 = \operatorname{cosec}^2\phi\sec^2\lambda.$$

172. A, B, C are three mountain peaks of which A is the lowest and B is at a known height h above A. At A the elevations of B and C are found to be β and γ, and the angle between the vertical planes through AB, AC is found to be θ. At B the angle between the vertical plane through BA and BC is found to be ϕ. Show that the height of C above A is $h\cot\beta\tan\gamma\sin\phi\operatorname{cosec}(\theta + \phi)$.

173. Two straight paths BC, CA on a plane hill-side have lengths a, b respectively and have the same upward gradient of 1 in m (1 vertical in m horizontal) while the gradient from B to A is 1 in p. Show that the inclination of the plane of the hill to the horizontal is α where

$$4ab\cot^2\alpha = (a + b)^2p^2 - (a \sim b)^2m^2.$$

174. Show that the distance between the centres of the inscribed and nine-point circles is equal to $\dfrac{R}{2} - r$.

Hence, deduce Feuerbach's Theorem, that the in-circle and nine-point circles of any triangle touch one another.

175. $ABCD$ is a quadrilateral such that $AB = 3$, $BC = 4$, $CD = 5$ and $DA = 6$ cm, and its area is $3\sqrt{3} + 9$ sq.cm. Show that there are two quadrilaterals satisfying these conditions, for which the values of the angle B are respectively 60° and $\cos^{-1}\left[\dfrac{-1-42\sqrt{3}}{74}\right]$, *i.e.*, 60° and 175°15′ nearly.

176. Eliminate α, β, γ from the equations

$$a\cos\alpha + b\cos\beta + c\cos\gamma = 0,$$
$$a\sin\alpha + b\sin\beta + c\sin\gamma = 0,$$

and

$$a\sec\alpha + b\sec\beta + c\sec\gamma = 0,$$

177. Eliminate θ from the equations

$$\tan(\theta - \alpha) + \tan(\theta - \beta) = x,$$

and

$$\cot(\theta - \alpha) + \cot(\theta - \beta) = y.$$

178. Eliminate ϕ from the equations

$$x\cos 3\phi + y\sin 3\phi = b\cos\phi$$

and
$$x\sin 3\phi + y\cos 3\phi = b\cos\left(\phi + \frac{\pi}{6}\right)$$

179. Two regular polygons, of m and n sides, are inscribed in the same circle, of radius a; show that the sum of the squares of all the chords which can be drawn to join a corner of one polygon to a corner of the other is $2mna^2$.

180. There are n stones arranged at equal intervals round the circumference of a circle; compare the labour of carrying them all to the centre with that of heaping them all round one of the stones; and prove that, when the number of stones is indefinitely increased, the ratio is that of $\pi : 4$.

181. By drawing a graph, or otherwise, find the number of roots of the equation

$$x + 2\tan x = \frac{\pi}{2}$$

lying between 0 and 2π, and find the approximate value of the largest of these roots.

Verify your result from the tables.

182. Find the least positive value of x satisfying the equation

$$\tan x - x = \frac{1}{2}$$

183. Draw the graph of the function $\sin^2 x$ and show from it that, if a is small and positive, the equation

$$x - a = \frac{\pi}{2}\sin^2 x$$

has three real roots.

184. Show that approximations to the larger real roots of the equation

$$ax + b = \tan\frac{\pi c x}{2}.$$

are given by
$$x = \frac{m}{c} - \frac{2}{\pi(am + bc)}$$

where m is any large odd integer.

185. By a graph determine approximately the numerically smallest positive and negative roots of the equation

$$x^2 \sin \pi x = 1$$

Prove that the large roots of this equation are given approximately by

$$x = n + \frac{(-1)^n}{n^2\pi}$$

where n is large.

186. Show that the roots of the equation

$$\tan x = 2x$$

which lies between 0 and $\frac{\pi}{2}$, is equal approximately to 1.1654, given that $\tan 1.1519 = 2.2460$ and $\tan 1.1694 = 2.3559$.

187. Show that $\tan\theta$ is always greater than

$$\theta + \frac{\theta^3}{3} + \frac{\theta^5}{15} + \ldots + \frac{\theta^{2n+1}}{4^{n-1}} + \ldots,$$

if θ be an acute angle.

188. Show that the equation

$$\cos(2\theta - \alpha) + a\cos(\theta - \beta) + b = 0$$

where a, b, α, β are constants, has four sets of roots; and denoting any four roots of different sets by $\theta_1, \theta_2, \theta_3, \theta_4$ prove that

$$\theta_1 + \theta_2 + \theta_3 + \theta_4 - 2\alpha$$

is an even multiple of π.

189. The equation

$$\cot(\theta + \alpha) + \cot(\theta + \beta) + \cot(\theta + \gamma)$$
$$= \operatorname{cosec}(\theta + \alpha) + \operatorname{cosec}(\theta + \beta) + \operatorname{cosec}(\theta + \gamma)$$

is satisfied by values of θ equal to θ_1, θ_2 and θ_3 no two of which differ by a multiple of four right angles. Show that

$$\theta_1 + \theta_2 + \theta_3 + \alpha + \beta + \gamma$$

is equal to a multiple of 2π.

190. Show that, in general, the equation

$$A\sin^3 x + B\cos^3 x + C = 0$$

has six distinct roots, no two of which differ by 2π, and that the tangent of their semi-sum is $-\frac{A}{B}$.

191. Show that the equation

$$\tan(\theta - \alpha) + \sec(\theta - \beta) = \cot\gamma.$$

has four roots (not differing by multiples of 2π) which satisfy the relation

$$\theta_1 + \theta_2 + \theta_3 + \theta_4 = 2(n\pi + \alpha + \beta - \gamma).$$

192. Show that if α, β, γ are three values of x satisfying the equation

$$\sin 2\theta(a\sin x + b\cos x) = \sin 2x(a\sin\theta + b\cos\theta)$$

and not differing from one another, or from θ by a multiple of 2π, then

$$\tan\frac{\alpha}{2}\tan\frac{\beta}{2}\tan\frac{\gamma}{2}\tan\frac{\theta}{2} + 1 = 0$$

193. Prove that if $\theta_1, \theta_2, \theta_3, \theta_4$ be four distinct roots of the equation $a\cos 2\theta + b\sin 2\theta + c\cos\theta + d = 0$

then $$\Sigma\sin\frac{\theta_2 + \theta_3 + \theta_4 - \theta_1}{2} = 0.$$

194. Prove the relation

$$\cos^{-1} x_0 = \frac{\sqrt{1 - x_0^2}}{x_1 \cdot x_2 \cdot x_3 \ldots \text{ ad inf.}}$$

where the successive quantities x_r are connected by the relation

$$x_{r+1} = \sqrt{\frac{1}{2}(1 + x_r)}$$

195. If a, b are positive quantities and if

$$a_1 = \frac{a + b}{2}, \ b_1 = \sqrt{a_1 b}, \ a_2 = \frac{a_1 + b_1}{2}, \ b_2 = \sqrt{a_2 b_1}$$

and so on, show that

$$a_\infty = b_\infty = \frac{\sqrt{b^2 - a^2}}{\cos^{-1} \dfrac{a}{b}}.$$

Hence, show that the value of π may be found.

196. If the equation

$$a_1 + a_2 \sin x + a_3 \cos x + a_4 \sin 2x + a_5 \cos 2x = 0$$

holds for all values of x, where all the constants $a_1, a_2, \ldots$ are independent of x, then each of these constants must be zero.

197. Prove that if α, β, γ do not differ by a multiple of π, and if

$$\frac{\cos(\alpha + \theta)}{\sin(\beta + \gamma)} = \frac{\cos(\beta + \theta)}{\sin(\gamma + \alpha)}$$

then each fraction is equal to $\dfrac{\cos(\gamma + \theta)}{\sin(\alpha + \beta)}$, and is also equal to ± 1.

198. Prove that $\dfrac{\cot 3x}{\cot x}$ never lies between 3 and $\dfrac{1}{3}$.

199. If A, B, C are the angles of an acute-angled triangle, show that $\tan A \cdot \tan B \cdot \tan C > 3\sqrt{3}$.

200. A log plank, of uniform rectangular section and of breadth b and thickness t, is being lowered with the side b horizontal through a plane circular hole in the deck of a ship. The hole is of diameter d, and the thickness of the deck is h. Prove that the least inclination to the horizontal at which the plank will pass through the deck is $\alpha + \beta$, where

$$\frac{\sin \alpha}{t} = \frac{\sin \beta}{h} = \frac{1}{\sqrt{d^2 + h^2 - b^2}}.$$

201. Two straight lines are taken on the side of a slope, which is an inclined plane, and their inclinations to the horizon are found to be α and β; also the angle between the vertical planes drawn through them is found to be γ. Show that the inclination of the slope to the horizon is θ, where

$$\sin \gamma \tan \theta = \sqrt{\tan^2 \alpha + \tan^2 \beta - 2 \tan \alpha \tan \beta \cos \gamma}$$

and that the vertical plane through the first of these two lines is inclined to the vertical plane through the line of greatest inclination at an angle

$$\tan^{-1}\left(\frac{\tan\alpha\cos\gamma - \tan\beta}{\tan\alpha\sin\gamma}\right).$$

202. Two roofs are inclined at angles α and β to the horizon respectively; the ridges of the two roofs are horizontal and meet at an angle γ. The intersection of the two roofs is inclined at θ_1 to the horizontal, and the vertical plane through this intersection is inclined at θ_2 to the vertical plane through the ridge of the first roof. Show that

$$\tan\theta_1 = \frac{\sin\gamma}{\sqrt{\cot^2\alpha + \cot^2\beta + 2\cot\alpha\cot\beta\cos\gamma}}$$

and that $$\tan\theta_2 = \frac{\cot\alpha\sin\gamma}{\cot\alpha\cos\gamma + \cot\beta}.$$

203. A plane is inclined towards the south at an angle α, and on it is a vertical post of height h; when the sun is β west of south and at an elevation γ, show that the length of the shadow of the post on the inclined plane is

$$\frac{h\cos\gamma}{\sin(\theta + \gamma)}, \text{ where } \tan\theta = \tan\alpha\cos\beta.$$

204. An observer looking up the line of greatest slope of an inclined plane sees a vertical tower due east of him. He walks l metres up the plane in *a* direction a north of east, and has then reached the level of the foot of the tower and finds its elevation is β. The plane makes an angle γ with the horizontal. Show that the height of the tower is

$$\frac{l\tan\beta\cos\gamma}{\sqrt{\cot^2\alpha + \cos^2\gamma}}.$$

205. The side of a hill slopes towards the south at an angle of 15°; show that the inclination to the horizon of a road on it which runs in a north-easterly direction is 10°44′ and that the bearing of a road on it whose slope is 5° to the horizon is 19°3′ N. of E.

206. A man starts up the line of greatest slope of an inclined plane and after walking 1000 metres finds that he has risen 50 metres. He turns to the right and after going 1000 metres has risen a further 33.33 metres. If the line of greatest slope is due north, find (i) the bearing of the new path, and (ii) the bearing of the original starting point as seen from the last position

ANSWERS

Answers have been given to the full number of figures which are likely to emerge from the student's work. They do not imply that in any practical situation the results are reliable to this number of figures.

Even if the data are regarded as exact, answers derived with the use of 5-figure tables have no more than 4-figure accoptability.

I (Page 4)

1. $\frac{2}{3}$ **2.** $\frac{301}{360}$ **3.** $\frac{45569}{64800}$ **4.** $1\frac{9}{20}$ **5.** $2\frac{3661}{10800}$

6. $4\frac{388}{3375}$ **7.** $33^g\,33'33.3''$ **8.** 90^g **9.** $153^g88'88.\dot{8}''$

10. $39^g76'38.\dot{8}''$ **11.** $261^g34'44.\dot{4}'$

12. $528^g3'33.\dot{3}''$ **13.** 1.2 rt. $\angle$; $108°$

14. 0.453524 rt. $\angle$; $40°49'1.776''$

15. 0.394536 rt. $\angle$; $35°30'29.664''$

16. 2.550809 rt. $\angle$; $22°34'22.116''$

17. 7.590005 rt. $\angle$; $683°6'1.62''$ **28.** $5°33'20''$; $66°40'$

29. $47\frac{7}{19}°$; $42\frac{12}{19}°$ **31.** $33°20'$; $10°48'$

II (Pages 8)

1. 40212 km nearly **2.** 848.2 cm per sec.

3. 20.36 km per hour nearly

4. 940600000 km nearly. **5.** 23 km nearly

III (Pages 11, 12)

1. $60°$ **2.** $240°$ **3.** $1800°$ **4.** $57°17'44.8''$

5. $458°21'58.4''$ **6.** 160^g **7.** $233_g33'33.\dot{3}''$

8. 2000^g **9.** $\frac{\pi}{3}$ **10.** $\frac{221}{360}\pi$ **11.** $\frac{703}{720}\pi$ **12.** $\frac{3557}{13500}\pi$

13. $\frac{79}{36}\pi$ **14.** $\frac{3\pi}{10}$ **15.** $\frac{1103}{2000}\pi$ **16.** $1.726268\,\pi$

17. $81°$; $9°$ **18.** $24°$, $60°$ and $96°$ **19.** $132°15'12.\dot{6}''$

20. $30°$, $60°$, and $90°$ **21.** $\frac{1}{2}$, $\frac{\pi}{3}$, and $\frac{2\pi}{3}-\frac{1}{2}$ radians

22. (1) $\frac{3\pi}{5}$; 108° (2) $\frac{5\pi}{7}$; $128\frac{4°}{7}$

(3) $\frac{3\pi}{4}$; 135° (4) $\frac{5\pi}{6}$; 150° (5) $\frac{15\pi}{17}$; $158\frac{14°}{17}$

23. 8 and 4 **24.** 10 and 8 **25.** 6 and 8 **26.** $\frac{\pi}{3}$

27. (1) $\frac{5\pi^c}{12} = 75° = 83\frac{1^g}{3}$; (2) $\frac{7\pi^c}{18} = 70° = 77\frac{7^g}{9}$;

(3) $\frac{5\pi^c}{8} = 112\frac{1}{2}° = 125^g$

28. (1) At $7\frac{7}{11}$ and 36 minutes past 4;

(2) at $28\frac{4}{11}$ and 48 minutes past 7.

IV (Pages 14, 15)

[Take $\pi = 3.14159\ldots$ and $\frac{1}{\pi} = 0.31831$]

1. 20.454° nearly **2.** $\frac{3}{5}$ radian; 34°22′38.9″

3. 68.75 cm nearly **4.** 0.05236 cm nearly

5. 24.555 cm nearly **6.** 0.53′43″ **7.** 3959.8 km nearly

8. 10π cm = 31.4159 cm **9.** 5 : 4 **10.** 3.1416

11. $\frac{4\pi}{35}$; $\frac{9\pi}{35}$; $\frac{14\pi}{35}$; $\frac{19\pi}{35}$ and $\frac{24\pi}{35}$ radians.

12. 65°24′30.4″ **13.** 687.5 m nearly

14. 1.5359 m nearly **15.** 3151.2 cm nearly

16. 32142.9 m nearly **17.** 3820 m nearly **18.** 19.099

19. 1788 km nearly **20.** 386000 km

VI (Pages 24, 25)

5. $\frac{\sqrt{15}}{4}$; $\frac{1}{\sqrt{15}}$, etc. **6.** $\frac{12}{5}$; $\frac{8}{13}$ **7.** $\frac{11}{60}$; $\frac{60}{61}$; $\frac{61}{60}$

8. $\frac{3}{4}$; $\frac{4}{3}$ **9.** $\frac{40}{9}$; $\frac{41}{40}$ **10.** $\frac{3}{4}$; $\frac{4}{5}$; $\frac{1}{5}$; $\frac{5}{3}$ **11.** $\frac{3}{4}$ **12.** $\frac{15}{17}$; $\frac{17}{8}$

13. $\frac{1}{2}\sqrt{5}$; $\frac{2}{5}\sqrt{5}$ **14.** 1 or $\frac{3}{5}$ **15.** $\frac{3}{5}$ or $\frac{5}{13}$ **16.** $\frac{5}{13}$

17. $\frac{12}{13}$ **18.** $\frac{1}{\sqrt{3}}$ or 1 **19.** $\frac{1}{2}$ **20.** $\frac{1}{\sqrt{2}}$ **21.** $1 + \sqrt{2}$

22. $\frac{2x(x+1)}{2x^2+2x+1}; \frac{2x+1}{2x^2+2x+1}$

VIII (Pages 35-37)

1. 17.32 m; 10 m **2.** 160 m **3.** 225 m **4.** 68.3 m
5. 146.4... m **6.** 367.9... metres; 454.3... metres
7. 17.32 metres **8.** 115.359... m **9.** 87.846... m
10. 43.3...m; 75 m from one of the towers
11. 94.641... m; 54.641... m **12.** 1366 metres
13. 30° **15.** 13.8564 km per hour
16. 23.66... m; 8.66... m; 28.66... m
17. $32\sqrt{5}$ (= 71.55...) m **19.** 10 km per hour
20. 86.6... metres **21.** 692.8... metres

IX (Pages 48, 49)

1. $\frac{2250}{6289}\pi, \frac{2500}{6289}\pi$ and $\frac{81}{331}\pi$ radians **2.** 68°45′17.8″
4. $\frac{2xy}{x^2+y^2}; \frac{2xy}{x^2-y^2}$ **8.** $\frac{1}{\tan^4 A} - \tan^4 A$ **9.** $\theta = 60°$
10. In $1\frac{1}{2}$ minutes

X (Page 58)

4. – 0.366... ; 2.3094... **15.** – 1.366... ; – 2.3094 **6.** 0; 2
7. 1.4142... – 2 **8.** 1.366... ; – 2.3094...
9. 45° and 135° **10.** 120° and 240°
11. 135° and 315° **12.** 150° and 330°
13. 150° and 210° **14.** 210° and 330°
15. – cos 25° **16.** sin 6° **17.** – tan 43°
18. sin 12° **19.** sin 17° **20.** – cot 24° **21.** cos 33°
22. – cos 28° **23.** cot 25° **24.** cos 30° **25.** cot 26°
26. – cosec 23° **27.** – cosec 36° **28.** negative
29. negtaive **30.** positive **31.** zero **32.** positive
33. positive **34.** positive **35.** negative
36. $\frac{1}{\sqrt{3}}$ and $\frac{-\sqrt{2}}{\sqrt{3}}; \frac{-1}{\sqrt{3}}$ and $\frac{\sqrt{2}}{\sqrt{3}}$.

XI (Pages 64, 65)

1. $n\pi + (-1)^n \frac{\pi}{6}$ **2.** $n\pi - (-1)^n \frac{\pi}{3}$

3. $n\pi + (-1)^n \frac{\pi}{4}$ **4.** $2n\pi \pm \frac{2\pi}{3}$

5. $2n\pi \pm \frac{\pi}{6}$ **6.** $2n\pi \pm \frac{3\pi}{4}$ **7.** $n\pi + \frac{\pi}{3}$ **8.** $n\pi + \frac{3\pi}{4}$

9. $n\pi + \frac{\pi}{4}$ **10.** $2n\pi \pm \frac{\pi}{3}$ **11.** $n\pi \pm (-1)^n \frac{\pi}{3}$

12. $n\pi \pm \frac{\pi}{2}$ **13.** $n\pi \pm \frac{\pi}{3}$ **14.** $n\pi \pm \frac{\pi}{6}$ **15.** $n\pi \pm \frac{\pi}{3}$

16. $n\pi \pm \frac{\pi}{4}$ **17.** $n\pi \pm \frac{\pi}{6}$ **18.** $(2n+1)\pi + \frac{\pi}{4}$

19. $2n\pi - \frac{\pi}{6}$

20. $105°$ and $45°$; $\left(n + \frac{m}{2}\right)\pi \pm \frac{\pi}{6} + (-1)^m \frac{\pi}{12}$ and $\left(\frac{m}{2} - n\right)\pi \mp \frac{\pi}{6} + (-1)^m \frac{\pi}{12}$ where m and n are any integers.

21. $187\frac{1}{2}°$ and $142\frac{1°}{2}$; $\left(n + \frac{m}{2}\right)\pi + \frac{\pi}{8} \pm \frac{\pi}{12}$ and $\left(n - \frac{m}{2}\right)\pi - \frac{\pi}{8} \pm \frac{\pi}{12}$

22. (1) 60° and 120°; (2) 120° and 240°; (3) 30° and 210°

23. (1) 2; (2) 1; (3) 1; (4) 1; (5) 1

XII (Page 67)

1. $n\pi + (-1)^n \frac{\pi}{6}$ **2.** $2n\pi \pm \frac{2\pi}{3}$

3. $n\pi + (-1)^n \frac{\pi}{3}$ **4.** $\cos\theta = \frac{\sqrt{5} - 1}{2}$

5. $n\pi + (-1)^n \frac{\pi}{10}$ or $n\pi - (-1)^n \frac{3\pi}{10}$ (Art. 120)

6. $\theta = 2n\pi \pm \frac{\pi}{3}$ **7.** $\theta = n\pi + \frac{\pi}{4}$ or $n\pi + \frac{\pi}{3}$

8. $\theta = n\pi + \frac{2\pi}{3}$ or $n\pi + \frac{5\pi}{6}$ **9.** $\tan\theta = \frac{1}{a}$ or $-\frac{1}{b}$

10. $\theta = n\pi \pm \frac{\pi}{4}$ **11.** $\theta = 2n\pi$ or $2n\pi + \frac{\pi}{4}$

12. $n\pi \pm \frac{\pi}{6}$ **13.** $n\pi$ or $2n\pi \pm \frac{\pi}{3}$

14. $2n\pi \pm \dfrac{\pi}{3}$ or $2n\pi \pm \dfrac{\pi}{6}$ **15.** $\sin\theta = 1$ or $-\dfrac{1}{3}$

16. $\dfrac{n\pi}{5} + (-1)^n \dfrac{\pi}{20}$ **17.** $\dfrac{n\pi}{4}$ or $\dfrac{(2n+1)\pi}{10}$

18. $2n\pi$ or $\dfrac{(2n+1)\pi}{5}$ **19.** $\dfrac{2r\pi}{m-n}$ or $\dfrac{2r\pi}{m+n}$

20. $\left(2n + \dfrac{1}{2}\right)\dfrac{\pi}{5}$ or $2n\pi - \dfrac{\pi}{2}$ **21.** $2n\pi$ or $\dfrac{2n\pi}{9}$

22. $\left(2r + \dfrac{1}{2}\right)\dfrac{\pi}{m+n}$ or $\left(2r - \dfrac{1}{2}\right)\dfrac{\pi}{m-n}$ **23.** $\left(n + \dfrac{1}{2}\right)\dfrac{\pi}{9}$

24. $\left(m + \dfrac{1}{2}\right)\dfrac{\pi}{n+1}$ **25.** $\dfrac{n\pi}{4} \pm \sqrt{1 + \dfrac{n^2\pi^2}{16}}$ **26.** $n\pi \pm \dfrac{\pi}{6}$

27. $\left(n + \dfrac{1}{2}\right)\dfrac{\pi}{3} \pm \dfrac{\alpha}{3}$ **28.** $\left(n + \dfrac{1}{2}\right)\dfrac{\pi}{4}$ **29.** $\dfrac{n\pi}{3} \pm \dfrac{\alpha}{3}$ **30.** $n\pi \pm \dfrac{\pi}{6}$

31. $\left(r + \dfrac{1}{2}\right)\dfrac{\pi}{m-n}$

32. $\tan\theta = \dfrac{2n + 1 \pm \sqrt{4n^2 + 4n - 15}}{4}$, where $n > 1$ or < -2

33. $\theta = \left(m + \dfrac{n}{2}\right)\pi \pm \dfrac{\pi}{6} + (-1)^n \dfrac{\pi}{12}$; $\phi = \left(m - \dfrac{n}{2}\right)\pi \pm \dfrac{\pi}{6} - (-1)^n \dfrac{\pi}{12}$

34. $\dfrac{1}{5}\left[(6m - 4n)\pi \pm \dfrac{\pi}{2} \mp \dfrac{2\pi}{3}\right]$; $\dfrac{1}{5}\left[(6n - 4m)\pi \pm \pi \mp \dfrac{\pi}{3}\right]$

35. 45° and 60° **36.** $\dfrac{1}{3}$ or $\dfrac{5}{3}$ **37.** $\pm\dfrac{1}{3}\sqrt{5}, \pm\dfrac{1}{2}\sqrt{5}$

XIII (Page 72)

1. $-\dfrac{133}{205}; -\dfrac{84}{205}$ **2.** $\dfrac{1596}{3445}; \dfrac{3444}{3445}$ **3.** $\dfrac{220}{221}; \dfrac{171}{221}; \dfrac{220}{21}$

XIV (Pages 76, 77)

30. $2\sin(\theta + n\phi)\sin\dfrac{3\phi}{2}$ **31.** $2\sin(\theta + n\phi)\cos\dfrac{\phi}{2}$

XV (Page 78)

1. $\cos 2\theta - \cos 12\theta$ **2.** $\sin 12\theta - \sin 2\theta$

3. $\cos 14\theta = \cos 8\theta$ **4.** $\cos 12° - \cos 120°$

XVI (Page 81)

1. $3; \frac{9}{13}$ **3.** 1

XVII (Page 87)

1. (1) $\pm \frac{24}{25}$; (2) $\pm \frac{120}{169}$; (3) $\frac{2016}{4225}$

2. (1) $\frac{161}{289}$; (2) $\frac{-7}{25}$; (3) $\frac{119}{169}$; **3.** a.

XVIII (Pages 99-101)

1. $\frac{\pm 2\sqrt{2} \pm \sqrt{3}}{6}; \frac{\pm 7\sqrt{3} \pm 4\sqrt{2}}{18}$

2. $\pm \frac{13}{12}; \pm \frac{\sqrt{13}}{2}$ or $\pm \frac{\sqrt{13}}{3}; \frac{169}{120}$ **3.** $\frac{16}{305}; \frac{49}{305}$

4. $\frac{7}{5\sqrt{2}}$ **5.** $\pm \frac{1}{3}; \pm \frac{3}{4}$ **6.** $\pm \frac{3}{4}$

7. $\frac{\sqrt{4 - \sqrt{2} - \sqrt{6}}}{2\sqrt{2}}; \sqrt{\frac{4 + \sqrt{2} + \sqrt{6}}{2\sqrt{2}}}; \sqrt{2} - 1; -(\sqrt{2} + 1) + \sqrt{4 + 2\sqrt{2}}$

8. $\sqrt{\frac{4 - a^2 - b^2}{a^2 + b^2}}$ **23.** + and – **24.** – and – **25.** – and –

29. (1) $2n\pi + \frac{\pi}{4}$ and $2n\pi + \frac{3\pi}{4}$; (2) $2n\pi + \frac{3\pi}{4}$ and $2n\pi + \frac{5\pi}{4}$;

(3) $2n\pi - \frac{\pi}{4}$ and $2n\pi + \frac{\pi}{4}$; (4) $2n\pi + \frac{\pi}{4}$ and $2n\pi + \frac{3\pi}{4}$

30. (1) $2n\pi - \frac{\pi}{4}$ and $2n\pi + \frac{\pi}{4}$; (2) $2n\pi + \frac{3\pi}{4}$ and $2n\pi + \frac{5\pi}{4}$;

(3) $2n\pi + \frac{5\pi}{4}$ and $2n\pi + \frac{7\pi}{4}$

XIX (Page 104)

12. The sine of the angle is equal to 2 sin 18°,

13. $\frac{n\pi}{8}$ or $\left(2n \pm \frac{1}{3}\right)\frac{\pi}{8}$.

XXI (Pages 114, 115)

1. $\frac{n\pi}{4}$ or $\frac{1}{3}\left(2n\pi \pm \frac{\pi}{3}\right)$ **2.** $\left(n + \frac{1}{2}\right)\frac{\pi}{4}$ or $\left(2n \pm \frac{1}{3}\right)\frac{\pi}{3}$

3. $\left(n+\frac{1}{2}\right)\frac{\pi}{2}$ or $2n\pi$ **4.** $\left(n+\frac{1}{2}\right)\frac{\pi}{3}$ or $n\pi+(-1)^n\frac{\pi}{6}$

5. $\frac{2n\pi}{3}$ or $\left(n+\frac{1}{4}\right)$ or $\left(2n-\frac{1}{2}\right)\pi$ **6.** $\frac{n\pi}{3}$ or $\left(2n\pm\frac{1}{3}\right)\frac{\pi}{4}$

7. $\left(n+\frac{1}{2}\right)\frac{\pi}{2}$ or $2n\pi\pm\frac{2\pi}{3}$ **8.** $\frac{n\pi}{3}$ or $\left(n\pm\frac{1}{3}\right)\pi$

9. $2n\pi$ or $\left(\frac{2n}{3}+\frac{1}{2}\right)\pi$

10. $n\pi+(-1)^n\frac{\pi}{6}$ or $n\pi+(-1)^n\frac{\pi}{10}$ or $n\pi-(-1)^n\frac{3\pi}{10}$

11. $\left(n+\frac{1}{2}\right)\frac{\pi}{8}$ or $\left(n+\frac{1}{2}\right)\frac{\pi}{2}$ **12.** $m\pi$ or $\frac{1}{n-1}\left[m\pi-(-1)^m\frac{\pi}{6}\right]$

13. $2m\pi$ or $\frac{4m\pi}{n+1}$ **14.** $\frac{2r\pi}{m+n}$ or $(2r+1)\frac{\pi}{m-n}$

15. $(2r+1)\frac{\pi}{m\pm n}$ **16.** $m\pi$ or $\frac{m\pi}{n-1}$ or $\left(m+\frac{1}{2}\right)\frac{\pi}{n}$

17. $2n\pi-\frac{\pi}{2};\frac{1}{5}\left(2n\pi-\frac{\pi}{2}\right)$ **18.** $n\pi+(-1)^n\frac{\pi}{4}-\frac{\pi}{3}$.

19. $2n\pi+\frac{\pi}{4}$ **20.** $n\pi+\frac{\pi}{6}+(-1)^n\frac{\pi}{4}$

21. $2n\pi+\frac{\pi}{4}\pm A$ **22.**

$-21°48° + n\,180° + (-1)^n\,[68°12']$

23. $2n.180° + 78°58'$; $2n.180° + 27°18'$

24. $n.180° + 45°$; $n.180° + 26°34'$ **25.** $2n\pi+\frac{2\pi}{3}$

26. $2n\pi$ or $2n\pi+\frac{\pi}{2}$ **27.** $2n\pi+\frac{\pi}{2}$ or $2n\pi-\frac{\pi}{3}$

28. $2n\pi+\frac{\pi}{6}$ **29.** $n\pi$ **30.** $\sin\theta=\frac{\pm\sqrt{17}-1}{8}$

31. $\cos\theta=\frac{\sqrt{17}-3}{4}$ **32.** $n\pi\pm\frac{\pi}{3}$ or $n\pi+\frac{\pi}{2}$

33. $2n\pi\pm\frac{\pi}{3};2n\pi\pm\frac{\pi}{4}$ **34.** $\left(n+\frac{1}{4}\right)\frac{\pi}{2}$ **35.** $n\pi\pm\frac{\pi}{4}$ **36.** $n\pi+\frac{\pi}{4}$

37. $\theta=\frac{n\pi}{2}$ or $n\pi\pm\frac{\pi}{3}$; also $\theta=n\pi\pm\frac{\alpha}{2}$, where $\cos\alpha=\frac{1}{3}$

38. $\left(n+\frac{1}{3}\right)\frac{\pi}{3}$ **39.** $n\pi\pm\frac{\pi}{3}$

XXIII (Pages 127, 128)

In obtaining the answers to Nos. 8—13, and in similar cases in later sets of Examples, seven-figure tables have been used. If the five-figure tables at the end of this book are used, less accurate results will in many cases be obtained.

1. $\bar{1}.90309; \bar{3}.4771213; \bar{2}.0334239; \bar{1}.4650389$

2. $0.1553361; \bar{2}.1241781; 0.5388340; \bar{1}.0759623$

3. $2; \bar{2}; 0; \bar{4}; \bar{2}; 0; 3$ **4.** 0.312936

5. 1.32057; 5.88453; 0.461791

6. (1) 21; (2) 13; (3) 30; (4) the 7th; (5) the 21st; (6) the 32nd.

7. (1) $\dfrac{4b}{c-b-a}$; (2) $\dfrac{a+2b}{4c-3b-2a}$; (3) $\dfrac{4a+7b}{a+3b-2c}$;

(4) $\dfrac{2b(2a-b)}{5ab+3ac-2b^2-bc}$ and $\dfrac{2ab}{5ab+3ac+2b^2-bc}$

where $a = \log 2$, $b = \log 3$, and $c = \log 7$

8. 0.22221 **9.** 8.6415 **10.** 9.6192 **11.** 1.6389 **12.** 4.7162

13. 0.41431

XXIV (Pages 136-138)

1. 4.5527375; 1.5527394 **2.** 4.7689529; $\bar{3}.7689502$

3. 478.475; 0.004784777 **4.** 2.583674; 0.0258362

5. (1) 4.7204815; (2) 2.7220462; (3) $\bar{4}.7240079$;

(4) 5273.63; (5) 0.05296726; (6) 5.26064

6. 0.6870417 **7.** 43°23′45″

8. 0.8455104; 0.8454509 **9.** 32°16′35″; 32°16′21″

10. 4.1203060; 4.1218748 **11.** 4.3993263; 4.3976823

12. 13°8′47″ **13.** 9.9147334 **14.** 34°44′27″

15. 9.5254497; 71°27′43″ **16.** 10.0229414 **17.** 18°27′17″

18. 36°52′12″

XXV (Page 140)

1. 13°27′31″ **2.** 22°1′28″ **3.** 1.0997340; 65°24′12.5″

4. 9.6198509; 22°36′28″ **5.** 10°15′34″ **6.** 44°55′55″

7. (1) 9.7279043; (2) 9.270857; (3) 10.1958917; (4) 10.0757907;

(5) 10.2001337; (6) 10.0725027; (7) 9.7245162

8. (1) 57°30′24″; (2) 57°31′58″; (3) 32°31′15″ (4) 57°6′39″

9. 0.5373602

10. (1) $\cos(x-y)\sec x\sec y$; (2) $\cos(x+y)\sec x\sec y$;
(3) $\cos(x-y)\operatorname{cosec} x\sec y$; (4) $\cos(x+y)\operatorname{cosec} x\sec y$;
(5) $\tan^2 x$; (6) $\tan x\tan y$

XXVI (Page 146)

1. $\frac{1}{5}, \frac{1}{2}$ and $\frac{9}{7}$ **2.** $\frac{4}{\sqrt{41}}, \frac{3}{5}$ and $\frac{8}{5\sqrt{41}}$; $\frac{40}{41}, \frac{24}{25}$ and $\frac{496}{1025}$

3. $\frac{3}{5}, \frac{4}{5}$ and 1 **4.** $\frac{5}{15}, \frac{12}{5}$ and ∞

5. $\frac{4}{5}, \frac{56}{65}$ and $\frac{12}{13}$ **6.** $\frac{7}{41}$ and $\frac{287}{816}$

7. 60°, 45°, and 75°

XXVII (Pages 150-152)

23. 16.8 cm **25.** $\frac{2}{5}$ **28.** $\frac{313}{338}$

XXVIII (Pages 154, 155)

1. 186.60... and 193.18 **2.** 26°33′54″; 63°26′6″; $10\sqrt{5}$ cm

3. 48°35′25″, 36°52′12″, and 94°32′23″ **4.** 75° and 15°

XXIX (Pages 156, 157)

1. 90° **2.** 30° **4.** 120° **5.** 45°, 120°, and 15°

6. 45°, 60°, and 75° **7.** 58°, 59′33″ **8.** 77° 19′ 11″

9. 76° 39′ 5″ **10.** 104°, 28′ 39″

11. 56° 15′ 4″, 59° 51′ 10″ and 63° 53′ 46″

12. 38° 56′ 33″, 47° 41′ 7″ and 93° 22′ 20″

13. 130° 42′20.5″, 23° 27′ 8.5″, and 25° 50′ 31″

XXX (Pages 160-162)

1. 63°13′2″; 43°58′28″ **2.** 117°38′45″; 27°38′45″

3. $8\sqrt{7}$ cm; 79°6′24″; 60°; 45°53′36″

4. 87°27′25.5″; 32°32′34.5″

5. 40°53′36″; 19°6′24″; $\sqrt{7}:2$ **6.** 71°44′30″; 48°15′30″

7. 78°17′40″; 49°36′20″ **8.** 108°12′26″; 49°27′34″

9. $A = 45°$; $B = 75°$; $c = \sqrt{6}$ **10.** $\sqrt{6}$; 15°; 105°

11. 0.8965 **14.** 40 m; 120°; 30°

15. 7.589467; 108°26′6″; 18°26′6″; 53°7′48″ **16.** 2.529823

17. 226.87; 73°34′50″; 39°45′10″

18. $A = 83°7′39; B = 42°16′21″; c = 199.099$

19. $B = 110°48′15″; C = 26°56′15″; a = 93.5192$

20. 73°1′51″ and 48°41′9″ 21. 88°30′1″ and 33°30′59″

XXXI (Pages 167, 168)

1. There is no triangle.
2. $B_1 = 30°, C_1 = 105°$, and $b_1 = \sqrt{2}; B_2 = 60°, C_2\ 75°$ and $b_2 = \sqrt{6}$.
3. $B_1 = 15°, C_1 = 135°$ and $b_1 = 50\ (\sqrt{6} - \sqrt{2}) = 51.76$;
   $B_2 = 105°, C_2 = 45°$, and $b_2 = 50(\sqrt{6} + \sqrt{2}) = 193.185$
5. $4\sqrt{3} \pm 2\sqrt{5}$, *i.e.* 11.4 and 2.46
6. $100\sqrt{3}$; the triangle is right-angled. 8. 34°27′ and 100°33′
9. 17.1 or 3.68
10. (1) The triangle is right-angled and $B = 60°$
    (2) $b_1 = 60°\ 3892, B_1 = 8°41′$
    and $C_1 = 141\ \ 19′$;
    $B_2 = 111°19′$ and $C_2 = 38°\ 41′$
11. 65°59′ and 41°56′12″ 12. 5.988... and 2.67... km per hour.
13. 63°2′12″ or 116°57′48″
14. 62°31′23″ and 102°17′37″, or 117°28′37″ and 47°20′23″
15. 5926.61

XXXII (Pages 168, 169)

1. 7 : 9 : 11 4. 79.063 5. 1 km ; 1.2197... cm
7. 20.976... km 8. 6.857 and 5.438 cm
9. 4.04435 metres 10. 233.2883 metres
11. 2.229 metres

XXXIII (Pages 173-175)

1. 100 m hight and 50 m broad; 25 metres
2. 25.78... m 3. 33.07... m; 17.5 m 4. 18.3... m
5. 12 metres 6. $h \tan \alpha \cot \beta$ 7. 1939.2... m
8. 10 metres 9. 61.22... metres 10. $100\sqrt[4]{2}$ (= 118.9 m)
15. $PQ = BP = BQ = 1000$ m
    $AP = 500\ (\sqrt{6} - \sqrt{2}) = 517.6$ m; $AQ = 1000\sqrt{2} = 1414.2$ m

16. 321.2 metres. **17.** 173.65 m; 984.81 m

18. 119.286 m **19.** 132.266 m **20.** 235.8 m

21. 1.4277 km **22.** 125.32 m

XXXIV (Pages 178-184)

3. 10 m; 20 m

4. I cosec γ, where γ is the sun's altitude; $\sin\gamma = \frac{2}{7}$,

so that $\gamma = 16°36'$.

5. 3.732... km; 12.342... km per hour at an angle whose tangents is $\sqrt{3}+1$, *i.e.*, 69°54′ *S.* of *E* **6.** 10.24... km per hour

7. 16.39 km; 14.697 km **8.** 2.39 km; 1.366 km

9. The angle whose tangent is $\frac{2}{3}$, *i.e.*, 33°41′ ; $\frac{9}{52}$ hour

13. $c \sin\beta \operatorname{cosec}(\alpha+\beta)$; $c \sin\alpha \sin\beta \operatorname{cosec}(\alpha+\beta)$

14. 9 m; 2 m **16.** $\frac{a}{3}$; $\frac{2a}{3}$

20. At a distance $\frac{375}{\sqrt{7}}$ (= 141.74) m from the cliff.

21. $c(1-\sin\alpha)\sec\alpha$ **22.** 114.4123 m **24.** 1069.75 m

26. The angle whose tangent is $\frac{1}{2}$, *i.e.*, 26°34′

29. 45° **32.** 18°26′6″ **34.** $\tan\alpha \sec\beta : 1$

37. 9.1896 m **38.** 1960.95 m **39.** 2.45832 km

40. 33.349 m **41.** 3.88 km

42. 492.4 and 459.17 metres **43.** 1.438 km

45. 251.13 metres per minute.

XXXV (Pages 185, 186)

1. 84 **2.** 216 **3.** 630 **4.** 3720 **5.** 270

6. 117096 **7.** 1470 **8.** 1.183... **12.** 35 m and 26 m

13. 14.9... cm **14.** 5, 7 and 8 cm **15.** 120°

17. 45° and 105°; 135° and 15° **18.** 17.1064... sq. cm

XXXVI (Pages 192, 193)

3. $8\frac{1}{2}, 1\frac{1}{2}$, 8, 2, and 24 respetively

XXXVII (Pages 199-202)

35. 2.1547... or 0.1547 times the radius of each circle.

39. $A_n = \frac{\pi}{3} + (-1)^n . 2^n . \left(A - \frac{\pi}{3}\right), \ldots$ **40.** 61°59′36″; 8.83 cm

XXXVIII (Pages 206, 207)

1. (1) $3\sqrt{105}$ (= 30.74) sq. cm; (2) $10\sqrt{7}$ = (= 26.46) sq. cm

3. $1\frac{5}{7}$ and $2\frac{1}{2}$ cm

XXXIX (Pages 210, 211)

1. 77.98 cm **2.** 0.5359

3. (1) 1.720...sq. m (2) 2.598... sq. m (3) 4.8284... sq. m (4) 7.694... sq. m (5) 11.196... sq. m

4. 1.8866... sq. m **5.** 3.3136... sq. m

6. $2 + \sqrt{2} : 4, \sqrt{2 + \sqrt{2}} : 2$ **12.** 3 **14.** 6 **15.** 9

16. 20 and 10

17. 6 and 5, 12 and 8, 18 and 10, 22 and 11, 27 and 12, 42 and 14, 54 and 15, 72 and 16, 102 and 17, 162 and 18, 342 and 19 sides respectively. **19.** $\frac{2}{3}\sqrt{3}; \sqrt{6}$

XL (Pages 216, 217)

1. 0.00204 **2.** 0.00007 **3.** 0.00029 **4.** 0.99999

5. 25783.10077 **6.** 1.0000011 **7.** 34′23″

8. 28°40′37″ **9.** 39′42″ **10.** 2°33′44″ **11.** 114.59... cm

XLI (Pages 218, 219)

1. 435.77 sq. m **2.** 4.9087... sq. cm

3. 127°19′26″ **4.** 6 sq. cm **5.** 13.8 cm

6. 0.0007855 cm **7.** $\frac{2}{3}\pi r$

XLII (Page 221)

1. 1°48′40″ **2.** 2.53 cm **3.** 974.77 m; 1°26′ nearly

8. 62 km. nearly

XLIII (Pages 227-229)

28. $\pm\sqrt{\sin 2\beta}$ **29.** $\frac{1}{6}$ **30.** $\pm\frac{1}{\sqrt{2}}$ **31.** $4\sqrt{\frac{3}{7}}$

32. $\frac{1}{4}$ **33.** $n\pi$ or $n\pi+\frac{\pi}{4}$ **34.** $\sqrt{3}$ **35.** $\frac{\sqrt{5}}{3}$

36. $\sqrt{3}$ or $-(2+\sqrt{3})$ **37.** $\sqrt{3}$ or $2-\sqrt{3}$

38. n or n^2-n+1 **39.** $\frac{1}{2}\sqrt{\frac{3}{7}}$ **40.** 13

41. x is given by the equation,

$$x^4 - x^2(ab+ac+ad+bc+bd+cd)+abcd=0$$

42. $x=ab$ **43.** $ab \div [\sqrt{a^2-1}+\sqrt{b^2-1}]$ **44.** $\frac{a-b}{1+ab}$

XLIV (Page 235)

1. $\frac{1}{2}\sin 2n\theta \operatorname{cosec}\theta$ **2.** $\cos\frac{3n-1}{4}A\sin\frac{3n}{4}A\operatorname{cosec}\frac{3}{4}A$

6. $\frac{1}{2}$ **7.** $\sin\left[\alpha+\left(n-\frac{1}{2}\right)\beta\right]\sin n\beta\sec\frac{\beta}{2}$

8. $-\sin\frac{n\theta}{n-2}$

9. $\sin 2nx(\cos 2nx+\sin 2nx)(\cos x+\sin x)\operatorname{cosec} 2x$

10. $\frac{1}{4}[(n+1]\sin 2\alpha-\sin(2n+2)\alpha]\operatorname{cosec}\alpha$

11. $\frac{1}{2}\sin(2n+2)\alpha.\sin 2n\alpha\operatorname{cosec}\alpha.$

12. $\frac{n}{2}\cos 2\alpha-\frac{1}{2}\cos(n+3)\alpha\sin n\alpha\operatorname{cosec}\alpha.$

13. $$\frac{\cos(2n\alpha-\alpha)\cos(n+1)\beta-\cos(2n\alpha+\alpha)\cos n\beta+\cos\alpha(1-\cos\beta)}{2(\cos\alpha-\cos 2\alpha)}$$

14. $\frac{1}{4}[(2n+1)\sin\alpha-\sin(2n+1)\alpha]\operatorname{cosec}\alpha$

15. $\frac{n}{2}-\frac{1}{2}\cos[2\theta+(n+1)\alpha]\sin n\alpha\operatorname{cosec}\alpha$

16. $\frac{3}{4}\sin\frac{n+1}{2}\alpha\sin\frac{n\alpha}{2}\operatorname{cosec}\frac{\alpha}{2}-\frac{1}{4}\sin 3\frac{n+1}{2}\alpha\sin\frac{3n\alpha}{2}\operatorname{cosec}\frac{3\alpha}{2}$

17. $\frac{1}{8}[3n-4\cos(n+1)\alpha\sin n\alpha\operatorname{cosec}\alpha+\cos(2n+2)\alpha \sin 2n\alpha\operatorname{cosec}2\alpha]$

18. $\frac{1}{8}$ [$3n + 4\cos(n+1)\alpha \sin n\alpha$ cosec α

$+ \cos(2n+2)\alpha \sin 2n\alpha$ cosec 2α]

19. $\frac{1}{4}\sin\frac{n\theta}{2}\left[\cos\frac{n-1}{2}\theta + \cos\frac{n+3}{2}\theta + \cos\frac{n+7}{2}\theta\right]$ cosec $\frac{\theta}{2}$

$+ \frac{1}{4}\sin\frac{3n\theta}{2}\cos\frac{3n+9}{2}\theta$ cosec $\frac{3\theta}{2}$

20. $-\frac{1}{2}\sin(2\alpha + 2n\beta)\sin 2n\beta \sec\beta$.

XLV (Page 240)

1. $a^2 + b^2 = c^2 + d^2$

2. $\frac{x^2}{a^2} + \frac{y^2}{b^2} - \frac{2xy}{ab}\cos(\alpha - \beta) = \sin^2(\alpha - \beta)$ **3.** $a(2c^2 - d^2) = bcd$.

4. $a\sin\alpha + b\cos\alpha = \sqrt{2b(a+b)}$ **5.** $\frac{x^2}{a^2} + \frac{y^2}{b^2} = 1$

6. $\frac{x^2}{a} + \frac{y^2}{b} = a + b$

7. $(p^3 + 1)^2 + 2q(p^2 + 1)(p + q) = 4(p + q)^2$

8. $(x^2 + y^2 - b^2)^2 = a^2[(x + b)^2 + y^2]$ **11.** $a^2 + b^2 = 2 + 2\cos\alpha$

12. $xy = (y - x)\tan\alpha$ **13.** $a^2(a - c)(a - d) = b^2(b - c)(b - d)$

14. $8bc = a\{4b^2 + (b^2 - c^2)^2\}$

15. $x(c^2 - a^2 - b^2) = y\sqrt{(a+b+c)(-a+b+c)(a-b+c)(a+b-c)}$

16. $b^2[x(b^2 - a^2) + a(a^2 + b^2)]^2 = 4c^4[b^2x^2 + a^2y^2]$

Miscellaneous Examples

(Pages 245-268)

4. 267 m approx; 4°30′ approx. **5.** 41, 50, and 21 cm

6. $\sin(\beta - \alpha) = \pm\sqrt{1-b}\sqrt{1-a^2} \mp a\sqrt{b}$ **9.** $n\pi$ + 38°7′27″

10. $\left(n + \frac{1}{4}\right)\frac{\pi}{3}$ **14.** $7 - 3\sqrt{5} : 2$

21. (i) $\theta = n\pi + (-1)^n\frac{\alpha + \beta}{2}$ or

$\tan\theta = (1 - \text{cosec}\,\alpha\,\text{cosec}\,\beta)\tan\frac{\alpha+\beta}{2}$;

(ii) $\theta = n\pi$ or $\left(n \pm \frac{1}{3}\right)\frac{\pi}{3}$

22. 51°19′ ; 78°28′ ; 180°13′

23. 1298 metres nearly; 13°31′ east of south.

28. 80 metres

30. $\frac{1}{2}\tan^{-1} x; \frac{x+y}{1-xy}$

31. $(l^2 + m^2)(1-n) = 2m(1+n)$

32. Two roots

35. $\left(m \pm \frac{1}{12}\right)\pi; \left(n \pm \frac{1}{6}\right)\pi$

47. $(\lambda^2 - 1)^3 = 27\lambda^2 \cos^2 \alpha \sin^2 \alpha$

48. 1.39 radians = 79°30′ nearly

49. $\sin^2(\beta - \gamma)\sec^2(\alpha - \beta)\sec^2(\alpha - \gamma)$

52. 11°12′ north of east

54. Six values

58. $\frac{1}{3}\left[n\pi + \frac{\pi}{2} - \alpha - \beta - \gamma\right]$

59. 72.77 cm

62. $c\sqrt{2a-b} = a\sqrt{2a} - (a-b)\sqrt{b}$

63. $118\frac{1}{2}^\circ$

64. $-1° 19'$, $+28\frac{1}{2}^\circ$, and $+50\frac{1}{2}$ nearly.

69. $\dfrac{a \sin \alpha \sin \beta}{\sqrt{\sin^2(\beta - \alpha)\sin(\beta + \alpha)}}$

73. $\cos(\alpha + \beta + \gamma + \delta) + \cos(\alpha + \beta - \gamma - \delta)$
$+ \cos(\alpha + \beta + \gamma - \delta) + \cos(\alpha - \beta - \gamma + \delta) - \cos(-\alpha + \beta + \gamma + \delta)$
$- \cos(\alpha - \beta + \gamma + \delta) - \cos(\alpha + \beta - \gamma + \delta) - \cos(\alpha + \beta + \gamma - \delta)$

76. $66° 19\frac{1}{2}'$ approx

82. $\tan\theta = 2 \pm \sqrt{11}$ or $2 \pm \sqrt{3}$; $\tan\phi = 2 \mp \sqrt{11}$ or $2 \mp \sqrt{3}$

84. 16.47 km

87. $27y^2 = x^2(9 - 8x^2)^2$

94. $2a^3 + c = 3a(1 + b)$

95. $\sin\frac{n\theta}{2}\sin\frac{(n+3)\theta}{2}[1 + 2\cos 2\theta]\operatorname{cosec}\frac{\theta}{2}$
$- \sin\frac{3n+9}{2}\theta \sin\frac{3n\theta}{2}\operatorname{cosec}\frac{3\theta}{2}$

96. 2.55 radians = 146°6′ nearly.

104. $\tan\theta = 0, 1, -1, -2$

108. 2.379 km

117. 11°27′

120. $x^2 + y^2 = a^2 + b^2$

128. $(a^2 + b^2)^2 - 4a^2 = \frac{8ab}{c}$

136. $(x+y)^{2/5} + (x-y)^{2/5} = 2$

138. $\dfrac{mc_1 + na_1 + \sqrt{m^2c_2^2 + n^2a_2^2 + 2mn\, a_2c_2 \cos(\alpha - \gamma)} \sin(nt - \beta)}{m+n}$

where $\tan\beta = (mc_2 \sin\gamma + na_2 \sin\alpha) \div (mc_2 \cos\gamma + na_2 \cos\alpha)$

146. $m^2 + m\cos\alpha = 2$ **148.** $77\frac{1}{3}°; 63\frac{1}{2}°$

151. $(x^2 + y^2 + 2ax)^2 = 4a^2(x^2 + y^2)$

161. $(1 - x^2 - y^2)\sin(\alpha - \delta)\sin(\beta - \gamma)$

176. $a^4 + b^4 + c^4 - 2b^2c^2 - 2c^2a^2 - 2a^2b^2 = 0$

177. $x^2y^2 - 4xy = (x + y)^2\tan^2(\beta - \alpha)$

178. $b^2(\sqrt{3}x - y)^2\{6(x^2 - y^2) - b^2\} = 8(x^2 - y^2)^3 + 4b^2(x^2 - y^2)$

181. 3 roots; 299° approx.

206. 48°13′31″ E. of N. : 24°7′18″ W. of S.

TABLES OF LOGARITHMS, NATURAL SINES, NATURAL TANGENTS, LOGARITHMIC SINES, LOGARITHMIC TANGENTS, AND RADIAN MEASURE OF ANGLES

TABLE I
LOGARITHMS OF NUMBERS

	0	1	2	3	4	5	6	7	8	9	Mean Differences								
											1	2	3	4	5	6	7	8	9
10	00000	00432	00860	01284	01703	02119	02531	02938	03342	03743	42	83	125	166	208	248	290	331	373
11	04139	04532	04922	05308	05690	06070	06446	06819	07188	07555	38	76	114	152	190	227	265	302	340
12	07918	08279	08636	08991	09342	09691	10037	10380	10721	11059	35	70	105	140	175	209	278	278	313
13	11394	11727	12057	12385	12710	13033	13354	13672	13988	14301	32	65	97	129	162	193	225	258	290
14	14613	14922	15229	15534	15836	16137	16435	16732	17026	17319	30	60	90	120	150	180	210	240	270
15	17609	17898	18184	18469	18752	19033	19312	19590	19866	20140	28	56	84	112	140	168	196	224	252
16	20412	20683	20952	21219	21484	21748	22011	22272	22531	22789	26	53	79	105	132	158	184	210	237
17	23045	23300	23553	23805	24055	24304	24551	24797	25042	25285	25	50	74	99	124	149	174	199	223
18	25527	25768	26007	26245	26482	26717	26951	27184	27416	27646	23	47	70	94	117	141	164	188	211
19	27875	28103	28330	28556	28780	29003	29226	29447	29667	29885	22	45	67	89	111	134	156	178	201
20	30103	30320	30535	30750	30963	31175	31387	31597	31806	32015	21	42	64	85	106	127	148	170	191
21	32222	32428	32634	32838	33041	33244	33445	33646	33846	34044	20	40	61	81	101	121	141	162	182
22	34242	34439	34635	34830	35025	35218	35411	35603	33793	35984	19	39	58	77	97	116	135	154	174
23	36173	36361	36549	36736	36922	37107	37291	37475	37658	37840	19	37	56	74	93	111	130	148	167
24	38021	38202	38382	38561	38739	38917	39094	39270	39445	39620	18	36	53	71	89	107	124	142	160
25	39794	39967	40140	40312	40483	40654	40824	40903	41162	41330	17	34	51	68	85	102	119	136	153
26	41497	41664	41830	41996	42160	42325	42488	42651	42813	42975	16	33	49	66	82	98	115	131	148
27	43136	43297	43457	43616	43775	43933	44091	44248	44404	44560	16	32	47	63	79	95	111	126	142
28	44716	44871	45025	45179	45332	45484	45637	45788	45939	46090	15	30	46	61	76	91	106	122	137
29	46240	46389	46558	46687	46835	46982	47129	47276	47422	47567	15	29	44	59	74	88	103	118	132
30	47712	47857	48001	48144	48287	48430	48572	48714	48855	48996	14	29	43	57	72	86	100	114	129
31	49136	49276	49415	49554	49693	49831	49967	50106	50243	50379	14	28	42	55	69	83	97	110	125
32	50515	50651	50786	50920	51055	51188	51332	51455	51587	51720	13	27	40	54	67	80	94	107	121
33	51851	51983	52114	52244	52375	52504	52634	52763	52892	53020	13	26	39	52	65	78	91	104	117
34	53148	53275	53403	53529	53656	53782	53908	54033	54158	54283	13	25	38	50	63	76	88	101	113
35	54407	54531	54654	54777	54900	55023	55145	55267	55388	55509	12	24	37	49	61	73	86	98	110
36	55630	55751	55871	55991	56110	56229	56348	56467	56585	56703	12	24	36	48	60	71	83	95	107
37	56820	56937	57054	57171	57287	57403	57519	57634	57749	57864	12	23	35	46	58	70	81	93	104
38	57978	58092	58206	58320	58433	58546	58659	58771	58883	58995	11	23	34	45	57	68	79	90	102

	0	1	2	3	4	5	6	7	8	9	1	2	3	4	5	6	7	8	9
39	59106	59218	59329	59439	59550	59660	59770	59879	59988	60097	11	22	33	44	55	66	77	88	99
40	60206	60314	60423	60531	60638	60746	60853	60959	61066	61172	11	21	32	43	54	64	75	86	97
41	61278	61384	61490	61595	61700	61805	61909	62014	62118	62221	10	21	31	42	52	63	73	84	94
42	62325	62428	62531	62634	62737	62839	62941	63043	63144	63246	10	20	31	41	51	61	71	82	92
43	63347	63448	63548	63649	62749	63849	63949	64048	64147	64246	10	20	30	40	50	60	70	80	90
44	64345	64444	65452	64640	64738	64836	64933	65031	65128	65225	10	20	29	39	49	59	68	78	88
45	65321	65418	65514	65610	65706	65801	65896	65992	66087	66181	10	19	29	38	48	57	67	76	86
46	66276	66370	66464	66556	66652	66745	66839	66932	67025	67117	9	19	28	37	47	56	65	75	84
47	67210	67302	67394	67486	67578	67669	67761	67852	67943	68034	9	18	27	37	46	55	64	73	82
48	68124	68215	68305	68395	68485	68574	68664	68753	68842	68931	9	18	27	36	45	53	61	71	80
49	69020	69108	69197	69285	69373	69461	69548	69366	69723	69810	9	18	26	35	44	53	67	70	79
50	69897	69984	70070	70157	70243	70329	70415	70501	70586	70672	9	17	26	34	43	52	60	69	77
51	70757	70842	70927	71012	71096	71181	71265	71349	71433	71517	8	17	25	34	42	51	59	67	76
52	71600	71684	71767	71850	71933	72016	72099	72181	72263	72346	8	17	25	33	42	50	58	66	75
53	72428	72509	72591	72673	72754	72835	72916	72997	73078	73159	8	16	24	32	41	49	57	65	73
54	73239	73320	73400	73480	73560	73640	73719	73799	73878	73957	8	16	24	32	40	48	56	64	72
55	74036	74115	74194	74273	74351	74429	74507	74586	74663	74741	8	16	23	31	39	47	55	62	70
56	74819	74896	74974	75051	75128	75205	75282	75358	75435	75511	8	15	23	31	39	46	54	62	69
57	75587	75664	75740	75815	75891	75967	76042	76118	76193	76268	8	15	23	30	38	45	53	60	68
58	76343	76418	76492	76567	76641	76716	76790	76364	76938	77012	7	15	22	30	37	45	52	59	67
59	77085	77159	77232	77305	77379	77452	77525	77597	77670	77743	7	15	22	29	37	44	51	58	66
60	77815	77887	77960	78032	78104	78176	78247	78319	78390	78462	7	14	22	29	36	43	50	57	65
61	78533	78604	78675	78746	78817	78888	78958	79029	79099	79169	7	14	21	28	35	42	49	56	64
62	79239	79309	79379	79449	79518	79588	79657	79727	79796	79865	7	14	21	28	35	42	49	56	63
63	79934	80003	80072	80140	80209	80277	80346	80414	80482	80550	7	14	21	27	34	41	48	55	62
64	80618	80686	80754	80821	80889	80956	81023	81090	81158	81224	7	13	20	27	34	40	47	54	60
65	81291	81358	81425	81491	81558	81624	81690	81757	81823	81889	7	13	20	26	33	40	46	53	59
66	81954	82020	82086	82151	82217	82282	82347	82413	82478	82543	7	13	20	26	33	39	46	52	59
67	82607	82672	82737	82802	82866	82930	82995	83059	83123	83187	6	13	19	26	32	39	45	52	58
68	83251	83315	83378	83442	83506	83569	83632	83696	83759	83822	6	13	19	25	32	38	44	50	57
69	83885	83948	84011	84073	84136	84198	84261	84323	84386	84448	6	13	19	25	31	37	44	50	56

(XX)

	0	1	2	3	4	5	6	7	8	9	1	2	3	4	5	6	7	8	9
70	84510	84572	84634	84696	84757	84819	84880	84942	85003	85065	6	12	18	25	31	37	43	49	55
71	85126	85187	85248	85309	85370	85431	85491	85552	85612	85673	6	12	18	24	30	36	42	49	55
72	85733	85794	85854	85914	85974	86034	86094	86153	86213	86273	6	12	18	24	30	36	42	48	54
73	86332	86392	86451	86510	86570	86629	86688	86747	86806	86864	6	12	18	24	30	35	41	47	53
74	86923	86982	87040	87099	87157	87216	87274	87332	87390	87448	6	12	18	23	29	35	41	47	52
75	87506	87564	87622	87679	87737	87795	87852	87910	87967	88024	6	12	17	23	29	35	40	46	52
76	88081	88138	88195	88252	88309	88366	88423	88480	88536	88593	6	11	17	23	29	34	40	46	51
77	88649	88705	88762	88818	88874	88930	88986	89042	89098	89154	6	11	17	22	28	34	39	45	50
78	89209	89265	89321	89376	89432	89487	89542	89597	89653	89708	6	11	17	22	28	33	39	44	50
79	89763	89818	89873	89927	89982	90037	90091	90146	90200	90255	5	11	16	22	27	33	38	44	49
80	90309	90363	90417	90472	90526	90580	90634	90687	90741	90795	5	11	16	22	27	32	38	43	49
81	90849	90902	90956	91009	91062	91116	91169	91222	91275	91328	5	11	16	21	27	32	37	43	48
82	91381	91434	91487	91540	91593	91645	91698	91751	91803	91055	5	11	16	21	26	32	37	42	47
83	91908	91960	92012	92065	92117	92169	92221	92273	92324	92376	5	10	16	21	26	31	36	42	47
84	92428	92480	92531	92583	92634	92686	92737	92788	92840	92891	5	10	15	21	26	31	36	41	46
85	92942	92993	93044	93095	93146	93197	93247	93298	93349	93399	5	10	15	20	25	30	36	41	46
86	93450	93500	93551	93001	93651	93702	93752	93802	93852	93902	5	10	15	20	25	30	35	40	45
87	93952	94002	94052	94101	94151	94201	94250	94300	94349	94399	5	10	15	20	25	30	35	40	45
88	94458	94498	94547	94596	94645	94694	94743	94792	94841	94890	5	10	15	20	25	29	34	39	44
89	94939	94988	95036	95085	95134	95182	95231	95279	95328	95376	5	10	15	19	24	29	34	39	44
90	95424	95472	95521	95569	95617	95665	95713	95761	95809	95856	5	10	14	19	24	29	34	38	43
91	95904	95952	95999	96047	96095	96142	96190	96237	96284	96332	5	9	14	19	24	29	33	38	43
92	96379	96426	96473	96520	96567	96614	96661	96708	96755	96802	5	9	14	19	24	28	33	38	42
93	96848	96895	96942	96988	97035	97081	97128	97174	97220	97267	5	9	14	19	23	28	33	37	42
94	97313	97359	97405	97451	97497	97543	97589	97635	97681	97727	5	9	14	18	23	28	32	37	41
95	97772	97818	97864	97909	97955	98000	98046	98091	98137	98182	5	9	14	18	23	27	32	36	41
96	98227	98272	98318	98393	98408	98453	98498	93543	98588	98632	5	9	14	18	22	27	32	36	41
97	98677	98722	98767	98811	98856	98900	98954	98989	99034	99078	4	9	13	18	23	27	31	36	40
98	99123	99167	99211	99225	99300	99344	99388	99432	99476	99520	4	9	13	18	22	26	31	35	40
99	99564	99607	99651	99695	99739	99782	99826	99870	99913	99957	4	9	13	17	22	26	30	35	39

TABLE II
NATURAL SINES

	0′	10′	20′	30′	40′	50′	60′		Mean differences 1′	2′	3′	4′	5′	6′	7′	8′	9′
0°	0.00000	0.00291	0.00582	0.00873	0.01164	0.01454	0.01745	89°	29	58	87	116	145	175	204	233	262
1°	0.01745	0.02036	0.02327	0.02618	0.02908	0.03199	0.03490	88°	29	58	87	116	145	175	204	233	262
2°	0.03490	0.03781	0.04071	0.04362	0.04653	0.04943	0.05234	87°	29	58	87	116	145	175	204	233	262
3°	0.05234	0.05524	0.05814	0.06105	0.06395	0.06685	0.06976	86°	29	58	87	116	145	174	203	232	261
4°	0.06976	0.07266	0.07556	0.07846	0.08136	0.08426	0.08716	85°	29	58	87	116	145	174	203	232	261
5°	0.08716	0.09005	0.09295	0.09585	0.09874	0.10164	0.10453	84°	29	58	87	116	145	174	203	232	261
6°	0.10453	0.10742	0.11031	0.11320	0.11609	0.11898	0.12187	83°	29	58	87	116	145	174	202	232	261
7°	0.12187	0.12476	0.12764	0.13053	0.13341	0.13629	0.13917	82°	29	58	87	116	145	173	202	231	260
8°	0.13917	0.14205	0.14493	0.14781	0.15069	0.15356	0.15643	81°	29	58	86	115	144	173	202	230	259
9°	0.15643	0.15931	0.16218	0.16505	0.16792	0.17078	0.17365	80°	29	57	86	115	144	172	201	230	258
10°	0.17635	0.17651	0.17937	0.18224	0.18509	0.18795	0.19081	79°	29	57	86	115	144	172	201	229	258
11°	0.19081	0.19366	0.19652	0.19937	0.20222	0.20507	0.20791	78°	29	57	86	114	143	171	200	228	257
12°	0.20791	0.21076	0.21360	0.21644	0.21928	0.22212	0.22495	77°	28	57	85	114	142	170	199	227	256
13°	0.22495	0.22778	0.23062	0.23345	0.23627	0.23910	0.24192	76°	28	57	85	113	141	170	198	226	255
14°	0.24192	0.24474	0.24756	0.25038	0.25320	0.25601	0.25882	75°	28	56	85	113	141	169	197	226	254
15°	0.25882	0.26163	0.26443	0.26724	0.27004	0.27284	0.27564	74°	28	56	84	112	140	168	196	224	252
16°	0.27564	0.27843	0.28123	0.28402	0.28680	0.28959	0.29237	73°	28	56	84	112	140	167	195	223	251
17°	0.29237	0.29515	0.29793	0.30071	0.30348	0.30625	0.30902	72°	28	56	83	111	139	166	194	222	250
18°	0.30902	0.31178	0.31454	0.31730	0.32006	0.32282	0.32557	71°	28	56	83	110	138	166	193	221	248
19°	0.32557	0.32832	0.33106	0.33381	0.33655	0.33929	0.34202	70°	27	55	82	110	137	164	192	229	247

	60′	50′	40′	30′	20′	10′	0′		1′	2′	3′	4′	5′	6′	7′	8′	9′
20°	0.34202	0.34475	0.34748	0.35021	0.35293	0.35565	0.35837	69°	27	55	82	109	137	164	191	218	246
21°	0.35837	0.36108	0.36379	0.36650	0.36921	0.37191	0.37461	68°	27	54	81	108	136	163	190	217	244
22°	0.37461	0.37730	0.37999	0.38268	0.38537	0.38805	0.39073	67°	27	54	81	108	135	161	188	215	242
23°	0.39073	0.39341	0.39608	0.39875	0.40142	0.40408	0.40674	66°	27	53	80	107	134	160	187	214	240
24°	0.40674	0.40939	0.41204	0.41469	0.41734	0.41998	0.42262	65°	27	53	80	106	133	159	186	212	238
25°	0.42262	0.42525	0.42788	0.43051	0.43313	0.43575	0.43837	64°	26	52	79	105	131	157	184	210	236
26°	0.43837	0.44098	0.44359	0.44620	0.44880	0.45140	0.45399	63°	26	52	78	104	130	156	182	208	234
27°	0.04399	0.45658	0.45917	0.46175	0.46433	0.46690	0.46947	62°	26	52	77	103	129	155	181	206	232
28°	0.46947	0.47204	0.47460	0.47716	0.47971	0.48226	0.48481	61°	26	51	77	102	128	154	179	204	230
29°	0.48481	0.48735	0.48989	0.49242	0.49495	0.49748	0.50000	60°	25	51	76	101	127	152	177	202	228
30°	0.50000	0.50252	0.50503	0.50754	0.51004	0.51254	0.51504	59°	25	50	75	100	125	150	175	200	225
31°	0.51504	0.51753	0.52002	0.52250	0.52498	0.52745	0.52992	58°	25	50	74	99	124	149	174	198	223
32°	0.52992	0.53238	0.53484	0.53730	0.53975	0.54220	0.54464	57°	25	49	74	98	123	147	172	196	221
33°	0.54464	0.54708	0.54951	0.55194	0.55436	0.55678	0.55919	56°	24	49	73	97	122	146	170	194	219
34°	0.55919	0.56160	0.56401	0.56641	0.56880	0.57119	0.57358	55°	24	48	72	96	120	144	168	192	216
35°	0.57358	0.57596	0.57833	0.58070	0.58307	0.58543	0.58779	54°	24	47	71	95	119	142	166	190	213
36°	0.58779	0.59014	0.59248	0.59482	0.59716	0.59949	0.60182	53°	23	47	70	94	117	140	164	187	211
37°	0.60182	0.60414	0.60645	0.60876	0.61107	0.61337	0.61566	52°	23	46	70	92	116	139	162	185	208
38°	0.61566	0.61795	0.62024	0.62251	0.62479	0.62706	0.62932	51°	23	46	68	91	114	137	159	182	205
39°	0.62932	0.63158	0.63383	0.63608	0.63832	0.64056	0.64279	50°	22	45	67	90	112	135	157	179	202
40°	0.64279	0.64501	0.64723	0.64945	0.65166	0.65386	0.65606	49°	22	44	66	88	111	133	155	177	199
41°	0.65606	0.65825	0.66044	0.66262	0.66480	0.66697	0.66913	48°	22	44	65	87	109	131	153	174	196
42°	0.66913	0.67129	0.67344	0.67559	0.67773	0.67987	0.68200	47°	21	43	64	86	107	129	150	172	193
43°	0.68200	0.68412	0.68624	0.68835	0.69046	0.69256	0.69466	46°	21	42	63	84	106	127	148	169	190
44°	0.69466	0.69675	0.69883	0.70091	0.70298	0.70505	0.70711	45°	21	42	62	83	104	124	145	166	187

NATURAL COSINES

(XXIII)

NATURAL SINES

	0′	10′	20′	30′	40′	50′	60′		Mean Differences								
									1′	2′	3′	4′	5′	6′	7′	8′	9′
45°	0.70711	0.70916	0.71121	0.71325	0.71529	0.71732	0.71934	44°	20	41	61	82	102	122	143	163	184
46°	0.71934	0.72136	0.72337	0.72537	0.72737	0.72937	0.73135	43°	20	40	60	80	100	120	140	160	180
47°	0.73135	0.73333	0.73531	0.73728	0.73924	0.74120	0.74314	42°	20	39	59	78	98	118	138	157	177
48°	0.74314	0.74509	0.74703	0.74896	0.75088	0.75280	0.75471	41°	19	39	58	77	96	116	135	154	173
49°	0.75471	0.75661	0.75851	0.76041	0.76229	0.76417	0.76604	40°	19	38	57	76	95	113	132	151	170
50°	0.76604	0.76791	0.76977	0.77162	0.77347	0.77531	0.77715	39°	19	37	56	74	93	111	130	148	167
51°	0.77715	0.77897	0.78079	0.78261	0.78442	0.78622	0.78801	38°	18	36	54	72	91	100	127	145	163
52°	0.78801	0.78980	0.79158	0.79335	0.79512	0.79688	0.79864	37°	18	35	53	71	89	106	124	142	159
53°	0.79864	0.80038	0.80212	0.80386	0.80558	0.80730	0.80902	36°	17	35	52	69	87	104	121	138	156
54°	0.80902	0.81072	0.81242	0.81412	0.81580	0.81748	0.81915	35°	17	34	51	68	85	101	118	135	152
55°	0.81915	0.82082	0.82248	0.82413	0.82577	0.82741	0.82904	34°	16	33	49	66	82	99	115	132	148
56°	0.82904	0.83066	0.83228	0.83389	0.83549	0.83708	0.83837	33°	16	32	48	64	80	96	112	138	144
57°	0.83867	0.84025	0.84182	0.84339	0.84495	0.84650	0.84805	32°	16	31	47	63	78	94	110	125	141
58°	0.84805	0.84959	0.85112	0.85264	0.85416	0.85567	0.85717	31°	15	30	46	61	76	91	106	122	137
59°	0.85717	0.85866	0.86015	0.86163	0.86310	0.86457	0.86603	30°	15	30	44	59	74	89	103	118	133
60°	0.86603	0.86748	0.86892	0.87036	0.87178	0.87321	0.87462	29°	14	29	43	57	72	86	100	114	129
61°	0.87462	0.87603	0.87743	0.87882	0.88020	0.88158	0.88295	28°	14	28	42	55	69	83	97	111	128
62°	0.88295	0.88431	0.88566	0.88701	0.88835	0.88968	0.89101	27°	13	27	40	54	67	81	91	108	121
63°	0.89101	0.89232	0.89363	0.89493	0.89623	0.89752	0.89879	26°	13	26	39	52	65	78	91	104	117
64°	0.89879	0.90007	0.90133	0.90259	0.90383	0.90507	0.90631	25°	13	25	38	50	63	75	88	100	113
65°	0.90631	0.90753	0.90875	0.90996	0.91116	0.91236	0.91355	24°	12	24	36	48	60	72	84	96	108
66°	0.91355	0.91472	0.91590	0.91706	0.91822	0.91936	0.92050	23°	12	23	35	46	58	70	81	93	104
67°	0.92050	0.92164	0.92276	0.92388	0.92499	0.92609	0.92718	22°	11	22	33	45	56	67	78	89	100
68°	0.92718	0.92827	0.92935	0.93042	0.93148	0.93253	0.93358	21°	11	21	32	43	53	64	75	85	96
69°	0.93358	0.93462	0.93565	0.93667	0.93769	0.93869	0.93969	20°	10	20	31	41	51	61	71	81	92

	60′	50′	40′	30′	20′	10′	0′		1′	2′	3′	4′	5′	6′	7′	8′	9′
70°	0.93969	0.94068	0.94167	0.94264	0.94361	0.94457	0.94552	19°	10	19	29	39	49	58	68	78	87
71°	0.94552	0.94646	0.94740	0.94832	0.94924	0.95015	0.95106	18°	9	18	28	37	46	55	64	74	83
72°	0.95106	0.95195	0.95284	0.95372	0.95459	0.95545	0.95630	17°	9	18	26	35	44	52	61	70	79
73°	0.95630	0.95715	0.95799	0.95882	0.95964	0.96046	0.96126	16°	8	17	25	33	41	50	58	66	74
74°	0.96126	0.96206	0.96285	0.96363	0.96440	0.96517	0.96593	15°	8	16	23	31	39	47	54	62	70
75°	0.96593	0.96667	0.96742	0.96815	0.96887	0.96959	0.97030	14°	7	15	22	29	36	44	51	58	65
76°	0.97030	0.97100	0.97169	0.97237	0.97304	0.97371	0.97437	13°	7	14	20	27	34	41	47	54	61
77°	0.97437	0.97502	0.97566	0.97630	0.97692	0.97754	0.97815	12°	6	13	19	25	32	38	44	50	57
78°	0.97815	0.97875	0.97934	0.97992	0.98050	0.98107	0.98163	11°	6	12	17	23	29	35	41	46	52
79°	0.96163	0.98218	0.98272	0.98325	0.98378	0.98430	0.98481	10°	5	11	16	21	27	32	37	42	48
80°	0.98481	0.98531	0.98580	0.98629	0.98676	0.98723	0.98769	9°	5	10	14	19	24	29	34	38	43
81°	0.98769	0.98814	0.98858	0.98902	0.98944	0.98986	0.99027	8°	4	9	13	17	22	26	30	34	39
82°	0.99027	0.99067	0.99106	0.99144	0.99182	0.99219	0.99255	7°	4	8	11	15	19	23	27	30	34
83°	0.99255	0.99290	0.99324	0.99357	0.99390	0.99421	0.99452	6°	3	7	10	13	17	20	23	26	30
84°	0.99452	0.99482	0.99511	0.99540	0.99567	0.99594	0.99619	5°	3	6	8	11	14	17	20	22	25
85°	0.99619	0.99644	0.99668	0.99692	0.99714	0.99736	0.99756	4°	2	5	7	9	12	14	16	18	21
86°	0.99756	0.99776	0.99795	0.99813	0.99831	0.99847	0.99863	3°	2	4	5	7	9	11	13	14	16
87°	0.99863	0.99878	0.99892	0.99905	0.99917	0.99929	0.99939	2°	1	3	4	5	7	8	9	10	12
88°	0.99939	0.99949	0.99958	0.99966	0.99973	0.99979	0.99985	1°									
89°	0.99985	0.99989	0.99993	0.99996	0.99998	1.00000	1.00000	0°									
90°	1.00000																

NATURAL COSINES

TABLE III
NATURAL TANGENTS

	0′	10′	20′	30′	40′	50′	60′		Mean differences								
									1′	2′	3′	4′	5′	6′	7′	8′	9′
0°	0.00000	0.00291	0.00582	0.00873	0.01164	0.01455	0.01746	89°	29	58	87	116	146	175	204	233	262
1°	0.01746	0.02037	0.02328	0.02619	0.02910	0.03201	0.03492	88°	29	58	87	116	146	175	204	233	262
2°	0.03492	0.03783	0.04075	0.04366	0.04658	0.04949	0.05241	87°	29	58	87	116	146	175	204	233	262
3°	0.05241	0.05533	0.05824	0.06116	0.06408	0.6700	0.06993	86°	29	58	88	117	146	175	204	234	263
4°	0.06993	0.07285	0.07578	0.07870	0.08163	0.08456	0.08749	85°	29	58	88	117	146	175	204	234	263
5°	0.08749	0.09042	0.09335	0.09629	0.09923	0.10216	0.10510	84°	29	59	88	118	147	176	206	235	265
6°	0.10510	0.10805	0.11099	0.11394	0.11688	0.11983	0.12278	83°	29	59	88	118	147	176	206	235	265
7°	0.12278	0.12574	0.12869	0.13165	0.13461	0.13758	0.14054	82°	30	59	89	118	148	178	207	237	266
8°	0.14054	0.14351	0.14648	0.14945	0.15243	0.15540	0.15838	81°	30	59	89	119	149	178	208	238	267
9°	0.15838	0.16137	0.16435	0.16734	0.17033	0.17333	0.17633	80°	30	60	90	120	150	179	209	239	269
10°	0.17633	0.17933	0.18233	0.18534	0.18835	0.19136	0.19438	79°	30	60	91	120	151	181	211	241	271
11°	0.19438	0.19740	0.20042	0.20345	0.20648	0.20952	0.21256	78°	30	61	92	121	152	182	212	242	273
12°	0.21256	0.21560	0.21864	0.22169	0.22475	0.22781	0.23087	77°	31	61	92	122	153	183	214	244	275
13°	0.23087	0.23393	0.23700	0.24008	0.24316	0.24624	0.24933	76°	31	62	92	123	154	185	216	246	277
14°	0.24933	0.25242	0.25552	0.25862	0.26172	0.26483	0.26795	75°	31	62	93	124	155	186	117	248	279
15°	0.26795	0.27107	0.27419	0.27732	0.28046	0.28360	0.28675	74°	31	62	94	125	157	188	219	250	282
16°	0.28675	0.28990	0.29305	0.29621	0.29938	0.30255	0.30573	73°	32	63	95	126	158	190	221	253	285
17°	0.30573	0.30891	0.31210	0.31530	0.31850	0.32171	0.32492	72°	32	63	96	128	160	192	224	256	288
18°	0.32492	0.32814	0.33136	0.33460	0.33783	0.34108	0.34433	71°	32	65	97	129	162	194	226	259	291
19°	0.34433	0.34758	0.35085	0.35412	0.35740	0.36068	0.36397	70°	33	65	98	131	164	196	229	262	294

	60′	50′	40′	30′	20′	10′	0′		1′	2′	3′	4′	5′	6′	7′	8′	9′
20°	0.36397	0.36727	0.37057	0.37388	0.37720	0.38053	0.38386	69°	33	66	100	133	166	199	232	265	298
21°	0.38386	0.38721	0.39055	0.39391	0.39727	0.40065	0.40403	68°	34	67	101	134	168	202	236	269	302
22°	0.40403	0.40741	0.41081	0.41421	0.41763	0.42105	0.42447	67°	34	68	102	136	170	205	239	273	306
23°	0.42447	0.42791	0.43136	0.43481	0.43828	0.44175	0.44523	66°	35	69	104	138	173	208	242	277	311
24°	0.44523	0.44872	0.45222	0.45573	0.45924	0.46277	0.46631	65°	35	70	105	140	176	211	246	281	316
25°	0.46631	0.46985	0.47341	0.47689	0.48055	0.48414	0.48773	64°	36	71	107	143	179	214	250	286	321
26°	0.48773	0.49134	0.49495	0.49858	0.50222	0.50587	0.50953	63°	36	73	109	.145	182	218	254	291	327
27°	0.50953	0.51320	0.51688	0.52057	0.52427	0.52798	0.53171	62°	37	74	111	148	185	222	259	296	333
28°	0.53171	0.53545	0.53920	0.54296	0.54673	0.55051	0.55431	61°	38	75	113	151	189	226	264	302	339
29°	0.55431	0.55812	0.56194	0.56577	0.56962	0.57348	0.57735	60°	38	77	115	154	192	230	269	307	346
30°	0.57735	0.58124	0.58513	0.58905	0.59297	0.59691	0.60086	59°	39	78	118	157	196	235	274	313	353
31°	0.60086	0.60483	0.60881	0.61280	0.61681	0.62083	0.62487	58°	40	80	120	160	200	240	280	320	360
32°	0.62487	0.62892	0.63299	0.63707	0.64117	0.64528	0.64941	57°	41	82	123	164	205	245	286	327	368
33°	0.64941	0.65355	0.65771	0.66189	0.66608	0.67028	0.67451	56°	42	84	126	167	209	251	293	334	376
34°	0.67451	0.67875	0.68301	0.68728	0.69157	0.69588	0.70021	55°	43	86	128	171	214	257	300	342	385
35°	0.70021	0.70455	0.70891	0.71329	0.71769	0.72211	0.72654	54°	44	88	132	176	220	263	307	351	395
36°	0.72654	0.73100	0.73547	0.73996	0.74447	0.74900	0.75355	53°	45	90	135	180	225	270	315	360	405
37°	0.75355	0.75812	0.76272	0.76733	0.77196	0.77661	0.78129	52°	46	92	139	185	231	277	324	370	416
38°	0.78129	0.78598	0.79070	0.79544	0.80020	0.80498	0.80978	51°	48	95	143	190	238	285	333	380	428
39°	0.80978	0.81461	0.81946	0.82434	0.82923	0.83415	0.83910	50°	49	98	147	196	245	293	342	391	440

NATURAL CONTANGENTS

(XXVII)
NATURAL TANGENTS

	0′	10′	20′	30′	40′	50′	60′		1′	2′	3′	4′	5′	6′	7′	8′	9′
40°	0.83910	0.84407	0.84906	0.85408	0.85912	0.86419	0.86929	49°	50	101	151	201	252	302	352	402	453
41°	0.86929	0.87441	0.87955	0.88473	0.88992	0.89515	0.90040	48°	52	104	156	208	260	311	363	415	467
42°	0.90040	0.90569	0.91099	0.91633	0.92170	0.92709	0.93252	47°	54	107	161	214	268	321	375	429	482
43°	0.93252	0.93797	0.94345	0.94896	0.95451	0.96008	0.96569	46°	55	111	166	221	277	332	387	442	498
44°	0.96569	0.97133	0.97700	0.98270	0.98843	0.99420	1.00000	45°	57	114	172	229	286	343	400	457	515
45°	1.00000	1.00583	1.01170	1.01761	1.02355	1.02952	1.03553	44°	59	118	178	237	296	355	414	474	533
46°	1.03553	1.04158	1.04766	1.05378	1.05994	1.06613	1.07237	43°	61	123	184	246	307	368	430	491	553
47°	1.07237	1.07864	1.08496	1.09131	1.09770	1.10414	1.11061	42°	64	127	191	255	319	382	446	510	573
48°	1.11061	1.11713	1.13029	1.13029	1.13694	1.14363	1.15037	41°	66	132	199	265	332	397	463	530	596
49°	1.15037	1.15715	1.17085	1.17085	1.17777	1.18474	1.19175	40°	69	138	207	276	345	413	482	552	620
50°	1.19175	1.19882	1.20593	1.21310	1.22031	1.22758	1.23490	39°	72	144	216	288	360	431	503	575	647
51°	1.23490	1.24227	1.24969	1.25717	1.26471	1.27230	2.7994	38°	75	150	225	300	376	451	526	601	676
52°	1.27994	1.28764	1.29541	1.30323	1.31110	1.31904	1.32704	37°	78	157	235	314	392	471	459	628	707
53°	1.32704	1.33511	1.34323	1.35142	1.35968	1.36800	1.37638	36°	82	164	247	329	411	493	576	658	740
54°	1.37638	1.38484	1.39336	1.40195	1.41061	1.41934	1.42815	35°	86	172	259	345	431	517	603	690	776
55°	1.42815	1.43703	1.44598	1.45501	1.46411	1.47330	1.48256	34°	91	181	272	363	453	544	634	725	816
56°	1.48256	1.49190	1.50133	1.51084	1.52043	1.53010	1.53987	33°	96	191	287	382	478	573	669	764	860
57°	1.53987	1.54972	1.55966	1.56969	1.57981	1.59002	1.60033	32°	101	201	302	403	504	604	705	806	907
58°	1.60033	1.61074	1.62125	1.63185	1.64256	1.65337	1.66428	31°	107	213	320	426	533	639	746	852	959
59°	1.66428	1.67530	1.68643	1.69766	1.70901	1.72047	1.73205	30°	113	226	339	451	565	677	790	903	1016
60°	1.7321	1.7437	1.7556	1.7675	1.7766	1.7917	1.8040	29°	12	24	36	48	60	72	84	96	108
61°	1.8040	1.8165	1.8291	1.8418	1.8546	1.8676	1.8807	28°	13	25	38	51	64	77	89	102	115
62°	1.8807	1.8940	1.9074	1.9210	1.9347	1.9486	1.9626	27°	14	27	41	54	68	82	95	109	122
63°	1.9626	1.9768	1.9912	2.0057	2.0204	2.0353	2.0503	26°	15	29	44	58	73	88	102	117	131
64°	2.0503	2.0655	2.0809	2.0965	2.1123	2.1283	2.1445	25°	16	31	47	63	79	94	110	126	141

(XXVIII)

	60′	50′	40′	30′	20′	10′	0′		1′	2′	3′	4′	5′	6′	7′	8′	9′
65°	2.1445	2.1609	2.1775	2.1943	2.2113	2.2286	2.2460	24°	17	34	51	68	85	101	118	135	152
66°	2.2460	2.2637	2.2817	2.2998	2.3183	2.3369	2.3559	23°	18	37	55	73	92	110	128	146	165
67°	2.3559	2.3750	2.3945	2.4142	2.4342	2.4545	2.4751	22°	20	40	60	80	100	119	139	159	179
68°	2.4751	2.4960	2.5172	2.5386	2.5605	2.5826	2.6051	21°	22	43	65	87	109	130	152	174	195
69°	2.6051	2.6279	2.6511	2.6746	2.6985	2.7223	2.7475	20°	24	47	71	95	119	142	166	190	213
70°	2.7475	2.7725	2.7980	2.8239	2.8502	2.8770	2.9042	19°	26	52	78	104	131	157	183	209	235
71°	2.9042	2.9319	2.9600	2.9887	3.1078	3.0475	3.0777	18°	29	58	87	116	145	174	202	231	260
72°	3.0777	3.1084	3.1397	3.1716	3.2041	3.2371	3.2709	17°	32	64	97	129	161	193	225	258	290
73°	3.2709	3.3052	3.3402	3.3759	3.4124	3.4495	3.4874	16°	36	72	108	144	181	216	253	289	325
74°	3.4874	3.5261	3.5656	3.6059	3.6470	3.6891	3.7321	15°	41	81	122	163	204	244	285	326	366
75°	3.7321	3.7760	3.8208	3.8667	3.9136	3.9617	4.0108	14°	46	93	139	185	232	278	325	371	418
76°	4.0108	4.0611	4.1126	4.1653	4.2193	4.2747	4.3315	13°	53	107	160	214	267	320	374	427	481
77°	4.3315	4.3897	4.4494	4.5107	4.5736	4.6382	4.7046	12°	62	124	186	248	311	373	435	497	559
78°	4.7046	4.7729	4.8430	4.9152	4.9894	5.0658	5.1446	11°	73	146	220	293	366	439	512	586	669
79°	5.1446	5.2257	5.3955	5.3955	5.4845	5.5764	5.6713	10°	88	175	263	350	438	526	613	701	788
80°	5.6713	5.7694	5.8708	5.9758	6.0844	6.19701	6.3138	9°									
81°	6.3138	6.4348	6.5606	6.6912	6.8269	6.9682	7.1154	8°									
82°	7.1154	7.2687	7.4287	7.5958	7.7704	7.9530	8.1443	7°									
83°	8.1443	8.3450	8.5555	8.7769	9.0098	9.2553	9.5144	6°									
84°	9.5144	9.7882	10.078	10.385	10.712	11.059	11.4301	5°									
85°	11.430	11.826	12.251	12.706	13.197	13.727	14.301	4°									
86°	14.301	14.924	15.605	16.350	17.169	18.075	19.081	3°									
87°	19.081	20.206	21.470	22.904	24.542	26.432	28.636	2°									
88°	28.636	31.242	34.368	38.188	42.964	49.104	57.290	1°									
89°	57.290	68.750	85.040	114.59	171.89	343.77	+ ∞	0°									
90°	+ ∞																

The differences change so rapidly here that they cannot be tabulated.

The cotangent of a small angle of n' or the tangent of $90° - n'$ is very nearly equal to 3437.7 divided by n.

NATURAL CONTANGENTS

TABLE-IV

Logarithmic Sines

	0′	10′	20′	30′	40′	50′	60′		Mean Differences								
									1′	2′	3′	4′	5′	6′	7′	8′	9′
0°	– ∞	7.46373	7.76475	7.94084	8.06578	8.16268	8.24186	89°	Differences vary so rapidly here that tabulation is impossible. for small angles of n minutes log sine n' or log cosine $(90° - n') = \log n + 4.46373$								
1°	8.24186	8.30879	8.36678	8.41792	8.46366	8.50504	8.54282	88°									
2°	8.54282	8.57757	8.60973	8.63968	8.66769	8.69400	8.71880	87°									
3°	8.71880	8.74226	8.76451	8.78568	8.80585	8.82513	8.84358	86°									
4°	8.84358	8.86128	8.87829	8.89464	8.91040	8.92561	8.94030	85°									
5°	8.94030	8.95450	8.96825	8.98157	8.99450	9.00704	9.01923	84°									
6°	9.01923	9.03109	9.04262	9.95386	9.06481	9.07548	9.08589	83°									
7°	9.08589	9.09606	9.10599	9.11570	9.12519	9.13447	9.14356	82°	96	192	288	384	480	576	672	768	864
8°	9.14356	9.15245	9.16116	9.16970	9.17807	9.18628	9.19433	81°	85	169	254	338	423	507	592	676	761
9°	9.19433	9.20223	9.20999	9.21761	9.22509	9.23244	9.23967	80°	76	151	227	302	378	453	529	604	680
10°	9.23967	9.24677	9.25376	9.26063	9.26739	9.27405	9.28060	79°	68	136	204	272	341	409	477	545	613
11°	9.28060	9.28705	9.29340	9.29966	9.30582	9.31189	9.31788	78°	62	124	186	248	310	373	435	497	559
12°	9.31788	9.32378	9.32960	9.33534	9.34100	9.34658	9.35209	77°	57	114	171	228	285	342	399	456	513
13°	9.35209	9.35752	9.36289	9.36819	9.37341	9.37858	9.38368	76°	53	105	158	210	263	316	368	421	473
14°	9.30368	9.38871	9.39369	9.39860	9.40346	9.40825	9.41300	75°	49	98	147	195	244	293	342	391	440
15°	9.41300	9.41768	9.42232	9.42690	9.43143	9.43591	9.44034	74°	46	91	137	182	228	273	319	364	410
16°	9.44034	9.44472	9.44905	9.45334	9.45758	9.46178	9.46594	73°	43	85	128	171	213	256	299	341	384
17°	9.46594	9.47005	9.47411	9.47814	9.48213	9.48607	9.48998	72°	40	80	120	160	201	241	281	321	361
18°	9.48998	9.49385	9.49768	9.50148	9.50523	9.50896	9.51264	71°	38	76	113	151	189	227	264	302	340
19°	9.51264	9.51269	9.51991	9.52350	9.52705	9.53056	9.53405	70°	36	71	107	143	179	214	250	285	321

	60′	50′	40′	30′	20′	10′	0′		1′	2′	3′	4′	5′	6′	7′	8′	9′
20°	9.53405	9.53751	9.54093	9.54433	9.54769	9.55102	9.55433	69°	34	68	101	135	169	203	237	270	304
21°	9.55433	9.55761	9.56085	9.56408	9.56727	9.57044	9.57358	68°	32	64	96	128	161	193	225	257	289
22°	9.57358	9.57669	9.57978	9.58284	9.58588	9.58889	9.59188	67°	31	61	92	122	153	183	214	244	275
23°	9.59188	9.59484	9.59778	9.60070	9.60359	9.60646	9.60931	66°	29	58	87	116	146	174	204	233	262
24°	9.60931	9.61214	9.61494	9.61773	9.62049	9.62323	9.62595	65°	28	56	83	111	139	166	195	222	250
25°	9.62595	9.62865	9.63133	9.63398	9.63662	9.63924	9.64184	64°	27	53	80	106	133	159	186	212	239
26°	9.64184	9.64442	9.64698	9.64953	9.65205	9.65456	9.65705	63°	25	51	76	102	127	152	178	203	229
27°	9.65705	9.65952	9.66197	9.66441	9.66682	9.66922	9.67161	62°	24	49	73	97	122	146	170	194	219
28°	9.67161	9.67398	9.67633	9.67866	9.68098	9.68328	9.68557	61°	23	47	70	93	117	140	163	186	210
29°	9.68557	9.68784	9.69010	9.69234	9.69456	9.69677	9.69897	60°	22	45	67	89	112	134	156	179	201
30°	9.69897	9.70115	9.70332	9.70547	9.70761	9.70973	9.71184	59°	22	43	65	86	107	129	150	172	193
31°	9.71184	9.71393	9.71602	9.71809	9.72014	9.72218	9.72421	58°	21	41	62	82	103	124	144	165	185
32°	9.72421	9.72622	9.72823	9.73022	9.73219	9.73416	9.73611	57°	20	40	59	70	99	119	139	159	178
33°	9.73611	9.73805	9.73997	9.74189	9.74379	9.74568	9.74756	56°	19	38	57	76	96	115	134	153	172
34°	9.74756	9.74943	9.75128	9.75313	9.75496	9.75678	9.75859	55°	18	37	55	74	92	110	129	147	165
35°	9.75859	9.76039	9.76218	9.76395	9.76572	9.76747	9.76922	54°	18	35	53	71	80	106	124	142	150
36°	9.76922	9.77095	9.77268	9.77439	9.77609	9.77778	9.77946	53°	17	34	51	68	86	103	120	137	154
37°	9.77946	9.78113	9.78280	9.78445	9.78609	9.78772	9.78934	52°	17	33	50	66	83	99	116	132	149
38°	9.78934	9.79095	9.79256	9.79415	9.79573	9.79731	9.79887	51°	16	32	48	64	80	95	112	127	143
39°	9.79887	9.80043	9.80197	9.80504	9.80504	9.80656	9.80807	50°	15	31	46	62	77	92	108	123	138
40°	9.80807	9.80957	9.81106	9.81254	9.81402	9.81549	9.81694	49°	15	30	44	59	74	89	104	118	133
41°	9.81694	9.81839	9.81983	9.82126	9.82269	9.82410	9.82551	48°	14	29	43	57	72	86	100	114	129
42°	9.82551	9.82691	9.82830	9.82968	9.83106	9.83242	9.83378	47°	14	28	41	55	69	83	97	110	124
43°	9.83378	9.83513	9.83648	9.83781	9.83914	9.84046	9.84177	46°	13	27	40	53	67	80	93	106	120
44°	9.84177	9.84308	9.84437	9.84566	9.84694	9.84822	9.84949	45°	13	26	38	51	64	77	90	102	115

LOGARITHMIC COSINES

LOGARITHMIC SINES
(XXXI)

	0′	10′	20′	30′	40′	50′	60′		Mean Differences								
									1′	2′	3′	4′	5′	6′	7′	8′	9′
45°	9.84949	9.85074	9.85200	9.85324	9.85448		9.85693	44°	12	25	37	50	62	74	87	99	112
46°	9.85693	9.85815	9.85936	9.86056	9.86170	9.80205	9.86413	43°	12	24	36	48	60	72	84	96	108
47°	9.86413	9.86530	9.86647	9.86763	9.86879	9.86993	9.87107	42°	12	23	35	46	58	70	81	93	104
48°	9.87107	9.87221	9.87334	9.87446	9.87557	9.87668	9.87778	41°	11	22	34	45	56	67	78	89	100
49°	9.87778	9.87887	9.87996	9.88105	9.88212	9.88319	9.88425	40°	11	22	32	43	54	65	76	86	97
50°	9.88425	9.88531	9.88636	9.88741	9.88844	9.88948	9.89050	39°	10	21	31	42	52	62	73	83	94
51°	9.89050	9.89152	9.89254	9.89354	9.89455	9.89554	9.89653	38°	10	20	30	40	50	60	70	80	90
52°	9.89633	9.89752	9.89849	9.89947	9.90043	9.90139	9.90235	37°	10	19	29	39	49	58	68	78	87
53°	9.90235	9.90330	9.90424	9.90518	9.90611	9.90704	9.90796	36°	9	19	28	37	47	56	65	75	84
54°	9.90796	9.90887	9.90978	9.91069	9.91158	9.91248	9.91336	35°	9	18	27	36	45	54	63	72	81
55°	9.91336	9.91425	9.91512	9.91599	9.91686	9.91772	9.91857	34°	9	17	26	35	44	52	61	70	78
56°	9.91857	9.91942	9.92027	9.92111	9.92194	9.92277	9.92359	33°	8	17	25	34	42	50	59	67	76
57°	9.92359	9.92441	9.92522	9.92603	9.92683	9.92763	9.92842	32°	8	16	24	32	41	49	57	65	73
58°	9.92842	9.92921	9.92999	9.93077	9.93154	9.93230	9.93307	31°	8	16	23	31	39	47	55	62	70
59°	9.93307	9.93382	9.93457	9.93532	9.93606	9.93680	9.93753	30°	8	15	23	30	37	45	52	60	67
60°	9.93753	9.93826	9.93898	9.93970	9.94041	9.94112	9.94182	29°	7	14	22	29	36	43	50	57	64
61°	9.94182	9.94252	9.94321	9.94390	9.94458	9.94526	9.45593	28°	7	14	21	27	34	41	48	55	62
62°	9.94593	9.94660	9.94727	9.94793	9.94858	9.94923	9.94988	27°	7	13	20	26	33	40	46	53	59
63°	9.94988	9.95052	9.95116	9.95179	9.94242	9.95304	9.95366	26°	6	13	19	25	32	38	44	50	57
64°	9.95366	9.95427	9.95488	9.95549	9.95609	9.95668	9.95728	25°	6	12	18	24	30	36	42	48	54
65°	9.95728	9.95736	9.95844	9.95902	9.95960	9.96017	9.96073	24°	6	12	17	23	29	35	40	46	52
66°	9.96073	9.96129	9.96185	9.96240	9.96294	9.96349	9.96403	23°	6	11	17	22	28	33	38	44	50
67°	9.96403	9.96456	9.96509	9.96562	9.98614	9.96665	9.96171	22°	5	10	16	21	26	31	36	42	47
68°	9.96171	9.96767	9.96818	9.96868	9.96917	9.96966	9.97015	21°	5	10	15	20	25	29	34	40	44
69°	9.97015	9.97063	9.97111	9.97159	9.97206	9.97252	9.97299	20°	5	9	14	19	24	28	33	38	42

70°	9.97299	9.97344	9.97390	9.97435	9.97479	9.97523	9.97567	19°	4	9	13	18	22	27	31	36	40
71°	9.97567	9.97610	9.97653	9.97696	9.97738	9.97779	9.97821	18°	4	9	13	17	21	26	30	34	38
72°	9.97821	9.97861	9.97902	9.97942	9.97982	9.98021	9.98060	17°	4	8	12	16	20	24	28	32	36
73°	9.98060	9.98060	9.98136	9.98174	9.98211	9.99248	9.98284	16°	4	8	11	15	19	22	26	30	34
74°	9.98284	9.98320	9.98356	9.98391	9.98426	9.98460	9.98494	15°	4	7	11	14	18	21	25	28	32
75°	9.98494	9.98528	9.98561	9.98594	9.98627	9.98659	9.98690	14°	3	7	10	13	17	20	23	26	30
76°	9.98690	9.98722	9.98753	9.98783	9.98813	9.98843	9.98872	13°	3	6	9	12	15	18	21	24	27
77°	9.98872	9.98901	9.98930	9.98958	9.98986	9.99013	9.99040	12°	3	6	8	11	14	17	20	22	25
78°	9.99040	9.99067	9.99093	9.99119	9.99145	9.99170	9.99195	11°	3	5	8	10	13	16	18	21	23
79°	9.99195	9.99219	9.99243	9.99267	9.99290	9.99131	9.99335	10°	2	5	7	9	12	14	16	19	21
80°	9.99335	9.99379	9.99379	9.99400	9.99421	9.99442	9.99462	9°	2	4	6	8	11	13	15	17	19
81°	9.99462	9.99482	9.99501	9.99520	9.99539	9.99557	9.99575	8°	2	4	6	8	10	11	13	15	17
82°	9.99575	9.99593	9.99610	9.99697	9.99643	9.99659	9.99675	7°	2	3	5	7	8	8	12	13	15
83°	9.99675	9.99690	9.99705	9.99720	9.99734	9.99748	9.99761	6°	1	3	4	6	7	7	10	12	13
84°	9.99761	9.99775	9.99787	9.99800	9.99812	9.99823	9.99834	5°	1	3	4	5	6	6	9	10	11
85°	9.99834	9.99845	9.99856	9.99866	9.99876	9.99885	9.99894	4°	1	2	3	4	5	6	7	8	9
86°	9.99894	9.99903	9.99911	9.99919	9.99926	9.99934	9.999940	3°	1	2	2	3	4	5	5	6	7
87°	9.99940	9.99947	9.99953	9.99959	9.99964	9.99969	9.99974	2°	1	1	2	2	3	3	4	4	5
88°	9.99974	9.99978	9.99982	9.99985	9.99988	9.99991	9.99993	1°	0	1	1	1	2	2	2	2	3
89°	9.99993	9.99995	9.99997	9.99998	9.99999	10.0000	10.0000	0°									
90°	10.0000																
	60′	**50′**	**40′**	**30′**	**20′**	**10′**	**0′**		**1′**	**2′**	**3′**	**4′**	**5′**	**6′**	**7′**	**8′**	**9′**

LOGARITHMIC COSINES

(XXXIII)

TABLE V

LOGARITHMIC TANGENTS

	0′	10′	20′	30′	40′	50′	60′		Mean Differences								
									1′	2′	3′	4′	5′	6′	7′	8′	9′
0°	$-\infty$	7.46373	7.76476	7.94086	8.06581	8.16273	8.24192	89°									
1°	8.24192	8.30888	8.36689	8.41807	8.46385	8.50527	8.54308	88°	Differences vary so rapidly here that tabulation is impossible. For small angles of n minutes log tan n' or log cot $(90° - n')$ = log n + $\bar{4}$.46373.								
2°	8.54308	8.57788	8.61009	8.64009	8.66816	8.69453	8.71940	87°									
3°	8.71940	8.74292	8.76525	8.78649	8.80674	8.82610	8.84464	86°									
4°	8.84464	8.86243	8.87953	8.89598	8.91185	8.92716	8.94195	85°									
5°	8.94195	8.95627	8.97013	8.98358	8.99662	9.00930	9.02162	84°									
6°	9.02162	9.03361	9.04528	9.05666	8.06775	9.07858	9.08914	83°									
7°	9.08914	9.09947	9.10956	9.11943	9.12909	9.13854	9.14780	82°	98	195	293	391	488	586	684	782	879
8°	9.14780	9.15688	9.16577	9.17450	9.18306	9.19146	9.19971	81°	97	173	260	346	433	519	606	692	779
9°	9.19971	9.20782	9.21578	9.22361	9.23130	9.23887	9.24632	80°	78	155	233	310	388	466	504	621	698
10°	9.24632	9.25365	9.26086	9.26797	9.27496	9.28186	9.28864	79°	71	141	212	282	354	420	492	564	635
11°	9.28865	9.29535	9.30195	9.30846	9.31489	9.32122	9.32747	78°	65	129	194	259	323	388	453	518	582
12°	9.32747	9.33365	9.33974	9.34576	9.35170	9.35757	9.36336	77°	60	120	179	239	299	359	419	478	538
13°	9.36336	9.36909	9.37446	9.38035	9.38589	9.39139	9.39677	76°	56	111	167	222	278	334	389	445	500
14°	9.39677	9.40212	9.40742	9.41266	9.41784	9.42297	9.42805	75°	52	104	156	208	261	313	365	417	469
15°	9.42805	9.44308	9.43806	9.44299	9.44787	9.45271	9.45750	74°	49	98	147	196	245	294	343	392	442
16°	9.45750	9.46224	9.44694	9.47160	9.47622	9.48080	9.48534	73°	46	93	139	186	232	278	325	371	418
17°	9.48534	9.48984	9.49430	9.49872	9.50311	9.50746	9.51178	72°	44	88	132	167	220	264	308	352	396
18°	9.51178	9.51606	9.52031	9.52452	9.52870	9.53285	9.53697	71°	42	84	126	168	210	252	294	336	378
19°	9.53697	9.54106	9.54512	9.54915	9.55315	9.55712	9.56107	70°	40	80	121	160	201	241	281	321	362

(XXXIV)

20°	9.55107	9.56498	9.56887	9.5774	9.57658	9.58039	9.58418	69°	39	77	116	154	193	231	270	308	347
21°	9.58418	9.58794	9.69163	9.59540	9.59909	9.60276	9.60641	68°	37	74	111	148	185	222	259	296	333
22°	9.60641	9.61004	9.61364	9.61722	9.62079	9.62433	9.62785	67°	36	72	107	143	179	214	250	286	322
23°	9.62785	9.63135	9.63484	9.63830	9.64175	9.64517	9.64858	66°	35	69	104	138	173	208	242	277	321
24°	9.64858	9.65197	9.65535	9.965870	9.66204	9.66537	9.66867	65°	34	67	101	134	168	201	235	268	302
25°	9.66867	9.67196	9.67524	9.67850	9.68174	9.68497	9.68818	64°	33	65	98	130	163	195	228	260	293
26°	9.68818	9.69138	9.69457	.69774	9.70089	9.70404	9.70717	63°	32	63	95	126	158	190	221	253	284
27°	9.70717	9.71028	9.71339	.71648	9.71955	9.72262	9.72567	62°	31	62	92	123	154	185	216	246	277
28°	9.72567	9.72872	9.71375	.73777	9.73777	9.74077	9.74375	61°	30	60	90	120	151	181	211	241	271
29°	9.74375	9.74673	9.74969	.75264	9.75558	9.75852	9.76144	60°	29	59	88	118	147	177	206	236	265
30°	9.67144	9.76435	9.76725	9.77015	9.77303	9.77591	9.77877	59°	29	58	87	116	144	173	202	231	260
31°	9.77877	9.78163	9.78448	9.78732	9.70015	9.79297	9.79579	58°	28	57	85	113	142	170	198	227	255
32°	9.79579	9.79860	9.80140	9.80419	9.80697	9.80975	9.81252	57°	28	56	84	112	139	167	195	223	251
33°	9.81252	9.81528	9.81803	9.82078	9.82352	9.82626	9.82899	56°	28	55	83	110	137	165	192	220	247
34°	9.82899	9.83171	9.83442	9.83713	9.83984	9.84254	9.84523	55°	27	54	81	108	136	162	190	217	244
35°	9.84523	9.84791	9.85059	9.85327	9.85594	9.85860	9.86126	54°	27	54	80	107	1347	160	188	214	241
36°	9.86126	9.86392	9.86656	9.86921	9.87185	9.87448	9.87711	53°	26	53	79	106	132	158	185	212	238
37°	9.87711	9.87914	9.88236	9.88498	9.88759	9.89020	9.89281	52°	26	52	78	105	131	157	183	209	236
38°	9.89281	9.89541	9.89801	9.90061	9.90320	9.90578	9.90837	51°	26	52	78	104	130	156	182	208	234
39°	9.90837	9.91095	9.91353	9.91610	9.91868	9.92125	9.92881	50°	26	52	77	103	129	155	180	206	232
40°	9.92381	9.92638	9.92894	9.93150	9.93406	9.93661	9.93916	49°	26	51	77	102	128	154	179	205	230
41°	9.93916	9.94171	9.94426	9.94681	9.94935	9.95190	9.95444	48°	25	51	76	102	127	153	178	204	229
42°	9.95444	9.95698	9.95952	9.96205	9.96459	9.96712	9.96966	47°	25	51	76	101	127	152	177	203	228
43°	9.96966	9.97219	9.97472	9.97725	9.97978	9.98231	9.98484	46°	25	51	76	101	127	152	177	202	228
44°	9.98484	9.98737	9.98982	9.99242	9.99495	9.99747	10.0000	45°	25	51	76	101	127	152	177	202	228
	60′	50′	40′	30′	20′	10′	0′		1′	2′	3′	4′	5′	6′	7′	8′	9′

45°	10.00000	10.00253	10.00505	10.00758	10.01011	10.01263	10.01516	44°	25	51	76	101	127	152	177	202	228
46°	10.01516	10.01769	10.02022	10.02275	10.02528	10.02781	10.03034	43°	25	51	76	101	127	152	177	202	228
47°	10.03034	10.03288	10.03541	10.03795	10.04048	10.043032	10.05556	42°	25	51	76	101	127	152	177	203	228
48°	10.04556	10.04810	10.05065	10.05319	10.05574	10.05829	10.06084	41°	25	51	76	102	127	153	178	204	229
49°	10.06084	10.06339	10.06594	10.06850	10.07106	10.07362	10.07619	40°	26	51	77	102	128	154	179	205	230
50°	10.07619	10.07875	10.08132	10.08390	10.08647	10.08905	10.09163	39°	26	52	77	103	129	155	180	206	232
51°	10.09163	10.09422	10.09680	10.09939	10.10199	10.10459	10.10719	38°	26	52	78	104	130	156	182	208	234
52°	10.10719	10.10980	10.11241	10.11502	10.11764	10.12026	10.12289	37°	26	52	78	105	131	157	183	209	236
53°	10.12289	10.12552	10.12815	10.13079	10.13344	10.13608	10.13874	36°	26	53	79	106	132	158	185	212	238
54°	10.13874	10.14140	10.14406	10.14673	10.14941	10.15209	10.15477	35°	27	54	80	107	134	160	188	214	241
55°	10.15477	10.15746	10.16016	10.16287	10.16558	10.16829	10.17101	34°	27	54	81	108	136	162	190	217	244
56°	10.17101	10.17374	10.17648	10.17922	10.18197	10.18472	10.18748	33°	28	55	83	110	137	165	192	220	247
57°	10.18748	10.19025	10.19303	10.19581	10.19860	10.20140	10.20421	32°	28	56	84	112	139	167	195	223	251
58°	10.20421	10.20703	10.20985	10.21268	10.21552	10.21837	10.22123	31°	28	57	85	113	142	170	198	227	255
59°	10.22123	10.22409	10.22697	10.22985	10.23275	10.23565	10.23856	30°	29	58	87	116	144	173	202	231	260
60°	10.23856	10.24148	10.24442	10.24736	10.25031	10.25327	10.25625	29°	29	59	88	118	147	177	206	236	265
61°	10.25625	10.25923	10.26223	10.26524	10.26825	10.27128	10.27433	28°	30	60	90	120	151	181	211	241	271
62°	10.27433	10.27738	10.28045	10.28352	10.28661	10.28972	10.29283	27°	31	62	92	123	154	185	216	246	277
63°	10.29283	10.29596	10.29911	10.30226	10.30543	10.30862	10.31182	26°	32	63	95	126	158	190	221	253	284
64°	10.31182	10.31503	10.31826	10.32150	10.32476	10.32804	10.33133	25°	33	65	98	130	163	195	228	260	293
65°	10.33133	10.33463	10.33796	10.34130	10.34465	10.34803	10.35142	24°	34	67	101	134	168	201	235	268	302
66°	10.35142	10.35483	10.35825	10.36170	10.36516	10.36865	10.37215	23°	35	69	104	138	173	208	242	277	311
67°	10.37215	10.37567	10.37921	10.38278	10.38636	10.38996	10.39359	22°	36	72	107	143	179	214	251	286	322
68°	10.39359	10.39724	10.40091	10.40460	10.40832	10.41206	10.41582	21°	37	74	111	148	185	222	259	296	333
69°	10.41582	10.41961	10.42342	10.42726	10.43113	10.43502	10.43893	20°	39	77	116	154	193	231	270	308	347

(XXXVI)

70°	10.43893	1044288	10.44685	10.45085	10.45488	10.45894	10.46303	19°	40	80	121	160	201	241	281	321	362
71°	10.46303	10.46715	10.47130	10.47548	10.47969	10.48394	10.48822	18°	42	84	126	168	210	252	294	336	378
72°	10.48822	10.49254	10.49689	10.50128	10.50570	10.51016	10.51466	17°	44	88	132	176	220	264	308	352	396
73°	10.51466	10.51920	10.52378	10.52840	10.53306	10.53776	10.54250	16°	46	93	139	186	232	278	325	371	418
74°	10.54250	10.54729	10.55213	10.55701	10.56194	10.56692	10.57195	15°	49	98	147	196	245	294	343	392	442
75°	10.57195	10.57703	10.58216	10.58734	10.59258	10.59788	10.60323	14°	52	104	156	208	261	313	365	417	469
76°	10.60323	10.60864	10.61411	10.61965	10.62524	10.63091	10.63664	13°	56	111	167	222	278	334	389	445	500
77°	10.63664	10.64243	10.64830	10.56424	10.66026	10.66635	10.67253	12°	60	120	179	239	299	359	419	478	538
78°	10.67253	10.67878	10.68511	10.69154	10.69805	10.70465	10.71135	11°	65	129	194	259	323	388	453	518	582
79°	10.71135	10.71814	10.72504	10.73203	10.73914	10.74635	10.75368	10°	71	141	212	282	354	420	494	564	635
80°	10.75368	10.76113	10.76870	10.77639	10.78422	10.79218	10.80029	9°	78	155	233	310	388	466	543	621	698
81°	10.80029	10.80854	10.81694	10.82550	10.83423	10.84312	10.85220	8°	87	173	260	346	433	519	606	692	779
82°	10.85220	10.86146	10.87091	10.88057	10.89044	10.90053	10.91086	7°	98	195	293	391	488	586	684	782	879
83°	10.91086	10.92142	10.93225	10.94334	10.95472	10.96639	10.97838	6°									
84°	10.97838	10.99070	11.00338	11.01642	11.02987	11.04373	11.05805	5°									
85°	11.05805	11.07284	11.08815	11.10402	11.12047	11.13757	11.15536	4°									
86°	11.15536	11.17390	11.19326	11.21351	11.23475	11.25708	11.28060	3°									
87°	11.28060	11.30547	11.33184	11.35991	11.38991	11.42212	11.45692	2°	Differences vary so rapidly here that tabulation is impossible.								
88°	11.45692	11.49473	11.53615	11.58193	11.63311	11.69112	11.75808	1°									
89°	11.75808	11.83727	11.93419	12.05914	12.23524	12.53627	+ ∞	0°									
99°	+ ∞																
	60′	50′	40′	30′	20′	10′	0′		1′	2′	3′	4′	5′	6′	7′	8′	9′

LOGARITHMIC CONTAGENTS

(XXXVII)

TABLE-VI

CIRCULAR, OR RADIAN, MEASURE

Degrees	Radians	Degrees	Radians	Minutes	Radians	Minutes	Radians
1°	0.1745	46°	.80285	1′	.00029	46′	.01338
2°	0.3491	47°	.82030	2′	.00058	47′	.01367
3°	0.5236	48°	.83776	3′	.00087	48′	.01396
4°	0.6981	49°	.85521	4′	.00116	49′	.01425
5°	0.8727	50°	.87266	5′	.00145	50′	.01454
6°	.10472	51°	.89012	6′	.00175	51′	.01484
7°	.12217	52°	.90757	7′	.00204	52′	.01513
8°	.13963	53°	.92502	8′	.00233	53′	.01542
9°	.15708	54°	.94248	9′	.00282	54′	.01571
10°	.17453	55°	.95993	10′	.00291	55′	.01600
11°	.19199	56°	.97738	11′	.00320	56′	.01629
12°	.20944	57°	.99484	12′	.00349	57′	0.1658
13°	.22689	58°	1.01229	13′	.00378	58′	0.1687
14°	.24435	59°	1.02974	14′	.00407	59′	0.1716
15°	.26180	60°	1.04720	15′	.00436	60′	0.1745
16°	.27925	61°	1.06465	16′	.00465		
17°	.29671	62°	1.08210	17′	.00495		
18°	.31416	63°	1.09956	18′	.00495		
19°	.33161	64°	1.11701	19′	.00524		
20°	.34907	65°	1.13446	20′	.00553		
21°	.36652	66°	1.15192	21′	.00611		
22°	.38397	67°	1.16937	22′	.00640		
23°	.40143	68°	1.18682	23′	.00669	Seconds	Radians
24°	.41888	69°	1.20428	24′	.00698	5″	.00002

25°	.43633	70°	1.22173	25′	.00727	10″	.00005
26°	.45379	71°	1.23918	26′	.00756	15″	.00007
27°	.47124	72°	1.25664	27′	.00785	20″	.00010
28°	.48869	73°	1.27409	28′	.00814	25″	.00012
29°	.50615	74°	1.29154	29′	.00844	30″	.00015
30°	.52360	75°	1.30900	30′	.00873	35″	.00017
31°	.54105	76°	1.32645	31′	.00902	40″	.00019
32°	.55851	77°	1.34390	32′	.00931	45″	.00022
33°	.57596	78°	1.36136	33′	.00960	50″	.00024
34°	.59341	79°	1.37881	34′	.00989	55″	.00027
35°	.61087	80°	1.39626	35′	.01018	60″	.00029
36°	.62832	81°	1.41372	36′	.01017		
37°	.64577	82°	1.43117	37′	.01076		
38°	.66323	83°	1.44862	38′	.01105		
39°	.68068	84°	1.46608	39′	.01134		
40°	.69813	85°	1.48353	40′	0.1164		
41°	.71558	86°	1.50098	41′	0.1193		
42°	.73304	87°	1.51844	42′	0.1222		
43°	.75049	88°	1.53589	43′	0.1251		
44°	.76794	89°	1.55334	44′	0.1280		
45°	.78540	90°	1.57080	45′	0.1309		

CONSTANTS

One Radian = 57°17′45″ nearly = 206265″:

log 206265 = 5.3144255

$\pi = 3.14159265$

$\frac{r}{\pi} = 0.31830989$

$\frac{\pi}{180} = 0.01745329$

$\frac{180}{\pi} = 57.2957795$

$\pi^2 = 9.86960440$

$\frac{1}{\pi^2} = 0.10132118$

$\sqrt{\pi} = 1.77245385$

$\frac{1}{\sqrt{\pi}} = 0.56418958$

$\sqrt[3]{\pi} = 1.46459189$

$\frac{1}{\sqrt[3]{\pi}} = 0.68278406$

$\log \pi = 0.4971499$

$\log \frac{1}{\pi} = \bar{1}.5028501$

$\log \frac{\pi}{180} = \bar{2}.2418774$

$\log \frac{180}{\pi} = 1.7581226$

$\log \pi^2 = 0.9942997$

$\log \frac{1}{\pi^2} = \bar{1}.0057003$

$\log \sqrt{\pi} = 0.2485749$

$\log \frac{1}{\sqrt{\pi}} = \bar{1}.7514251$

$\log \sqrt[3]{\pi} = 0.1657166$

$\log \frac{1}{\sqrt[3]{\pi}} = \bar{1}.8342834$

$\sqrt{2} = 1.4142135\ldots$

$\sqrt{3} = 1.7320508\ldots$

$\sqrt{5} = 2.2360679$

$\sqrt{6} = 2.4494897\ldots$

$\sqrt{7} = 2.6457513\ldots$

$\sqrt{8} = 2.828427$

$\sqrt{10} = 3.1622776\ldots$

Classic Texts Series

C046	Plane Trigonometry Part 1	*SL Loney*	95
C047	Coordinate Geometry Part 1	*SL Loney*	140
C048	Higher Algebra	*Hall & Knight*	195
C181	Mathematical Analysis	*GN Berman*	180
C182	Problems in Mathematics	*V Govorov, & P Dybow*	160
C183	Problems in General Physics	*IE Irodov*	130
C259	Fundamental Laws of Mechanics	*IE Irodov*	105
C260	Integral Calculus for Beginners	*Joseph Edwards*	95
C261	Science for Everyone Aptitude Test Problems in Physics	*SS Krotov*	90
C262	Differential Calculus for Beginners	*Joseph Edwards*	95
C263	Basic Laws of Electromagnetism	*IE Irodov*	125
C264	Higher Algebra	*Barnard & Child*	245
C265	Algebra for Beginners	*Hall & Knight*	130
C266	A School Geometry	*HS Hall & FH Stevens*	120
C267	Elementary Algebra for School	*HS Hall & FH Stevens*	195
F042	Statics & Dynamics Part I (Statics)	*SL Loney*	115
F043	Statics & Dynamics Part II (Dynamics)	*SL Loney*	95
G437	Problems in Calculus of One Variable	*IA Maron*	160

New Pattern JEE Books

B062	New Pattern JEE Problems Physics	*DC Pandey*	675
B061	New Pattern JEE Problems Chemistry	*Dr RK Gupta*	795
B070	New Pattern JEE Problems Mathematics	*Dr SK Goyal*	805

37 Years' Chapterwise IIT JEE Solved

C051	39 Years' IIT JEE Physics (Chapterwise)	*DC Pandey*	405
C050	39 Years' IIT JEE Chemistry (Chapterwise)	*Dr RK Gupta*	405
C049	39 Years' IIT JEE Mathematics (Chapterwise)	*Amit M Agarwal*	405
C093	विगत 39 वर्षों के अध्यायवार IIT JEE हल भौतिकी	*Om Narayan*	380
C094	विगत 39 वर्षों के अध्यायवार IIT JEE हल रसायन	*Preeti Gupta*	390
C095	विगत 39 वर्षों के अध्यायवार IIT JEE हल गणित	*Dr RP Singh*	395

IIT JEE Questions & Solutions (Yearwise)

C007	14 Years' Solved Papers IIT JEE Physics (Main & Advanced)	560
C008	14 Years' Unsolved Questions Papers	290
C009	14 Years' Objective Solved Papers IIT JEE (Main & Advanced)	390

Master Resource Books for JEE Main

B063	Master Resource Book for JEE Main Physics	*DB Singh*	799
B064	Master Resource Book for JEE Main Chemistry	*Sanjay Sharma*	799
B065	Master Resource Book for JEE Main Mathematics	*Prafull K Agarwal*	799
B031	सम्पूर्ण स्टडी पैकेज JEE Main भौतिकी	*धर्मवीर सिंह*	799
B032	सम्पूर्ण स्टडी पैकेज JEE Main रसायन विज्ञान	*अभय कुमार*	799
B033	सम्पूर्ण स्टडी पैकेज JEE Main गणित	*मंजुल त्यागी*	799

Solved Papers & Mock Tests for JEE Main

C019	15 Years' JEE Main Solved Papers	420
C016	15 Years' JEE Main सॉल्वड पेपर्स	420
C102	16 Years' JEE Main Chapterwise Solutions Physics	205
C103	16 Years' JEE Main Chapterwise Solutions Chemistry	205
C104	16 Years' JEE Main Chapterwise Solutions Maths	205

40 Days Revision Books for JEE Main

C142	40 Days JEE Main Physics	*Saurabh A*	380
C143	40 Days JEE Main Chemistry	*Dr Praveen Kumar*	380
C144	40 Days JEE Main Mathematics	*Rajeev Manocha*	380
C127	40 Days JEE Main भौतिकी	*देवेन्द्र कुमार*	370
C126	40 Days JEE Main रसायन	*हसराज मोदी*	370
C125	40 Days JEE Main गणित	*डॉ आरपी सिंह*	370

Objective Books for JEE Main & Advanced

B122	Objective Physics (Vol 1)	*DC Pandey*	645
B123	Objective Physics (Vol 2)	*DC Pandey*	645
B121	Objective Chemistry (Vol 1)	*Dr. RK Gupta*	795
B130	Objective Chemistry (Vol 2)	*Dr. RK Gupta*	795
B048	Objective Mathematics (Vol 1)	*Amit M Agarwal*	780
B053	Objective Mathematics (Vol 2)	*Amit M Agarwal*	780

BITSAT 2018
BITSAT Prep Guide
Code : C064 ₹810

JEE Main Prepguide 2018
(with CD)
Code : C211 ₹1295

Solved & Mock Tests for Engineering Entrances

Solved Papers & Mock Tests (2-Edge Series)

C084	VIT Solved Papers & Mock Tests	355
C023	BVP Engineering 2-Edge Solved Papers & Mock Tests	370
C136	AMU Engineering 2-Edge Solved Papers & Mock Tests	345
C092	Manipal Engineering 2-Edge Solved Papers & Mock Tests	380

Andhra Pradesh

C154	27 Years' Chapterwise EAMCET Physics	300
C155	27 Years' Chapterwise EAMCET Chemistry	260
C156	27 Years' Chapterwise EAMCET Mathematics	340
C061	17 Years' Solved Papers EAMCET Engineering	410

Bihar

C042	BCECE Previous Years' Solved Papers	330
C043	12 Years' Solved Papers BCECE Mains Entrance Exam	335

Chhattisgarh Complete Success Packages

F022	Chhattisgarh PET Complete Success Package	795
F028	छत्तीसगढ़ PET सक्सेस पैकेज	775
F036	Chhattisgarh PMT Complete Success Package	790
F037	छत्तीसगढ़ PMT सक्सेस पैकेज	790

Solved Papers & Mock Tests

C105	Chhattisgarh PET 2-Edge Solved Papers & Mock Tests	350
C137	छत्तीसगढ़ PET 2-Edge मॉक टेस्ट सॉल्वड पेपर्स	335
C106	Chhattisgarh PMT 2-Edge Mock Tests & Solved Papers	355
C138	छत्तीसगढ़ PMT 2-Edge मॉक टेस्ट सॉल्वड पेपर्स	335

Delhi

C059	GGSIPU Engineering Entrance Exam *2-Edge Solved Papers & Mock Tests*	355

Haryana/Jammu & Kashmir (Solved Papers & Mock Tests)

C081	J&K CET Medical Entrance Exam	385
C091	J&K CET Engineering Entrance Exam	385

Jharkhand (Solved Papers & Mock Tests)

C045	16 Years' Solved Papers JCECE Engineering Entrance Exam	340

Kerala (Solved Papers & Mock Tests)

C076	16 Years' Solved Papers Kerala CEE Engineering Entrance Exam	475

Karnataka/Maharashtra (Solved Papers & Mock Tests)

C032	16 Years' Solved Papers K-CET Engineering Entrance Exam	375
C107	MHT-CET Engineering Entrance Exam	310

Uttar Pradesh (Complete Success Packages)

F029	UPTU/UPSEE संपूर्ण सक्सेस पैकेज 2018	775
F024	Complete Study Guide UPTU/UPSEE 2018 Physics	390
F025	Study Guide Chemistry for SEE-GBT	380
F026	Study Guide Mathematics for SEE-GBTU	380

Solved Papers

C014	14 Years' सॉल्वड पेपर्स UPTU/UPSEE	390
C072	14 Years' Solved Papers UPTU/UPSEE	405

West Bengal

C075	WB JEE Engineering Solved Papers & Mock Tests	415

Science & Mathematics Olympiads

B056	Indian National Physics Olympiad	*Saurabh A*	360
B068	Indian National Chemistry Olympiad	*Dr.Praveen Kumar*	275
B044	Indian National Mathematics Olympiad	*Rajeev Manocha*	390
B043	Indian National Biology Olympiad	*Dr. RK Manglik*	275

NCERT Exemplar Solutions

Class XI

F259	NCERT Exemplar - Physics	150
F251	NCERT Exemplar - Chemistry	150
F280	NCERT Exemplar - Mathematics	175
F260	NCERT Exemplar - Biology	175

Class XII

F281	NCERT Exemplar - Physics	150
F279	NCERT Exemplar - Chemistry	175
F282	NCERT Exemplar - Mathematics	175
F278	NCERT Exemplar - Biology	150